Rebecca Zacher
215 Main Street
Leechburg, Pa. 15656

Other Champion Books:

Dee O'Hara
ASTRONAUTS' NURSE

Ken Boyer
GUARDIAN OF THE HOT CORNER

Art Arfons
FASTEST MAN ON WHEELS

Elaine Moore Moffat
BLUE RIBBON HORSEWOMAN

Philip Vampatella
FIGHTER PILOT

This is an Authorized Biography

Dixie Cline
ANIMAL DOCTOR

The complete life story of a girl who fought to make her way in the "man's world" of veterinary medicine

BY VIRGINIA McDONNELL

A RUTLEDGE BOOK
THOMAS NELSON & SONS
Edinburgh • New York • Toronto

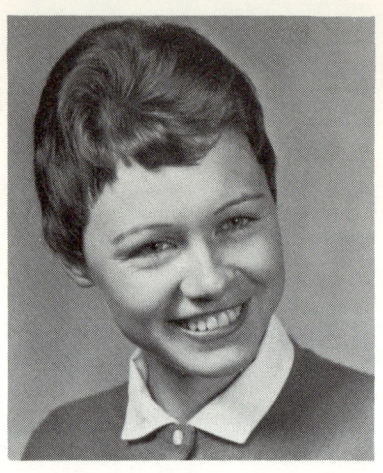

PHOTO CREDITS
*All photographs are from Dixie Cline's own collection
except the following:*
R. Blatt, pages 2, 86, 92, 100, 104, 107, 109, 113
G. Hinze, pages 79, 82, 89, 96, 102, 111, 115, 120, 124, 128
Colorado State University, pages 58, 62, 66

Copyright © 1966, by Rutledge Books, Inc.
Prepared and produced by Rutledge Books, Inc.
All rights reserved under International and Pan-American Conventions
Published by Thomas Nelson & Sons
Simultaneously published in Canada
Library of Congress Catalog Card Number 66-15984
Printed in the United States of America

CONTENTS

chapter 1   PIONEER SPIRIT, *page 7*

chapter 2   CATCH A PIG!, *page 19*

chapter 3   A MAN'S WORK, *page 29*

chapter 4   AS GOOD AS ANY BOY!, *page 45*

chapter 5   FIRST HURDLES PASSED, *page 59*

chapter 6   DIXIE CLINE, D.V.M., *page 73*

chapter 7   TO BE A CELEBRITY, *page 83*

chapter 8   "MARRY A VETERINARIAN", *page 101*

chapter 9   A LONG WAY TO GO, *page 117*

Dixie lavishes affection on Old Yellow, one of a succession of pets

CHAPTER 1

PIONEER SPIRIT

"Doesn't she ever play with dolls?" the neighbor asked.

Dixie Cline's mother smiled. "Yes, but she likes animals, too. Live things appeal to Dixie."

With her kitten firmly clutched in her arms, Dixie sidled toward the door, hoping to escape. This woman asked too many questions—questions to which a shy little girl like Dixie had trouble finding answers. She wished the woman would go home. Didn't she have any chores to do? Here at the Clines', hands were never idle. But Dixie realized that her mother was enjoying her caller. Visitors were rare on this lonely Colorado farm.

Dixie had almost made it to the door when the neighbor's voice stopped her. "What are you going to be when you grow up, dear?"

This was a question Dixie had never answered before, even to herself. Her mind scurried around. Should she say she wanted to be a teacher, like her mother? Should she say she wanted to get married and have a big family? Then she remembered the man with the black bag who had come to take care of Daddy's sick horse. "I want to be an animal doctor," she said firmly.

The visitor laughed. "Do you, really?" She turned to Dixie's mother. "Well, she's only five—plenty of time to change her mind a dozen times."

Dixie made her escape. Outside, she put the kitten down and went to get feed for the chickens. "I will not change my mind," she thought. "That's what I'll be when I grow up. I'll take care of sick animals all my life!"

When the chickens were fed, Dixie went off to find her father. He wouldn't laugh at her, she was sure.

And he didn't. Mac Cline hunkered down so that his eyes were on a level with his daughter's. "That's a very fine thing to be," he agreed. "Of course, I don't think there are very many women veterinarians—mostly men. And the ones there are treat little animals, like pet dogs and cats and birds. But don't let that stop you, honey. The Clines have always been pioneers—you be a pioneer, too."

Dixie inherited her pioneer spirit from both sides of her family. Grandfather and Grandmother Cline had traveled west by covered wagon to Akron, Colorado.

They had built a sod house, cutting the "bricks" from the earth itself, and had homesteaded with their six children, one of whom was Mac, Dixie's father. Akron, about a hundred miles east of Denver, is in hilly country. Later, they moved farther west, to still wilder country in the Rocky Mountains. They settled in the town of Loveland, and there Mac met Ruby Prescott, whose parents were also homesteaders.

Ruby had ambitions. She refused to marry Mac until she had completed college and had taught school for three years. But Mac was the kind of man who appealed to her—strong, not afraid of work, loving toward animals and good at winning their trust. They both felt that their life together would be a good one.

And so, in 1934, Mac Cline and Ruby Prescott were married. Mac decided to return to Akron, where the old sod house, built years ago by his parents, was vacant. There Stan was born and, a year later, Dixie.

To augment the family income, Ruby Cline continued to teach after Stan was born, and went back again after she had Dixie, hiring a woman to take care of the children. But when Stan was old enough for school, Ruby decided that little Dixie was old enough to go, too, in spite of the fact that she was not yet quite four.

Conditions were primitive at the one-room Rock Springs School, where Dixie's education began. There was no well, so water had to be toted from the Clines' farm for all the students. Each morning, Mac Cline

Home to little Dixie—an old sod house built by Grandpa and Grandma Cline when they arrived in Akron by covered wagon

saddled a horse, helped his wife into the saddle, tied water bags on either side, boosted up the two children—one before their mother, one behind—and the whole edifice moved off. Besides those journeys to and from school, Ruby also rounded up the cows on horseback. Riding was just routine for Ruby, but for Dixie it was one long joyride. She loved the horses.

But one day the routine of rounding up the cows turned into a nightmare. The herd bull was very gentle and had never given any of the Clines cause to fear him, until that afternoon, when suddenly and without any apparent reason, he attacked the mare on which Dixie was riding with her mother.

The jolt of the big bull striking the shoulder of the

mare was totally unexpected. Dixie lost her hold and fell to the ground—at the mercy of the enraged bull, although she didn't realize that.

Ruby Cline dug her heels into the mare and rode off at top speed. The bull took out in pursuit. Ruby circled the field and rode back toward Dixie. The little girl was still on the ground, watching with pleasure this diverting show that her mother and the bull were putting on.

The bull was still close behind Ruby as she came near Dixie. So she veered off again, calling over her shoulder, "Next time I come around, hold up your arms!"

Delighted, Dixie got to her feet and stretched up her arms. What fun—Mom was going to scoop her up off the ground, just like the trick riding in that rodeo Daddy had taken her to! "Come on, Mom," she yelled.

On the third round, Ruby scooped Dixie up and rode pell-mell out of the field. She slid off the horse, let go of Dixie, and slammed the gate. Then she dropped to the ground, weak with relief.

This amazed Dixie. Mom practically never sat idly by while there was work to do. "You tired, Mom?" she inquired anxiously. "Come on—let's do it again!"

Dixie was wildly anxious to ride alone. She had been begging her father to let her ride alone for more than a year. She pleaded her cause so well, and so often, that he finally agreed. He boosted her up on a gentle mare, gave her the reins, and told her, "All

Animals around the Cline home were numerous—and some of them looked very big indeed to a small two-year-old girl

right, honey, you're on your own. Good luck to you!"

As soon as the horse realized that this featherweight was alone on her back, she decided to go wherever she pleased. Where she pleased was under a clothesline, conveniently low enough to sweep off her passenger.

Sitting on the ground, Dixie looked up at the mare indignantly. "Daddy, will you boost me up again? Stan says you've got to let a horse know who's boss."

Obligingly, Mac Cline hoisted his daughter back to the saddle.

Dixie broke into a sudden giggle, looking down at her short legs, which were sticking out almost at right angles. "Anyway, I'll let this horse know who's boss just as soon as my legs get long enough. Hup, Bessie!"

By the time Ruby Cline decided to give up teaching, Dixie was long-legged enough to ride to school on her own—but barely, for she was still very small for her age, a fact that irked her. If she'd only get big, she was certain, Stan wouldn't mind her tagging along behind him wherever he went. She even followed her brother when he went hunting—not because she wanted to participate in stocking the family larder, but because it gave her a chance to set holding traps for animals, such as badgers, to add to her collection.

It was fortunate for Dixie that her parents sympathized with her love of animals, because by now her pets were a menagerie. There were the jack rabbits that Dixie bottle fed every two hours, night and day, until they were old enough to shift for themselves. There was the skunk, Petunia, tame enough so that she never forgot her manners with her squirt-gun weapon. There were wild and domestic birds of all kinds—pheasants, ducks, geese, turkeys, and even prairie-dog owls, little birds that nest in holes dug by prairie dogs. And kittens and puppies of all colors and sizes and breeds. Each one had a name, and each one had Dixie's love and tender care to make its life worthwhile.

One afternoon, Dixie discovered some baby magpies out in the pasture and brought them home. Looking at them, her mother smiled reminiscently. "I remember that Uncle Edgar and I had some pet magpies when we were little. Once, when one was sick, I gave it an aspirin tablet. The bird died—and I never found out whether it died of its sickness, or because of the aspirin."

The little magpies throve for a while. Then one began to droop. In spite of all Dixie's efforts, it became sicker and sicker.

"Why don't you try aspirin?" Stan asked her.

"I'm afraid to," Dixie objected. "I don't know if it would work."

So Stan gave the little magpie aspirin—and, like their mother's pet before it, the magpie died.

Dixie swallowed her tears. "It's just the way it was with Mom," she told Stan. "I don't know, either, if it was the aspirin that killed Robber." Then she stopped, thinking. Her eyes began to shine, and the day's tragedy was forgotten. "But some day I'll know," she told her brother. "Some day I'll know all there is to know about taking care of animals, when I'm a veterinarian."

"Aw, you never will!" Stan teased.

But Mac Cline, coming up behind the children, said, "She will, Stan. Anything you want that much, you get. Dreams come true if you *make* them come true—if you work hard and study hard and make your dream the most important thing in the world."

Abashed, Stan turned away as Mac held out his hand to his daughter. "Come on, honey—I'll dig a hole for you to bury your little bird in, and then I want you to see something—I've got a surprise for you."

The surprise was wonderful beyond Dixie's wildest imaginings. An animal, of course—what else would delight Dixie so? A horse all her own, a strawberry roan mare.

"I'll name her Lady," Dixie told her father, her voice tender. "I'll take such good care of her, Dad, and I'll ride her to school every day, and get the cows on her, and—oh, she's beautiful, she's just beautiful!"

This was a considerably flattering description of Lady, who was tall and skinny and knob-kneed. The horse, in fact, was so high off the ground, and Dixie was so close to the ground, that it seemed to the little girl she'd never be able to mount. But a little thinking solved that. Whenever Dixie wanted to mount, she'd

Everything was new and strange for Stan and Dixie when they moved to Grandpa and Grandma Prescott's farm at Loveland

15

wait for Lady to put her head down to graze. Then Dixie, facing the horse's tail, would fling her left leg over Lady's neck. When Lady raised her head, Dixie would slide downhill, turn quickly around, and be all set to go.

Dixie loved and enjoyed Lady, but even the mare couldn't replace Tiny in her affections. Tiny was a scrap of a white puppy, one wriggling bundle of love for Dixie, from his moist nose to his ever-wagging tail.

Because there was a certain amount of traffic on the road that ran past the farm, Tiny was kept tied up when Dixie was away from home. When she could be with him, she generally carried the puppy to keep him safe.

One morning, when she was in the fifth grade, Dixie was all ready for school. She had finished her morning chores; all that was left to do was to feed Tiny, then mount Lady, her own private school bus, and be off.

Not yet tied up for the day, the puppy buried his nose in his pan of breakfast food, while Dixie crouched beside him, watching his evident enjoyment.

All of a sudden, the puppy raised his head and cocked it to one side, listening.

At first, Dixie could hear nothing. Then she made out the sound of a car. That would be Miss McKie, one of her teachers, driving by on her way to school, as she did every morning.

Tiny listened a moment longer and then, just as Dixie realized what he was going to do, he took off.

If it was alive and they could catch it, Dixie and Stan added every available creature to their growing menagerie

Her hand, flashing out to grab him, got only a fluff of fur. Tiny streaked away, straight for the road.

"Tiny, come back!" Dixie leaped to her feet and ran in pursuit. But the little dog shot her a impish glance and ran on.

"Stop—Miss McKie, stop, stop!" But the teacher, her car windows rolled up against the morning chill, didn't hear the little girl's plea.

The car ran by just as Tiny slithered through the hedge onto the road. There was a shrieking of brakes, a sharp yelp of protest. And then, in one second, it was over.

As she dropped to her knees in the dirt beside the still little ball of fur, Dixie knew that Tiny was dead.

17

Duck watching provided amusement and knowledge for the future vet

CHAPTER 2

CATCH A PIG!

Mac Cline came running out of the house. He reached his daughter at about the same time as Miss McKie, who was white-faced and on foot now.

"Dixie, I'm so sorry—I'm so terribly sorry," the teacher said, her voice breaking.

In Dixie, wild grief welled up, and a desire to hit out at everyone, to hurt as she was being hurt.

"Get away from me!" she cried. "You killed Tiny!"

"Not on purpose." That was Mac Cline's voice as he dropped down and put his arms around his daughter's shoulders. "It's not Miss McKie's fault."

Dixie was fair. "I know, I know," she sobbed. "It's really my fault. I should have had him tied up."

Mac pulled the little girl close to him. "It was an accident, honey. It's one of those things that happen that's nobody's fault. Dixie, that's what the whole world

Smooky and Jingle were among the many dogs who lived at the Cline farm and served as playmates for Dixie and Stan

is about—living and dying. If you're going to be a veterinary, honey, you'll have to get used to death, and to feeling helpless to stop it."

Dixie stumbled to her feet. She wanted to run and run and never stop running, to hide from pain and death and the aching void that Tiny had left in her heart. "I'm going—I'm going—" she began.

Her father's hand closed gently, firmly on her arm. "You're going to go get Lady and ride to school."

She knew he was right. "Yes, Dad."

It was a long and miserable day. The picture of Tiny, like a crumpled and discarded piece of fur in the road, came between Dixie and her books. But finally the day ended, and she rode Lady back home.

"Dad wants you," her mother said. "He's up in the back pasture."

Dixie found him there, mending a fence. He put down his post-hole digger and came to meet her. "Honey, you and I have a little trip to make. I found out today that the Eastons have a new litter of pups. We'd better get up there and pick one out while there's still a choice."

The puppy was, like all puppies, warm and eager, falling all over himself to show how happy he was at being chosen as Dixie's own dog. Because he was black and because he felt his rightful place to be close at Dixie's heels, she named him Shadow—and a faithful shadow he remained for seventeen years, until he died of old age.

About this time, something happened that made a big difference in Dixie's life. Her father's brother— called Monk—brought his wife and three children to live just across the road from Dixie's family. One of these three children was a girl, Lorene, close to Dixie's age. At last, Dixie had someone to pal around with, someone to talk to, to share secrets with.

At first, Dixie thought that Lorene might be a disappointment, after all. She preferred to play only with dolls. But Lorene was an amiable child, as eager as Dixie for company. And Dixie had learned by now that in this life you have to compromise. Sometimes they went Lorene's way and played with dolls, and some-

Shadow was a very special pup, given to Dixie by her dad to fill the void left when her beloved Tiny was run over

times they went Dixie's way and played with animals.

On her eighth birthday, Dixie's most exciting present was a bay-and-white spotted colt, a gift to Dixie from her father as a replacement for Lady, who was getting rather old to make the trip to and from school.

"What shall I name her?" was the big question. Lorene and Dixie debated it for hours.

"I like 'Princess' best," Dixie decided at last.

Together, Dixie Cline and her father broke Princess to saddle and bridle, and finally, for the first time, Dixie rode Princess to school, so proud she could hardly see straight.

"When you get something really good, like Princess, there's usually responsibility attached to it," Mac told his daughter when she got home that day. "Now that you've got a fine horse to ride, Dixie, you're going to take over rounding up the cows and bringing them in from pasture each night. All right?"

All right? It was wonderful. Getting the cows had always been fun, but now she was going to do it all by herself, be responsible for it herself—well, herself and Princess! It was a job—one that Dixie did well and proudly—that took many of her evening hours and, on weekends and vacations, her morning hours, too—taking the cows out to pasture.

One of the big events of summer vacation was the County Fair, fortunately held in Akron, which was the county seat. The fair was exciting, with all sorts of exhibits, shows, and contests.

The contests the children enjoyed most were the "Catch a" contests—Catch a Pig, Catch a Calf, Catch a Sheep. In each, a number of animals was turned loose. A mad scramble among the youngsters ensued. The first boy to catch his animal and get it to the judges' stand was the winner, but, winner or not, it was a point of honor with each boy to catch one of the animals. Having caught it, he was entrusted with it for a year, to keep, care for, and finally, bring back to next year's fair to be caught again.

Stan had caught a sheep last year. This year, Dixie determined, she was going to enter one of the contests.

She approached Stan obliquely. "What contest you going to enter this year, Stan?"

"I think I'll try pigs this time."

"So'll I. Bet I catch a pig before you do!"

The boy gave her a quelling look. "Catch a pig? Why, you can't even get into the contest!"

"I can so!" his sister told him, furious. "This year I'm old enough."

Stan shook his head. "It wouldn't matter if you were a hundred. You're a girl—and girls don't enter."

"There's no law against girls," she retorted, tossing her head. She wasn't sure she was right about that, but it turned out she was—the rules didn't have a word to say about the sex of the contest participants.

The grandstand was jammed to capacity on the great day. And there was little Dixie Cline, jaw set and ready for action—the only girl among nine boys entered in Catch a Pig.

"Ready!" the judge called. "Get set! Go!" A gate was opened, and out tumbled pigs—big ones and little ones and medium-sized ones, pink and black and white and spotted. They took off in all directions, and after them pelted nine assorted-sized boys and one very small girl.

A huge black pig dashed close to Dixie, so close that she got her hands on him. But he was too big, too strong —he might as well have been a greased pig, he got away so easily. After that, Dixie didn't even touch a pig.

Finally, just before the contest ended, the smallest pig of all, a little runt of a red porker, came close to Dixie. With a cry of joy, she leaped on him, knocking all the wind out of herself and her captive. A roar of applause greeted her, and all at once Dixie was her shy self again, wishing to be anywhere but here, in the spotlight. She hardly heard the judge congratulate her.

Bella, as Dixie christened the pig, became another of Dixie's chores, along with feeding the chickens and getting the cows.

One spring day, Dixie found Bella down on her side, making little groaning noises in her throat. Dixie called, "Bella—here I am!" a statement usually guaranteed to get Bella up and running to her mistress, for whom she had apparently formed a deep affection. Today, however, Bella only rolled her eyes and groaned.

"Bella's sick," Dixie told her father that evening. "Come and look at her, Dad."

Mac inspected Bella, shaking his head. "A pig is one of the things I know least about," he admitted. "Never raised any. Run and ask your Uncle Monk."

Uncle Monk came and looked at Bella, too. But he couldn't say what ailed her. However, he did have some hog medicine left by a veterinarian when one of his hogs had been sick, and he offered Dixie that.

Dixie was doubtful. She remembered the magpie and the aspirin. "I don't want to experiment on Bella," she told her father.

But two days later, when Bella seemed no better, she got Mac to help her administer a dose to Bella. They waited, hopefully. Bella seemed no worse, but no better, either.

When this had been going on for a week—a week in which Dixie spent every moment she could with Bella, having to be called for meals and for homework and for bed—Mac decided to take a hand. "She's in pain, honey," he told Dixie. He hesitated. Then, "Wouldn't it be best to put her out of her misery?"

Dixie sat back on her heels. Her eyes were dark with misery. "Dad, if I only knew what to do for her! When I get to be a veterinarian, I'll *know* what to do, and—and no animal will die, ever!"

It was wonderful to have cousins living right across the road. Dixie introduced Lorene and Patsy to the new puppies

Mac Cline put his arm around his daughter's shoulders. "Honey, you're going to be a fine doctor. I know that."

"And Dad, about—about putting Bella out of her misery. That can wait till tomorrow, anyway, can't it?"

Next morning, for some reason, Bella was as lively as a pig ever is, tucking into her food with gusto, walking around her pen easily, painlessly.

Dixie looked at her with a mixture of exasperation and affection. "The trouble is," she said, "I don't know *why* you got well. I don't know if you got well because of what I did or in spite of what I did. But someday I'll know. People's animals will get sick, and the first thing they think will be, 'Call Dr. Dixie!' You wait and see!"

Old Grant provided transportation for Dixie and baby brother Arthur

CHAPTER 3

A MAN'S WORK

The year that Dixie was ten, Uncle Monk and his family moved away. Dixie missed Lorene terribly. Even though Lorene had a deplorable tendency not to play with animals, she was fun, and she was company, and Dixie was very lonely without her.

But good things happened that year Dixie was ten, as well. Grandma and Grandpa Prescott came to live in a trailer right next to the Clines' house. And shortly after that, Dixie's mother had her third child, Arthur. He was a beautiful, dark-eyed baby, and a delight to Dixie—a real, live doll to play with. She took her responsibility seriously when her mother allowed her to help tend Arthur, and became very skillful at feeding him, changing him, and bathing him.

"Even young as she is, Dixie's good with her hands," Ruby Cline told Mac. "And careful. She keeps her mind on what she's doing. I guess you're right, Mac. She'll make a good doctor of some kind, animal or people."

Mac smiled fondly at his small daughter. "Whatever she decides to do, it'll be good. But somehow I think she'll stick to doctoring animals. Anybody as set on a thing as she is on that isn't likely to cast it aside." Mac watched his daughter, her head bent close to the baby's. "I'm going to get Dixie a new horse, Ruby. A good one. As crazy about animals as she is, she ought to have a good one—and we know she'll take care of it."

The new horse was Flame, a part-Arabian colt. She was the reddish-brown color that is called "bay" when it occurs in horses, and she had black streaks—which had given her her name—in her mane and tail. Later, full grown, she would shed the bay color and become white.

Mac had Flame in a field, and brought Dixie to the gift rather than the gift to Dixie. "Nice colt," he said noncommittally.

"Beautiful!" Dixie cried. And she was—so proud, so handsome, so quiveringly alive that she made Dixie's heart beat faster and her eyes mist. "Whose is she, Dad? Is she—is she ours?"

"Not ours," said Mac.

The little girl felt a sharp disappointment. In just those few minutes since she'd first seen her, Dixie had felt a particular attachment to the lovely colt, as if there were some special bond between them. Then she looked up and saw the light dancing in her father's eyes, the look that meant he was teasing her. "Dad—she is ours, isn't she?"

Mac shook his head. "Not ours—yours."

If someone had given her the sun, with the moon and stars thrown in, it wouldn't have meant half as much to Dixie. With a shout of joy she flung herself on her father. "Daddy—thank you, thank you!"

"No call to break my neck, honey. Listen, if you're going to be a veterinarian, you ought to know as much about animals as you can, for a head start. Breaking and riding your own colt's one way."

"Breaking? Dad, can I break her? When?"

"How's right now for a starter? I'll give you a hand."

After considerable maneuvering, Dixie managed to get a bridle on Flame. Her father held the filly with one hand and, with the other, helped boost Dixie up on her back. For a moment it seemed as if Flame, standing docile and innocent-looking, might turn out not to need breaking. But only for a moment. Then she hunched her back and effortlessly shot Dixie high in the air, stepping daintily aside to get out of the way of Dixie's return trip.

Dixie landed with a dismal thud. She looked up groggily at her father, who hurried over. "Dad, when you get a bump like that, you really *do* see stars!"

Dixie won several awards with Flame, a part-Arabian colt. When Flame foaled, Dixie named the lovely colt Janella

"Want to knock off for today?"

Dixie shook her head. "The time to try again is right off," she said, and Mac, knowing she was quoting him, didn't protest.

"Try again" was Dixie's approach to any problem. "Keep at it till you lick it" was her philosophy, and she never for a moment admitted, no matter what the difficulty, that a problem might be too big for her to lick. . . .

Dixie joined 4-H, taking Flame as her year's project. The organization (4-H stands for "Head, Heart, Health, and Hands") is run by the U.S. Department of Agriculture. Professors from all land-grant colleges make themselves available for guidance and assistance. The objective is to have members "learn by doing" those skills that will be useful in their own homes. The club is open to anyone between the ages of nine and nineteen, without charge, and operates in urban as well as rural areas. Dixie became one of two-and-a-third million 4-H members in this country, and one of six million throughout the world, for the program has been "exported" to other countries.

Through 4-H, Dixie knew, she could learn the latest methods of raising dairy cattle and be a help to her father. She could also learn how best to care for her beloved Flame. All that was fun. The hard part of 4-H to Dixie was the report she was required to deliver, before an audience, on her year's project. For a girl who was shy with everyone except her family, that was really hard. Mac, as always, had something to say that helped her.

"Look at it this way, honey—let's say the speech you have to make is payment for all you've learned at 4-H. You've taken so much out, a short little report isn't much to trade for it all, is it?"

So, looking at it Mac's way, Dixie squared her shoulders and delivered her report; it wasn't easy, but she got through it. And then it was behind her.

Once, when Dixie and her dad were feeding the cattle, Mac said, "Honey, you know there's another part to this family, too. Your mother, in the house. She's got a lot of women's chores to do, and it seems to me you ought to give her a hand sometimes. You'd learn a lot a girl needs to know, that way."

Dixie shrugged. "I help with Arthur, Dad, and I make the beds in the morning, and set the table for breakfast and supper, to help Mom. Honest, I don't need to learn all that stuff. If I'm going to do a man's job when I grow up, I might as well do man's work now."

To her amazement, her father burst out laughing. Stung, she demanded, "What's so funny?"

Mac curbed his mirth. "Honey, I'm sorry. But if you were standing in my boots, it'd strike you funny, too. You're such a half pint, looks like you may never make five feet tall. And you're pretty, in case you hadn't noticed it—the kind of pretty that'll make the fellows whistle when you get older. Everything about you is tiny and cute. You're about the most female-looking female I ever laid eyes on."

Dixie couldn't help laughing with him. But, "Never mind," she told him. "Maybe even when I'm grown up it'll be funny to see me doing a man's work—but I'll be doing it, all the same."

Mac nodded agreement. "I wouldn't make any bets against that, Dixie. I'd surely lose."

Comforted, Dixie went back to work. She liked what she was doing. She liked everything about her life. Well, she wasn't so crazy about school, but she knew she had to have an education to get where she

Thumper and Jumper were two star boarders in the private zoo conducted, with parental approval, by Stan and Dixie

wanted to get, so she worked hard at her lessons. It was a pretty good world, her world, one in which nothing much ever seemed to go wrong....

And then, just a few days later, it was brought forcibly home to Dixie that things can, indeed, go wrong in anybody's world.

She came home from school as usual that afternoon, in time to bring home the cows for their evening milking. Taking a treat for the filly, she went to get Flame. This was the best part of the day, to Dixie's thinking. School was behind her and, dressed in jeans, she was ready to go to work. She and Flame would round up the cows and herd them back to the barn, where they would be milked by machine. Then she and her brother

Stan would strip the cows, removing the last drops of milk by hand. After that, the milk would have to be dumped into large cans, for transportation and sale. Then the animals must all be fed and bedded down for the night. After that... well, then there were lessons to do for school next day, but that less pleasant task was a long way off, and Dixie wouldn't think about it now.

As she reached the fence, she held up the carrot she had brought. "Come and get it!" she called to Flame.

The mare pricked up her ears, wheeled, and pounded across the field, nickering a welcome. She accepted the carrot, munched it gratefully, and then stood quietly while Dixie saddled up.

In the saddle, Dixie stroked the mare's satin neck. "Got to get the cows," she said. "Let's go!" and she touched her heels to the mare's flanks. They had between three and four miles to go, and if they lagged, they'd hold up Mac and Stan. On a farm, time regulates everything.

They streaked across the fields, stirring the grazing cattle, turning them, and heading them back toward the barn. Dixie kept a rough count as she went so that no lazy stray, hiding out somewhere, would be left behind.

From a distance, she saw a brown hump on the ground. "Looks as if one of the cows is down," she told Flame, and turned the mare in that direction for a closer look. The cow might, of course, be simply taking her ease, but that wasn't too likely. Any animal lying down

Midnight, sleek and aloof, looked down disdainfully on the pets with whom he was forced to share Dixie's affections

calls for prompt investigation. It may be sick. It may be injured. It may even be dying. Dixie's heart thumped unpleasantly as she ordered, "Get up—get up there, you—up."

Her pulse steadied as the animal began to lumber to its feet, but quickened again as the cow sank back.

Sliding quickly to the ground, Dixie went over to prod it. "Come on! Up—up!" she urged, trying to help the cow.

She wasn't successful. This was serious, for a cow is a valuable commodity to a dairy farmer. To Mac Cline, the herd represented years of struggle and hardship. "Please," Dixie begged, shoving as hard as she could. She knew that if you could get a sick animal to

37

its feet and walking, chances were it would come through all right. This was where being a girl, a tiny girl, was such a disadvantage. She'd have to go for help.

Flinging herself into the saddle, Dixie headed Flame back, racing across the fields. Past the sod house they flew, past the new house, to the dairy barn.

"Trouble?" Mac asked, reaching for Flame's bridle.

"Cow's down," Dixie gasped.

"Go back and keep trying to get her up," Mac instructed. "I'll call the vet and meet you out there with the pickup truck."

Back they raced and again Dixie leaped to the ground beside the stricken animal. Once more, the cow struggled to get her feet, and once more gave up the futile effort.

Then the pickup came bumping over the rough ground and screeched to a halt. Mac jumped out, took a quick look at the cow, shook his head and began unloading feed and water.

"I called Dr. Weickum, over in Yuma," he told Dixie as he worked. "Trouble is, Yuma's twenty-five miles away, and the doc's out on another call. No telling when he'll be able to get here."

Dixie glanced at him in dismay. This was an old, familiar problem—you worked your heart out caring for animals on which you depended for a living, never knowing whether you could get help in an emergency.

This cow was sick; she needed professional help, a veterinarian who would understand what the trouble was. But would the vet get there in time?

"What do you suppose ails her?" Dixie asked.

Mac frowned. "Wish I knew," he answered, offering water to the animal. "I surely wish I knew!"

By morning, they still didn't know. It had been a long night, with the Clines taking turns staying by the sick animal, trying to aid her. She was worse, now. She would make no effort to get up. Sometimes she bellowed in pain; sometimes she was so quiet that she seemed to be drifting away. And still no veterinarian.

"I'll stay home from school," Dixie told her mother that morning. "Dad can use an extra pair of hands." Regardless of the sick animal, the farm work must go on. She could fill in anywhere she was needed.

But Ruby Cline shook her head. "No, Dixie, you go on to school. The work's most important to your Dad and me, but school's most important for you. Stan's to go, too. If your Dad needs extra hands today, they'll be my hands. I can let the housework go."

Only a total disaster or impassable roads were grounds for missing school, to her mother's way of thinking. Well, Mom had been a teacher, so that wasn't too surprising.

"I hope the doctor gets here soon," Dixie said, as she and Stan started off.

"He'll come as soon as he can," Stan answered her.

39

Not all parents would tolerate a skunk in the vicinity of the house, but Ruby and Mac Cline accepted Dixie's Petunia

"But he has an awful lot of territory to cover. I don't suppose there's ever a day or night when some farmer or rancher isn't waiting for him to arrive, hoping he'll make it in time."

"What do you suppose is wrong with the cow?" Dixie wondered.

"I'd give a lot to know."

Dixie realized only too well that this might be a catastrophe. The loss of one cow would be bad enough, but suppose the illness was something that could spread to the whole herd; suppose, after all these years of struggle, the entire herd would have to be destroyed?

The cow was still alive when Dixie and Stan got home. But, close to sundown, she died. Now the Clines had cause for desperate concern—what about the rest of the herd? Was the illness contagious?

In the middle of the evening, Dr. Weickum finally arrived, his face gray with fatigue. "Sorry," he said wearily. "I've been working since yesterday morning with no sleep. I just couldn't make it any sooner."

The doctor decided to do a post-mortem at once. Perhaps emergency measures would have to be taken to save the rest of the herd. To determine that, he needed to know why this cow had died.

"Can I watch you?" Dixie asked.

The veterinarian gave her a quick, sharp look. What he saw in her eyes must have reassured him, for he said, "Be glad to have you."

Fascinated, Dixie watched as he made his incision and examined the vital organs. In answer to his questions, she told the veterinarian all she knew of the cow's sickness, relating every symptom she had observed from the moment she had found the cow down.

"You keep your eyes open," he told her approvingly.

At long last, the doctor sat back on his heels. "From what I can see here, and from what you've told me, I'd say she was poisoned," he told Dixie.

"Poisoned?" Fear gripped her. Why, if the other cows in the herd found the poison, the Clines would be wiped out.

"I don't mean somebody deliberately set out poison

for your cows, intending to ruin your dad," the doctor went on. "This looks more like an accident. Sometimes the grass or wheat, when it's in a fast-growing stage, can cause this reaction."

Dixie nodded. She had heard of such cases. "What shall we do?" she asked.

"Graze the herd in a different field for a few days," the doctor advised.

Dixie wanted to know all there was to be known. "Is there anything that can be done if a cow gets sick this way?"

The doctor nodded. "There are ways of clearing the poison out of the system—if I can get there in time."

"You mean—the cow didn't have to die?"

"If I could have come sooner, I probably could have saved her," the doctor agreed. "I'm the only veterinarian for miles around, and there are literally hundreds of animals in the area. I do the best I can, but I can't spread myself thin enough."

"I wasn't saying it was your fault," Dixie told him hastily. "It's just—well, we need more vets."

"Try to find them!"

The moment had come, and Dixie forgot about being shy. She seized it.

"There—there'll be one more, when I'm old enough." There, it was said. Would he laugh at her? Would he make fun of her?

He smiled gently, wearily. "It's a big ambition—

Old Grant was a favorite among all children in the area. Patiently, he permitted them to take turns learning to ride

and you're a mighty little girl. Looks to me as if you'll always be a little one. It takes physical strength to care for large animals. It's hard work."

"I'm little, but I'm strong," Dixie told him, her jaw set stubbornly. "I round up the cows. I help mow. I've helped when cows calved and horses foaled. I—I *like* to work hard."

"Women veterinarians—and there aren't a lot of them—generally work in towns, taking care of pets."

"I don't want that. I want to tend farm animals."

The doctor studied her quietly for a long moment. Then, "You really do want it, don't you? Your mind's really set on it. All right, then, good luck to you, youngster. Don't let anything stand in your way!"

Arthur grinned with triumph as he "helped" tame Ready, the pheasant

CHAPTER 4

AS GOOD AS ANY BOY!

As Dixie put it, "I'm graduating from eighth grade with more distinction than anybody, ever. Who else has ever been at the head of the class and at the bottom of the class!"

Dixie *was* the class. In fact, she and two other children were the entire student body of Rock Springs Grammar School. There seemed little point in holding graduation exercises for one lone pupil, so Dixie went to Platner, a little town east of Akron, to take part in the exercises there.

High school was going to be fun, Dixie thought. Sure, it was going to be hard, at first, with all those new people to get acquainted with. "I won't be shy," Dixie vowed. "I'll look them straight in the eye, and I'll find something to say, and—and everything will be fine."

It wasn't.

That first morning, when she and Stan started off for Akron in the old Model A Ford that Stan drove, Dixie found herself breathing as hard as if she'd just run a race. Even Stan, his mind usually occupied by more important things than his sister, such as guns and hunting, said, "What's eating you? You sound like a foundered horse."

"Stan, I—I'm scared."

"Well, don't be," he told her superiorly. "There's nothing to be scared of."

"That's easy for you to say. You're a boy."

He threw her a quick look. Something in her small face, pinched-looking this morning, must have struck a note of sympathy, for he said the right thing. "So I'm a boy—so what. You can do anything a boy can. You're as good as any boy."

This was a compliment, indeed! Dixie comforted herself with the beautiful words all the rest of the way to Akron High School.

But once there, they didn't help a bit. To the others in the freshman class, she was a baby—at least two years younger than anyone else, because Ruby Cline had started her to school when she had no baby sitter for her. The shyness came back a hundredfold, sweeping over Dixie. She blushed, she was tongue-tied. If only Lorene could have been there. With somebody to chum around with, Dixie knew, she could make her way.

"It'll get better," Stan told her, on the way home.

And, "It'll get better," her mother said, getting out the cookies and milk. "It'll get better," Mac Cline said, when she brought in the cows.

But it didn't. They said it all year long, and all year long it didn't get one bit better. To Dixie, the whole of her freshman year in high school was sheer misery, alleviated only when she could be home, with her family and the animals she loved.

There were new animals now. Sharing his daughter's love for Arabians, Mac Cline had bought an Arabian stallion, Janow, that had come from Iran. He was an old horse, but still full of spirit.

Shortly after he'd been added to the Cline menagerie, Janow broke his leg at the shoulder joint. He limped around for six months. Then infection set in and he went down. But before he died, Flame had been bred to him. When Flame foaled, the colt was, to Dixie's delight, the picture of her dam.

"I'll name her Janella," Dixie decided. "When she's two, I'll break her and use her to bring the cows in."

At that time, Stan's joy was a spotted Hambletonian natural pacer mare named Shooting Star. Together, Stan and Dixie broke her. They also broke an Arabian filly named Rackanna, that Mac had given to Stan.

With so much work to do, Dixie had little time to brood over her dislike of school, but she was relieved when summer vacation came around. "I'm not going to think about having to go back," she told her father. "That would spoil the whole summer."

"You will have to go back," Mac Cline said slowly. "Sooner or later you'll have to face up to it."

"Oh, I know. You don't get to be a veterinarian by dropping out of high school. Dad, there are going to be a lot of rough spots along the way. I don't expect it to be easy. This is one of the rough spots, that's all. Don't worry—I'll go back, and I'll survive!"

Mac grinned at her. "That's my girl. Don't let anybody try to tell me you won't make it. Don't let anybody try to tell me it's a man's job and a girl shouldn't even attempt it. *This* girl should! Stick to your guns, honey." He paused, slipping his arm around his daughter's shoulders. "Dixie, I've got some news that ought to make next year look a little brighter. Your Uncle Monk is going to bring his family back here to live."

"Oh, Dad—that means I'll have Lorene to go to school with. That'll make all the difference."

And it did. When sophomore year began, Lorene and Dixie faced it together. What can be a grind for one, Dixie realized, can be fun when there's someone to share it with. Soon Dixie and Lorene settled down to a pleasant routine. The two girls went to school with Stan in the Model A each morning, and returned with him after school—except there was a difference from last year. Stan had gone out for football. This gave the girls some after-school time to themselves. They could join clubs and get into extracurricular activities, as Dixie hadn't been able to last year. Sometimes, because there were chores waiting at home, Dixie and Lorene went to Grandma Cline's house in Akron and did their homework. Other days, they went to JUGS meetings.

The JUGS—short for "Just Us Girls"—had been chosen by Dixie with a purpose. Ideally, she would have joined a club of prospective veterinarians, had there been such a club. The JUGS, composed mainly of girls who wanted to go into nursing, was the next best thing.

The JUGS worked in the local hospital, both in the office and in the wards, assisting nurses. They learned hospital procedures, and when they had passed a test to determine what they had learned, they were awarded caps and pins for proficiency in nurses' aide work.

"At least," Dixie reasoned, "it's medical work. If I learn how to take care of people, that will certainly help when I learn how to take care of animals."

The prospective nurses of JUGS didn't think much of Dixie's ambition to be a veterinarian. "You're crazy even to think about it," one of them told her.

"You'll drop out the first year," another predicted.

"Drop out?" a third put in. "Why, she'll never

even get into veterinary school. They won't let her in, I'll bet you anything. Besides, what farmer or rancher in his right mind would trust valuable dairy stock to a girl—a little bit of a girl at that!"

"You're right—they probably don't even accept girls in veterinary school! It's men's work!"

Such comments only stiffened Dixie's resolve. "If they've never accepted a girl in veterinary school, then I'll be the first," she told them calmly. "I'll be a pioneer."

The idea that veterinary school might not even accept her was a new one—and it bore investigation, Dixie decided. She wrote a letter of inquiry to the School of Veterinary Medicine at Colorado Agricultural and Mechanical College, at Fort Collins, Colorado. Stan was going to Colorado A&M next fall. Dixie, regardless of what course she took, would follow a year later.

The whole family was in on it, helping to compose the letter, the gist of which was: What are my chances of getting in?

Fingers crossed, Dixie waited for the reply. She knew that two years of pre-veterinary college work were required before admission to the School of Veterinary Medicine. She wanted to know if she had a chance, before investing two years. Could they refuse her, just because she was a girl?

Days and days of waiting dragged by. Surely,

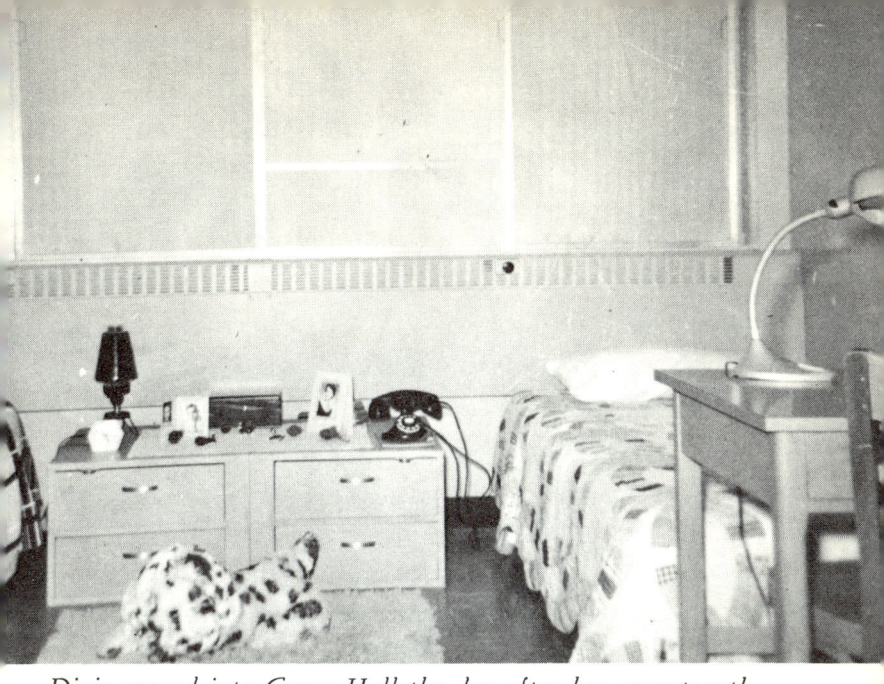

Dixie moved into Green Hall the day after her seventeenth birthday when she entered college as a pre-veterinary student

surely they wouldn't turn her down! Why, she could hold her own against any boy when it came to farm work, especially working with livestock. And she *cared* about animals so much, they meant so much to her. Had she managed to get that across in the letter?

Finally, the answer came. At the first sentence, her heart lifted. But as she read on, disappointment made her feel sick.

In part, the letter said:

"We have no regulations which state that women students cannot enroll in the School of Veterinary Medicine. All things being equal, however, the places usually go to well-qualified men students, as we do not feel that women are particularly suited to follow

51

the profession of veterinary medicine.... It would be necessary for you to carry your subjects in a very outstanding manner and to have other qualifications which would recommend you for serious consideration. Otherwise, I do not feel that you would be accepted as a member of the class after the pre-veterinary college work has been completed."

Dixie stood very still, thinking it through. After a moment, she read the letter again. Then her eyes began to light up. "They didn't come right out and say *no*," she told herself. "I'll just have to be good, that's all. I'll just have to be such an outstanding student, and prove that I have such outstanding qualifications, that the School of Veterinary Medicine simply can't afford to pass me by. That's what it comes down to."

She wrote back to Colorado A&M, requesting permission to register as a pre-veterinary student. To her delight, permission was granted. One barrier had been hurdled.

Dixie was sixteen the year she graduated from high school. In the fall, she'd go off to college. Would it be, she wondered with a pang of fear, like her freshman year in high school? Would it be a repetition of the misery, the horrible shyness, the feeling of not belonging? Akron had a population of six hundred; Fort Collins, nearly fifteen thousand. How easy to get lost in a place like that!

Well, Dixie told herself, there'd be no more of that nonsense. Every minute of every day at college had to count. She had to make such a showing that the School of Veterinary Medicine would welcome her. There'd be no time for misery, no time to feel sorry for herself. It would be all work, work, work!

The day after her seventeenth birthday, Dixie entered Colorado A&M. It was like entering another world—and, to her surprise and delight, she found her new world exciting and altogether wonderful.

She settled down in Green Hall, one of the women's dormitories. Dorothy Hinkle, from southeastern Colorado, was her roommate. Dorothy's sister Barbara had a room with Laura Franklin, from Nebraska. A little farther down the hall was Pat Corbin, from Wiley, Colorado. These girls became Dixie's closest friends.

Each entering freshman was assigned to an advisor. Dixie's was Dr. Chow, who advised pre-veterinary students. It was his responsibility to help her arrange her courses so that she would have the proper credits for entrance into the School of Veterinary Medicine by the end of her sophomore year.

But, Dr. Chow warned her—as everyone else had—her chances of getting into the school were slim. "You see," he explained, "there are always many more candidates for admission to the school than can be accommodated. All of them are students whose records in pre-veterinary are acceptable, so the final selection is made on the basis of a personal interview. They'll take into consideration the fact that you are a woman, for, whether or not you consider it fair, this is still thought of as a man's field. They'll also take physical characteristics into consideration."

His eyes measured her—slim, feminine-looking, only five feet three inches tall when she stood her straightest.

"I still want to try," Dixie said.

"Now, if you wanted to do laboratory work," Dr. Chow went on, "or, if you wished to specialize in the care of pet animals..." His voice trailed off.

Dixie shook her head. "Cattle, horses, farm animals of all kinds—I know them and love them, and I want to take care of them."

The doctor smiled suddenly. "Well, you can certainly try. I believe the examining board takes spirit into consideration, as well, and you have plenty of that. Let's work out a program of studies for you."

Dixie dug into her studies. An outstanding record—she had to have that, or she'd never even get before that examining board. As for the personal interview—well, she'd think about that when the time came.

It was hard work, pre-veterinary school. Chemistry, biology, botany, zoology, English, history... round and round they went with, Dixie thought ruefully, chemistry turning up more often than the others because she found it her hardest subject to master.

But it wasn't all work. Something wonderful and brand-new happened in Dixie's life that first year in college—she found that she was popular with boys. She had always been pretty, but the boys in school at home had considered her too young for them, and her shyness had kept her from trying to demonstrate that she wasn't. Here, nobody seemed to bother about age, and her shyness was, at last, fading away. There were dates—the offer of more dates than her work load would allow her to accept. But she did date, going to dances, fraternity parties, rodeos—and she had a wonderful time.

Freshman year flew by, and then, once more, she and Stan were home. "Glad to have you back," said

Rockwell Hall at Colorado State University was Dixie's home when she began the exciting study of veterinary medicine

Mac Cline, and the shine in his eyes told her that this was the understatement of the year. "I could use a little help around here."

Back to the chores—rounding up the cattle, riding the tractor, bringing in the hay, milking. Sometimes Dixie worked with a book in her hand, reviewing the demon chemistry.

And then, summer over, it was time to return to college, now renamed Colorado State University.

It was another year of concentrated study for Dixie —the home stretch in her fight to get into veterinary school.

In the spring, before the semester was over, Dixie was summoned for that interview toward which all her work had been directed. She found, to her dismay, that there were four hundred applicants for admission to the School of Veterinary Medicine, from CSU and from other colleges. Of this group, only sixty-five would be selected, on the basis of grades, background, and aptitude, for entrance to the school in the coming autumn.

In grim determination, Dixie waited her turn. When at last her name was called, she thought, "I will never be this scared again in my whole life!" She got to her feet, threw back her shoulders, and marched into the examination room. She tried to smile as the board examiners looked her over—measuring her height, she thought, estimating her weight, wondering what on earth gave this half pint the notion that she could be a veterinarian.

"Miss Cline, will you tell us why you want to become a veterinarian?" someone asked, and the examination had begun.

When it was over, Dixie remembered only bits and pieces of the ordeal. She had answered every question, she knew that. She had tried hard. She had done the best she could. She had given a good account of herself. And now there was nothing to do but wait.

When she went home for the summer, she still didn't know. By now she was beginning to be edgy. Nothing was as bad as waiting, she thought.

"You'll make it. Don't worry," Mac told her a dozen times. Of course *he* thought so. But how about those men who had asked her all the questions, who had weighed her answers with unreadable eyes—what did they think?

Day after day the mail arrived, and still no answer.

She was out in the field, mowing, when the answer finally came. Arthur dashed out to get the mail as soon as it was delivered. Dixie could see him in the distance, leafing through it. Then, all at once, he leaped on his bike, waving a letter over his head.

Dixie killed the tractor engine and jumped to the ground. She started to meet Arthur, but her shaking knees wouldn't let her. So she stood there, leaning against the tractor. In a moment, she would know.

Obstacles overcome, Dixie entered the College of Veterinary Medicine

CHAPTER 5

FIRST HURDLES PASSED

"What does it say? Open it!" Arthur demanded.

"Give me a chance," Dixie told him. Her face was pale beneath her tan. Her whole body shook. Now that the answer was here, she was strangely reluctant to know what it was.

"Open it!" Arthur repeated impatiently. "If you're scared to, let me—"

"I'll do it." Dixie fumbled with the flap, finally tearing the envelope open. Her eyes caught the first few words, and color rushed back to her cheeks.

"It gives me great pleasure to inform you that the faculty offers you admission to the College of Veterinary Medicine of this institution, beginning the fall quarter, 1957," the letter began.

"What does it *say?*" Arthur was jumping up and down in his anxiety.

"I made it," said Dixie. The words came out an awed whisper. Then she flung her arms around her little brother and shouted "I made it!" at the top of her lungs. With Arthur at her heels, she raced to the house to spread the good news.

The freshman veterinary class was divided into two sections. There were two other girls among the sixty-five entering freshmen, but they were both in the other section. Dixie found herself the lone girl in a group of men, all of them considerably older than she, most of them married. They treated her like a little sister—and, like a little sister, she became the prime target for their jokes and pranks. But she didn't mind. It was all part of this wonderful world she had hoped for and she was honored by their acceptance.

The courses were completely different from anything in her previous experience, highly specialized and progressively more difficult. Dixie had known it was going to be hard—but not this hard! Each course presented its unique problems. And each required so much time!

There were lectures in virology—the study of viruses—by Dr. Chow, who had been Dixie's pre-vet advisor. Pathology—the study of the nature of diseases and of the changes caused by them—took many of Dixie's Saturdays and many nights as well; she spent long hours poring over slides, learning the characteristics of various kinds of diseased tissues. Parisitology was the study of small bugs and worms that invade animals. Learning to identify each required great concentration. In fact, "Just learning to pronounce them is quite a feat," Dixie thought, as she recited out loud, *"Dioclaphyma renale,* the giant kidney worm; *exyuris equi,* the pin worm of horses; *tetrameres americana,* stomach worm found in turkeys . . ."

"I suppose you have to look at them, too," her roommate said, wrinkling her nose in disgust.

"Naturally," Dixie told her, grinning. "We look at them in jars and under microscopes, and—"

"Spare me the gory details," the other girl begged. "I can smell formaldehyde on your clothes, even though you leave your coveralls in the lab. That's enough."

Dixie herself had had trouble getting accustomed to some things she learned. Her first day in anatomy had shaken her. A ghastly, pungent smell filled the room. "What is it?" Dixie had gasped, fighting down a wave of nausea.

"Formaldehyde," the professor said. "The animals on which you will work are preserved in it. You'll get used to it. . . ."

Dixie understood what he left unsaid. If they didn't get used to it, they couldn't be veterinarians. All right, then, she'd get used to it. It was absolutely necessary to study, at first hand, every muscle, bone, nerve, and

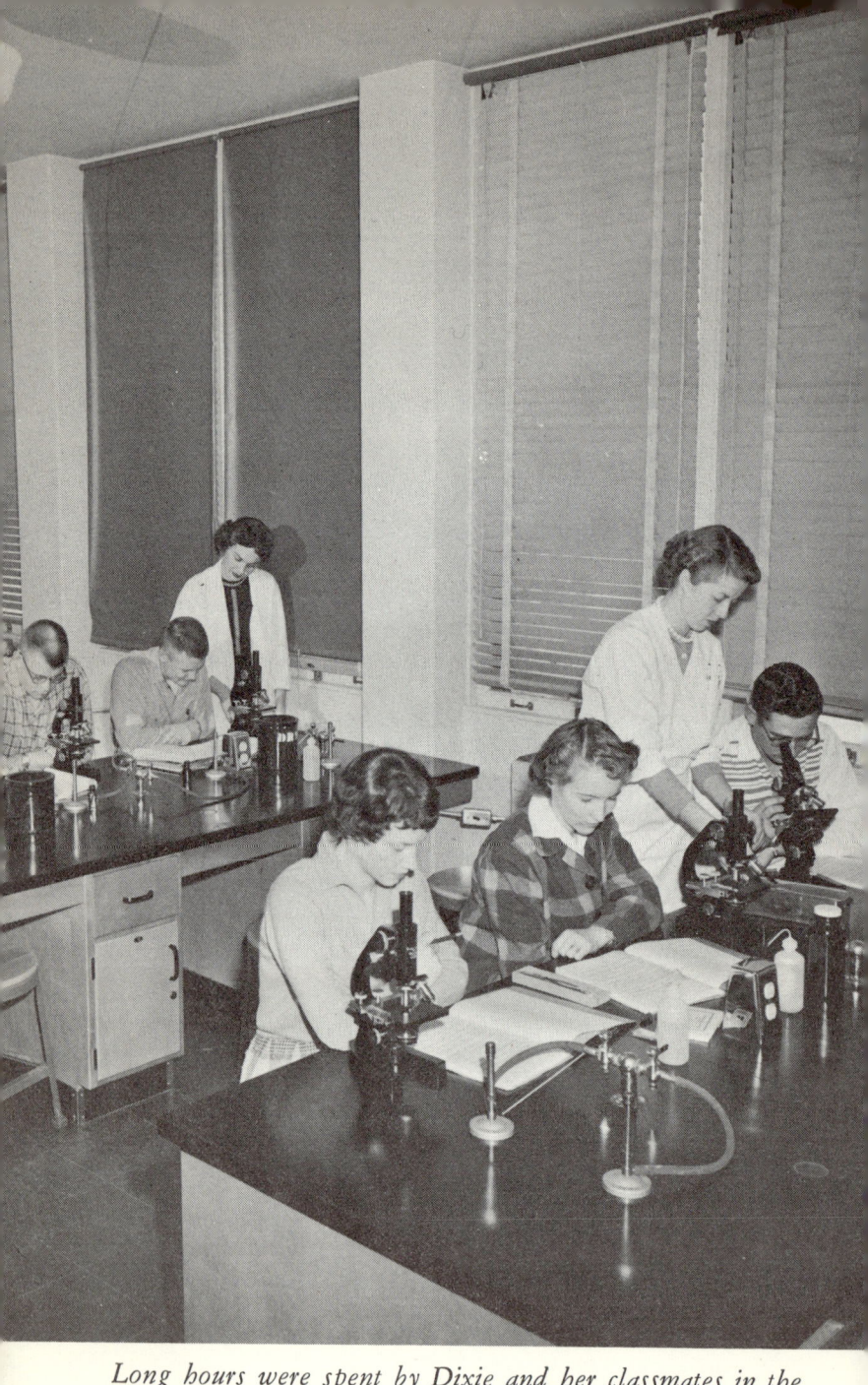

Long hours were spent by Dixie and her classmates in the laboratory, intently absorbing knowledge of microbiology

blood vessel in the many types of animals they would eventually treat.

The class was divided into groups of three for the study of anatomy. Within each group, one member would read aloud the information about the various parts of the animal, while the other two partners dissected. They started with a preserved greyhound for each group.

Through Dixie's mind ran that phrase she had heard so often, *It's a man's work.* Straightening her shoulders, she grimly began her dissection. The thought of stripping the body of the greyhound down, piece by piece, was unnerving, but soon she became so absorbed that she forgot her nervousness. She was learning, from this cadaver, the way that living beings were constructed—how fascinating!

As time went on, Dixie found she could work on the body of a cow or a horse without flinching. She could forget the smell of the lab, forget everything but her intense interest in what she was learning.

Much of her time outside the classroom was spent in studying, in preparation for the next day's classes and for examinations.

The veterinary students always had an examination of one kind or another coming up, and they were always worried about exams. They had good reason to worry. As the year wore on, the class shrank in size. A couple of the men had nervous breakdowns.

Four failed and were dropped. Several others were forced to withdraw because of family situations that made demands on their time which they could not reconcile with the time required by their studies.

Those who remained became a close-knit, dedicated group. The College of Veterinary Medicine operated on a self-imposed, self-supervised honor system. In Dixie Cline, the sense of personal integrity was a part of her way of life.

With such a demanding schedule, it was necessary for the vet students to let off steam occasionally. Every quarter they had a picnic, the freshmen and the sophomores together, and the juniors and seniors together. At these get-togethers, Dixie became better acquainted with Pat Cross, one of the other three girls in college.

At the picnics, the men would rig up barrels, saddle them, and tie them between two trees. Then they would attach ropes, which, when pulled, made the "horses" buck wildly. Naturally, they insisted that the girl students do the riding. "Up you go," the girls would be told, and it would have been folly to refuse, for if they had they would have been forcibly hoisted into the saddle. But the girls were good sports and accepted with good humor the bumps and bruises they acquired during their rides.

Each November at CSU there was a livestock show known as the "Little National Western." It included horse shows, exhibitions of cattle showmanship, and judging. Dixie took Flame to Fort Collins for the show during her sophomore year. With little time to practice, she won no awards, but it was fun.

"College Days," an annual event in May, provided another break in routine. The sophomore vet students were responsible for building a float, and Dixie's class won the sweepstakes with theirs. It was a wagon bearing the inscription, *Have Syringe, Will Travel.* Mounted on the wagon was a giant syringe, operated by a dummy driver who gave continuous shots to the horse that pulled the wagon.

Although her time was filled to overflowing, Dixie did manage an occasional weekend at home. On one of those weekends, Dixie took five of her classmates along to help her father with the branding. "You hold the animals," Dixie directed the men, "and I'll do the branding."

Obligingly, the men threw the animals down and held them while Dixie applied the branding iron. Suddenly, one of the men began to laugh. "Some vet you'll be! You've got all the brands upside down!"

Dixie supposed this was just part of their customary teasing, but she took a closer look, just to be sure. To her chagrin, it was all too true. How was she ever going to live this down?

Then she had an idea. "That's because I'm accustomed to branding with the cows standing up. When you threw them down, I didn't want to embar-

At the Veterinary Hospital at CSU, the veterinary students view actual cases and learn to make the correct diagnoses

rass you, so I didn't say anything," she told them with a straight face.

It was a reasonable-sounding alibi, but it didn't save her. The joke followed her for years and became a vet school classic. But a laugh was a laugh, a means of relieving the constant strain, so Dixie accepted it with good humor.

During her junior and senior years, Dixie lived in a comfortable apartment; she and her roommates called it "Sherwood Forest" because it was located on North Sherwood Avenue.

Her roommates were a home economics major and Pat Cross from vet school. Pat owned a little orange Volkswagen, a luxury far superior to the bicycle Dixie had previously ridden the fifteen blocks to and from classes.

During her junior year, Dixie's brother Stan was married. He had graduated from CSU, after the required five-year course, with a degree as a soil scientist. He had little interest in farming or cattle, and was awaiting a civil service appointment.

The appointment came through sooner than expected. The wedding date was hastily set and Dixie and her family went to Ault, Colorado, to see Stan married to Doris Lightsy.

Dixie was a bridesmaid. A forestry major named Cory Mordeux was one of the ushers and, getting better acquainted, Dixie began to wish she could stay for

An annual event, "College Days," provided a needed break in routine. Dixie's class won the sweepstakes for their float

all the wedding festivities, instead of having to hurry back to vet school. But her conscience wouldn't let her stay. There was too much work to be done, and every moment was more precious than the last.

Later in the semester, Cory asked her for a date. By this time, Dixie had done some inquiring and some thinking. Inquiry had elicited the information that Cory Mordeux had "quite a temper." Thinking had made Dixie decide that she didn't want to get involved in something that might well end unhappily. "When I marry," she told herself, "it will have to be a veterinarian. Veterinary medicine is my whole life. I'll have to have a husband who understands and shares it, or I'll never be happy . . . and neither will my husband."

So Dixie, regretfully, turned Cory down.

By now, vet school required more night hours than ever before, especially hours devoted to the dissection laboratory. The class was at work on horses. They had started with fifteen horse cadavers, suspended by hooks from the ceiling. By the end of the quarter there was very little left of them.

One night, Dixie looked up from her work to see a classmate viewing her speculatively. She didn't like the wicked gleam in his eye, or the way his glance shifted between her and one of the now-empty hooks. She could practically read his mind.

"We've just about run out of horses," he remarked. "Isn't it time we got ourselves a small animal? How about Dixie—she looks to be the right size."

Dixie backed away. He came after her.

"Don't you dare!" she cried, ducking out of reach.

But there was no escape. Several other pranksters got into the act. They cornered Dixie, ran a meat hook through the back of her coveralls, and hoisted her up in the air. There she remained until they took pity on her.

She didn't really mind, though. They all laughed, and for a few moments, the tension that always dogged them was relieved. They all went back to work the better for their prank.

When her junior year was over, Dixie spent the summer in Denver, working for a veterinarian with a small animal practice. She needed the experience, and although she was going to specialize in farm animals, she wanted to know all there was to know about her chosen profession. There is no internship for veterinarians, as there is for medical doctors, so working for a licensed vet is standard practice in obtaining necessary on-the-spot experience.

While she was in Denver, Cory Mordeux came to see her. This time she went out with him. He proved to be as fascinating a companion as she had hoped—or feared—he would be. When she went back to school for her senior year that fall, Cory Mordeux was her steady date.

It was a stormy romance. They fought; they could never seem to see eye to eye on anything. They broke up, made up, broke up, and made up again.

At one point, Dixie began to date other men, but Cory was in her mind. The others seemed hardly alive compared to him. Soon she was back dating Cory again. She argued with herself that their personalities clashed, that he was not a veterinarian and she could only be happy with someone in her profession, could only make someone in her own profession happy. But the arguments did little good.

Then Cory made it necessary for her to come to a decision. "Let's stop the everlasting analyzing and reasoning," he said, "and just get married!"

The proposal came at a time when Dixie was very

During her summer vacations, Dixie worked at the Brentwood Animal Hospital in Denver, to gain veterinary experience

busy, and so tired that she felt she could hardly take another step or read another page. There were classes. There were lectures. There was endless laboratory work. There were clinics. Added to all that was the task of preparing for State Boards. To practice in any given state, a veterinarian must pass the examinations given by that state, in order to obtain his license.

"Why am I killing myself?" Dixie asked herself. "Why am I driving myself into a nervous breakdown? I've proved what I set out to prove—that I can be a veterinarian. I can do a man's job. Now that I've proved it, why don't I give up and be a woman, as I was meant to be? Why don't I marry Cory, and be a wife and a mother, and forget this man's world?"

A full-fledged D.V.M. at long last, Dixie Cline goes out on a cal

CHAPTER 6

DIXIE CLINE, D.V.M.

But it didn't take Dixie long to realize that her thinking was prompted by nervousness and weariness, not by conviction. A marriage for which she had given up her career would have no chance of success.

"I want to practice veterinary medicine," she told herself. "And not just long enough to prove that I can get into practice. I want to work at it all my life—because it is my life, the way I've chosen. Of course I want to marry. But marriage will have to be all of a piece with my work. That's why it'll have to be a veterinarian. I'll have to wait."

So she said "no" to Cory—regretfully, and yet with a feeling of relief. She hadn't made a mistake.

Dixie settled down to work. Exams were coming up. So were State Boards. If possible, the veterinary students were busier than ever before.

One small break in the routine came when a group of Russian ranchers toured the College of Veterinary Medicine. Dixie was assigned to small animal medicine that week and, when the Russians arrived, was busily clipping a poodle. Pat Cross was working on large animal medicine at the time.

The Russians made a great fuss over these two young women, working side by side with men, and Dixie almost giggled when the interpreter said the visitors were marveling at two girls "doing men's work."

The story made the news, and Dixie and Pat had the fun of hearing their names on the radio and reading about themselves in the newspaper. But the excitement soon died down, and the grind of work, work, work filled their days.

The senior class took the Colorado State Boards a couple of weeks before graduation. Those who planned to practice in Colorado could now heave a deep sigh of relief. Ahead of them lay only school finals. Then they could, as one of them expressed it, "grab the diplomas and run!"

Dixie, however, wasn't content with a license to practice only in Colorado. A week before graduation, she and twenty other seniors went to Manhattan, Kansas, and took the three-day Kansas Boards.

And then, at last, the great day came—the culmination of six years of backbreaking effort—graduation.

Mac Cline got to his daughter first, when the ceremonies were over. "Congratulations, Doctor!"

Dixie grinned at him. Oh, the delight of hearing herself called "Doctor!" She took her father's hand and extended her other hand to her mother. "I would never have even gotten started, let alone graduated, without all the encouragement you gave me."

"Now what?" Ruby Cline asked. "Are you coming home?"

"Not yet." Dixie looked down at the precious paper that told the world she was a D.V.M. "I don't know exactly where I want to practice. I just might set up near Stan, in Montana. That means I have to take the Montana State Boards—tomorrow."

In order to get to Montana in time, Dixie and two classmates drove all night. They arrived, sleepless, just in time to start two full days of exams.

Finally Dixie headed home to rest a little before deciding where to hang out her shingle.

During those weeks, nearly everybody Dixie met—old friends and strangers alike—reminded her that a veterinary was badly needed right there. "We have no local vets at all. The closest ones are at Brush, twenty-three miles west, and at Yuma, twenty-five miles east. Why not go into practice right here?"

She talked it over with her father. "I don't know if it's a good idea, Dad."

"Why not? You could live at home."

A pickup truck provides a happy solution to the problem of transporting the bulky instruments of a veterinarian

"I know, and I'd love that. But everyone around here remembers me as the little kid who rode horseback to Rock Springs School, or as the little girl who caught a pig at the fair. Are they going to accept me as Dr. Cline? Are they going to be willing to entrust valuable livestock to me?"

As it turned out, it wasn't only difficult for the people around Akron to accept the small, pretty girl as Dr. Cline—it was impossible. Everyone had called her Dixie for too many years. Fortunately, someone came up with the compromise, "Dr. Dixie." The name stuck, and she liked it.

Dixie thought long and hard about it, and finally decided to gamble; she'd set up practice here at home. She rented a vacant office building out on the highway. She moved in her equipment—the precious instruments that had cost so much, that must be paid for out of her earnings. She hung out a modest sign, *Akron Animal Hospital,* and settled down to wait for business to come her way.

The wait seemed endless. Were there no sick animals nearby? Dixie knew better; more, she knew what must be happening. Ranchers and farmers were still calling on the vets in Brush and Yuma. Days passed and more days. The doorbell was silent. The phone never rang.

"Just one call!" Dixie thought. "Just one! That would break the ice. One call, and I'll be on my way!"

The phone just sat there.

"Ring, darn you!" she told it one evening, just before she closed up shop.

Obediently, the phone rang.

Dixie jumped. She was so startled by the broken silence that the phone rang twice more before she picked it up.

"Dr. Cline," she said.

A man's voice came back to her. "This is Henry Pilt. I just took over the old Bollit farm out on Rock Road. Is the doctor in?"

"This is the doctor," Dixie told him.

There was a long pause. "Oh. Well, the two veterinarians—I mean, the *other* veterinarians—they're busy. But I don't think—"

"What seems to be the trouble?" Dixie asked briskly.

"I've got a cow coming to calf, but she's not getting anywhere. But—"

"I'll be there in about ten minutes," Dixie said, and hung up before he could say "but" again.

Quickly she gathered up the equipment she might need and headed for the car. As she drove, she ran over in her mind her knowledge of dystocias—difficult births caused by abnormal positions of the calves or lambs or colts, or whatever the species.

Dixie found Mr. Pilt out in the barn with the cow.

"I'm Dr. Cline," she said.

Her patient safely restrained in a squeeze stall, Dixie injects procaine prior to performing a surgical procedure

His eyes—as so many pairs of eyes had before—measured her, coming out with a scant-five-feet-three answer. "No," said Mr. Pilt. "Listen, lady, that cow's a valuable animal. I'm not going to have some—"

"She won't be very valuable to you dead," Dixie told him bluntly.

He hesitated, and Dixie seized the moment to move over to the cow and start her examination. Mr. Pilt followed her, watching anxiously.

"I'll try chains," Dixie said. After cleansing her hands, she manipulated the calf's legs and head, in order to get the chains around it. When the chains were in place, she showed Mr. Pilt how to help her pull on them.

Together, they pulled. But the calf did not emerge.

Mr. Pilt seemed resigned to having her there, now that she was at work. "Will you have to operate?" he asked.

"We'll wait and see," she decided. "I'll have a try with the calf pullers first."

After much pulling and straining, the calf pullers worked.

Tired, but relieved and elated, Dixie turned to Mr. Pilt. "Both patients are fine," she said. What she thought was: And I'm on my way!

Mr. Pilt shook his head. "Hey, you *do* know what you're doing," he said, his voice full of amazement. Then he grinned sheepishly. "Beg your pardon, Doc."

Mischievous Dr. Dixie is not above catching a ride on a donkey if there is no other transportation available

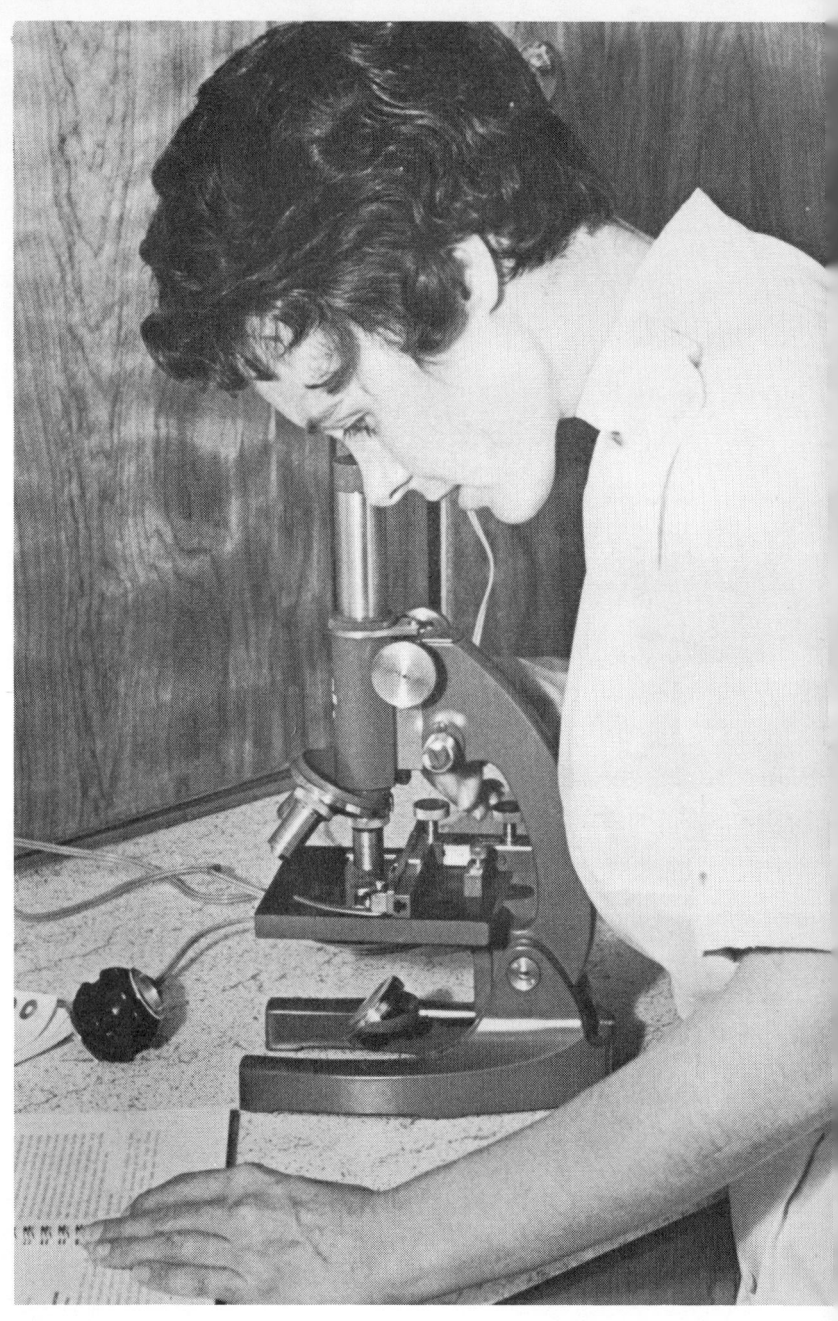

The examination of skin scrapings aids in diagnosing disorders

CHAPTER 7

TO BE A CELEBRITY

After that initial effort, Dixie's practice began to grow quickly and steadily. She immunized many dogs against rabies and distemper, and vaccinated many hogs against hog cholera. Soon she was so busy she could no longer spare the time to travel back and forth from the homestead. She located and rented an apartment in town.

Shortly before she moved, an old friend, Bob Graves, called and asked her for a date. He was a dairy cattleman, and she had dated him a few times during her last year of school, after she'd said "no" to Cory Mordeux.

The night of the date, while she was waiting for Bob to arrive, there was the sound of a car outside. Thinking it was Bob, Dixie went to the door—and found Cory there, instead.

"I'm on my way to an Army base in Kansas," he explained. "Come on, Dixie—spend my last civilian evening with me."

Dixie wasn't at all sure how she felt about Cory after the long lapse of time since she had last seen him. But one thing was certain. "I can't go out with you, Cory. I've got a date—with Bob Graves."

Cory grinned. "I'll stick around. Bob won't mind, when he hears I'm going in the Army."

It was now a little after seven, and Bob had said he'd pick Dixie up promptly at seven o'clock. They waited until eight, and then left, deciding that something had come up to prevent Bob's keeping the date.

Dixie and Cory went bowling. They were uneasy with each other—at least, Dixie felt uneasy with Cory. She asked him to take her home early.

When she got in, Mac Cline told Dixie that Bob had come, then gone back to town to try to find his date. "Said he'd be back if he didn't find you."

Shortly, back he came—not in the best of tempers. But Dixie apologized sincerely, and he calmed down.

"Come in and have breakfast with me in the morning, will you?" he asked.

Dixie promised that she would, and Bob went off to the motel, where he had engaged a room for the night.

Somewhat to her surprise, over breakfast next morning, Bob told her, "I think it would be better if we broke off dating. There's really no future for us."

As she wasn't in love with him, Dixie readily agreed. He had found someone else, she decided. But later in the morning, when Cory showed up at her office, she learned the reason for Bob's statement. Bob and Cory had had rooms next to each other in the motel. Cory had seized the opportunity to make it clear to Bob that Dixie was his girl. "He wished me luck," Cory told her, smiling blandly.

She gazed at him with mingled exasperation and affection. How fond she was of him—and how awfully mad he could make her!

"I'll see you when I get back from Korea," Cory said, and he was gone.

By now the phone that had once been so ominously silent seemed to ring continuously in the office of Dixie Cline, D.V.M. Each call was a challenge. She never knew what kind of crisis she'd be called upon to face.

One day, however, she received a very different kind of call. "This is the Denver *Post*," said a strange voice. "We once did a feature story about the JUGS, and now we are following up to see how many of those girls went into nursing. We know you didn't, but you are in a branch of the medical profession. We'd like to send someone down to interview you."

"All right," Dixie agreed, astonished, but pleased.

In due course a reporter and a photographer showed up in Akron. They interviewed Dixie and

Patients come in all sizes and varieties, and Dr. Dixie checks on their hearts and lungs with her stethoscope

another ex-JUG, who was a nurse in Washington County Hospital. It was interesting, and it was exciting to read the story and see the pictures in the Sunday magazine section of the Denver *Post*. But Dixie had immunizations to do and fractures to set and operations to perform. She soon forgot the incident.

Then came another surprise phone call, this one from Bob Palmer, who had a television show on station KOA, in Denver. "I'd like to do a show about you," he said.

This time there was quite a flurry in Akron. Bob Palmer and his crew arrived and followed Dixie around watching her treat cows, horses, and bulls.

"You obviously have the trust and respect of these

cattlemen," Bob told her. "It's great to see a little bit of a thing like you doing a man's job."

It was time, Dixie decided, to set this straight. "It's a woman's job," she said. "It's the job of anyone who can do it and wants to do it, man or woman, big or small. And," she added, smiling, "I love it!"

The show, when it appeared on television, was a sensation in Akron and for many miles around. Dixie, once again, enjoyed it, and once again went back to work.

But the excitement still wasn't over. The next call came from the *Saturday Evening Post*. Again, Dixie was interviewed and photographed, and in the January 27, 1962, issue of the magazine, a story about the twenty-three-year-old doctor of veterinary medicine appeared, complete with pictures. Dixie smiled and thanked everyone who told her how interesting the article was and how pretty she looked in the pictures, and went back to work.

The fourth call began, "My name is Ann Kaminsky. I'm an associate producer of the CBS television show, 'What's My Line?' "

"I ought to be more excited," Dixie thought, as she hung up the phone. "Oh, I am; it'll be wonderful to have such a trip, and wonderful to be on a big network television show. But—well, I guess it's just that that's *not* my line. I'm a veterinarian—that takes first place."

The trip and the program turned out to be all

Dixie had imagined, and more. Dixie bought herself a new green knit suit to travel in, and a becoming black dress to wear on the show. Her impression of New York was that it was big, *big,* BIG, but she didn't get lost, got to the television studio in plenty of time. The important people she met—John Daly, Bennett Cerf, Dorothy Kilgallen, Arlene Francis—were pleasant and friendly. On the air, Dixie found she wasn't at all nervous. She laughed and talked as if she were in the Clines' living room at home, with friends.

When it was all over, and everyone had told her how photogenic she was, she made a tour of New York, seeing the sights, including the United Nations. She visited Greenwich Village and took in a Broadway show. Then she told herself, "Enough of this—there's work to do!" and went back home to Akron.

As Dixie's practice continued to enlarge, she outgrew her little makeshift hospital. She bought a new, light-blue station wagon and began practicing from it. Many of her patients were too big to be brought to her office, anyway, and now she could take a portable hospital to the various farms and ranches.

The station wagon was a great improvement, but Dixie needed even better facilities as time went on. She began to make plans for building a real hospital. At about that time, she acquired a "partner."

"I have a little black dog," the local medical doctor told her. "He has a rather disagreeable temper. On

Calls come in at all hours and, many a night, Dr. Dixie loads up her car and sets out to take care of an emergency

occasion, he's bitten some of my patients. Do you think you might find a home for him somewhere?"

"I don't know," Dixie answered. "I'll ask around."

"If you can't," the M.D. decided, "I'll have to ask you to put him to sleep."

Occasionally, Dixie had euthanized (a painless causing of death) many an animal that had been seriously injured, when the owner wanted to end its misery. But killing a perfectly well animal didn't appeal to Dixie. She picked up the dog, whose name was Binx, and took him out to her parents' place.

Her father phoned shortly afterward. "Binx is gone."

"Binx is back here," an exasperated doctor reported a bit later.

Dixie retrieved the dog and decided to keep him herself. She always took him with her when she went to her parents' to visit. Once, one of the cows began unaccountably to chase Binx. Dixie picked him up and carried him all the way back to the house. From that time on, he was her constant, loving companion.

Binx was company for Dixie when she went on night calls, often a lonely business.

One of her clients, knowing how overworked Dixie was, asked her, "Have you ever thought of hiring an assistant?"

"I've thought about it—but I never have time to do anything about it."

"I have a niece who's looking for work of this kind," the man said. "She's had some training as a medical assistant. Name's Jeanne Bishop."

"By all means, send her over," Dixie replied. And when the girl arrived, Dixie found that she liked her on sight. Two years Dixie's junior, she had a pleasant personality and was anxious to learn. She was, in short, a godsend, and Dixie hired her on the spot.

Shortly afterward, the new Akron Animal Hospital was completed, and Dixie and Jeanne moved into the four-room apartment that was part of the building.

In addition to the living quarters, the new hospital had reception and waiting rooms, a kennel room, examination rooms for both large and small animals, an operation room, a combination X-ray and dark room, and a laboratory. Delighted with it, Dixie and Jeanne settled in. They worked well together, and the younger girl soon became an accomplished aide. She accompanied Dixie on calls Tuesdays and Thursdays and on all night calls. The rest of the time she stayed in the office and handled the phone, with a young girl substituting for her Tuesdays and Thursdays.

One day, Jeanne answered the phone while Dixie was in the middle of an operation. She turned pale. "The woman on the line says her dog's under the kitchen table. He's foaming at the mouth. She's afraid he has rabies."

A mad dog is a danger to every person and every

Having a pig for a patient reminds Dr. Dixie of the day, long ago, when she had entered the Catch a Pig Contest

unvaccinated animal for miles around. The disease is transmitted by the bite of an infected animal. Such a dog is likely to turn on anyone and attack viciously.

Dixie's mind raced over the problem as her hands went ahead mechanically with the operation. The dog suspected of rabies must be caught and isolated. If it survives two weeks, the suspicion of rabies was a false alarm. If it dies, the head must be sent to the state laboratory for investigation. Everyone the animal has bitten must begin the long and painful Pasteur treatment, the only chance for survival.

"Tell her I'll be there as soon as I can," Dixie said. "I can't just leave this dog here with the incision wide open. Tell her to get out of that kitchen and shut the door. Keep everyone out and keep the dog captive."

Jeanne relayed the message and hung up. Dixie went ahead with her surgery.

Before she got the incision closed, the phone rang again. Jeanne answered, listened, then burst into shouts of laughter. "That same woman," she reported a moment later. "She just noticed a bag of marshmallows on the floor with the bag chewed through. The dog was trying furiously to dislodge a candy stuck in his teeth. He was foaming marshmallow all over the place."

Not every case was that simple. One night in particular the girls were hoping that there would be no calls. It was Easter eve, and they wanted very much to attend sunrise services the next morning.

At four A.M., the phone rang.

"I have a cow trying to calf." It was the old, familiar story. "Could you—"

"Be right there," Dixie promised.

She woke Jeanne and they drove to the farm, some twenty miles away. Dixie began her examination. If this were a dystocia, perhaps she could pull the calf and still have time to get cleaned up and back to town for the services.

But, "The calf's too big," she reported, when her examination was over. "I'll have to do a Caesarean."

They stretched the cow out and tied her down. Dixie laid out her instruments and set up for surgery.

Then she gave the cow a local anesthetic, waited for it to take effect, and made her incision, cutting through the abdominal wall to reach the calf.

When she had pulled the calf out, she began to laugh. "He's in fine shape! He's trying to nurse before I get the incision sewed up. Somebody hold him out of my way."

As Dixie finished suturing, Jeanne pointed to the shafts of light showing through the cracks in the old barn. "The sun's up."

"Happy Easter," said Dr. Dixie. "Maybe next year..."

A few days later, back at their apartment, Jeanne looked up from the letter she was reading to say, "A friend of mine is coming up to see me from my home town. Why don't I ask him to bring another man along, so we can double date?"

It was a good idea, Dixie thought.

Her blind date turned out to be very attractive. He was tall and blond, with blue eyes. Better yet, he was fun to be with. His name was Jack Lycan, and Dixie liked him from the first.

During that evening, Dixie found herself telling Jack that she would never marry anyone but a veterinarian. And then she wondered, "Am I warning him off—or am I warning myself?"

"What did you think of your date?" Jeanne asked, when the men had left them.

"I liked him," Dixie said. "I liked him a lot."

"You seemed to hit it off very well."

Dixie laughed. "Oh, we did. But we have nothing in common. He owns a grocery store. What would we ever find to talk about?" She paused, then went on in a determined voice, "It was fun, but that's that. I'll never see him again. Now, let's get to bed—we've a hard day tomorrow."

The next day, Dixie got a letter from Cory Mordeux, saying he hoped to come home soon on leave. She was delighted to hear from him. Cory was an old friend, and very dear to her. If she did ever marry someone who wasn't a veterinarian—and she wasn't saying that she would!—it would certainly be Cory Mordeux.

Just before Christmas week, Jack Lycan phoned Dixie. Would she go with him to the Cowboys' Ball, a big event to be held in Lamar, about seventy miles from Jack's home town of Walsh? Jeanne urged her to accept, so that she and her friend from Walsh could go along. Dixie agreed, provided the men would come the two hundred miles to Akron to pick them up.

Then, shortly before the dance, another letter arrived from Cory. His leave was definite now. He was coming home for a weekend, and wanted to see Dixie.

She answered him immediately, saying yes, she'd be waiting for his phone call. Then her eyes lighted on the calendar. "Why, that's the weekend of the

Cowboys' Ball," she told Jeanne. "Why does everything happen at once?"

"You *can't* break the date with Jack," Jeanne pleaded. Dixie did some quick figuring. "Why don't I ask Jack to drive me to Pueblo, where Cory's family lives, after the dance? That would save him hundreds of miles of driving. You and your date could come along for the ride and then you could all go back to Walsh together, and I could spend the night with Cory's folks."

Jeanne was horrified. "You're out of your mind! You can't go out with one man and then, at the end of the evening, ask him to deliver you to another man!"

Dixie laughed. "Of course I can. There's nothing

In the operating room of her Akron hospital, the small veterinarian performs routine surgery on large animals

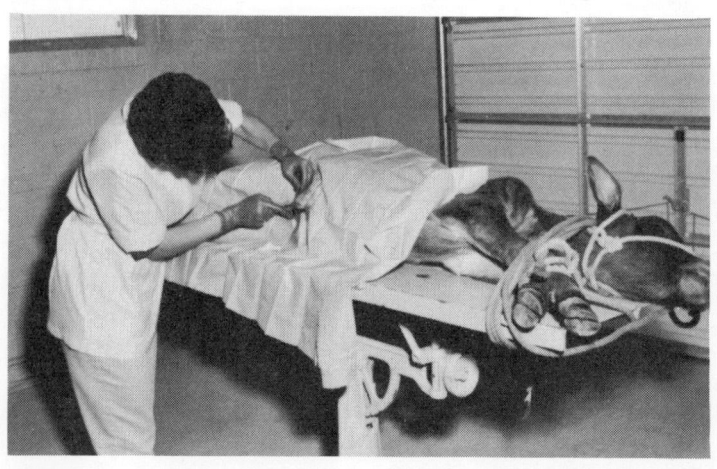

between Jack and me. This will be only my second date with him."

"You'll never see him a third time."

But Dixie planned to manage it that way, and changed the subject. They were spending too much time on this. There was work to do. Plenty of work.

There was the cow with milk fever, for instance—an infection which often occurs in dairy cattle shortly after calving, and is characterized by paralysis. Dixie drove out to the owner's farm and found that the cow, which had recently calved, was unable to get up.

The medical procedure was a tricky one. Dixie inserted a needle into the cow's jugular vein and drained in calcium solution. She did this slowly and carefully, listening to the animal's heart through her stethoscope during the whole slow process. While calcium might cure the cow, it might also stop the animal's heart completely within ten to thirty minutes.

When the danger was passed, she gave the cow a push. "Get up, you," she ordered.

To everyone's relief, the cow managed to lurch to her feet. She promptly began to graze, as if nothing had ever been wrong.

With all she had to do, the days slipped by for Dixie, each one running into the next before she realized it. Suddenly, it was time for the Cowboys' Ball.

Before the men came to pick them up, Jeanne

delivered a long lecture on the subject of not spoiling the evening by asking Jack Lycan, in advance, to drive her to Cory's home town of Pueblo. Dixie promised not to bring the subject up until the dance was over, and she kept her promise.

But when the two couples piled into the car after a wonderful evening, Dixie asked, "Jack, will you drive me to Pueblo instead of back to Akron? An old friend is home on leave, and I want to see him."

Jack gave her a quick, sharp look but he said, "Sure. Why not? It'll be a much shorter drive."

On the way, he asked casual questions—or, at least, they sounded casual—about Cory. When they reached the big, old-fashioned red brick house, Dixie took her friends inside and introduced them to Cory and his parents. After a few moments, Jack shepherded his passengers out. Dixie went to the car with them.

"See?" she whispered to Jeanne. "I told you Jack wouldn't mind."

"You wait," Jeanne whispered back. "Of course he was polite about it. But he'll never call you again. And Cory will go back to the Army—and then where will you be?"

Dixie chuckled. "I'll be out looking for a veterinarian to marry—that's where I'll be."

The next day, on the way back to Akron, Cory told her that he was thinking of making the Army his career. "How would you like to be an Army wife?"

"I wouldn't," Dixie told him honestly. "Army people keep moving around. What about my career? I'd never have a chance to establish a practice. Besides, I already *have* a practice established now, in Akron."

"You wouldn't have to work at all," Cory told her. "You could be a lady of leisure."

"I wouldn't like that, either," Dixie told him firmly. "I'd hate it!"

They rode a while in silence. Then Cory said, "All right, suppose I give up the idea of the Army and get a job in forestry around here somewhere."

That was no solution, Dixie pointed out. Marriage shouldn't force anyone to give up a career he wanted. Or she wanted.

"Why don't we quit talking about it and just get married?" Cory urged. "We can straighten out the problems afterwards."

"That's all wrong," Dixie answered. "If we can't settle our differences first, we'd never settle them. No marriage could survive under such circumstances."

There was a long silence, and then, "I won't ask you again," Cory said quietly.

"I know."

When she was back home in the animal hospital at Akron, Dixie thought, "Now, where do I go from here? I've sent Cory away. And I've probably fixed it so Jack Lycan will never see me again."

Dr. Dixie makes regular rounds, testing animals for brucellosis

CHAPTER 8

"MARRY A VETERINARIAN"

As time went by, Dixie found that Jack Lycan was more often in her thoughts than Cory Mordeux ever had been. She was lonely for him, although they had spent only two evenings together. His face kept coming unbidden into her mind.

But he didn't call her.

Work, Dixie told herself, was the best antidote for loneliness. Anyway, brooding was a waste of time, so why brood?

Her days were busy enough. There was regular testing to be done for erysipelas—an infectious disease of the skin—and brucellosis. There were accident victims to be patched up, ruptures to be repaired. She didn't want for something to keep her occupied.

Occasional blood transfusions were necessary for injured animals. For this, Dixie fortunately had a

Detailed medical records are kept on every animal she treats. Dr. Dixie often devotes long hours to paper work

willing and handy donor. Out at the farm her family had a "combination-type" dog that was part Labrador. His name was Wilfred, but Dixie had nicknamed him "Blood Bank," since he seemed quite content to sit quietly while she inserted a needle in his vein and withdrew the required blood. If a drop spilled when she withdrew the needle, Wilfred would tidily lick it up and then go about his business. The animals of the surrounding countryside, Dixie said, owed a great debt to good old Wilfred.

After a long stretch of nothing but work, work, work, which made even so dedicated a worker as Dixie feel dull, Jack Lycan called her. Giving the lie to Jeanne's dire predictions, he came up from Walsh—bringing Jeanne's friend with him—not once, but many times.

"Are you two getting serious?" Jeanne asked, after a while. Romance was on Jeanne's mind. She was seeing more and more of an Akron boy.

Dixie's answer was no. "I like Jack a great deal. He gets my mind off my work. We find a lot to talk about. But basically, Jeanne, Jack and I have nothing in common. I still plan to marry a veterinarian."

The trouble was, she hadn't met that veterinarian.

As time went on, Dixie found herself growing restless. "I'm coming down with something," she told herself. When nothing materialized, she found an-

All sorts of animals still enchant Dr. Dixie and, as she had during her childhood, she finds time to stop and play

other excuse. "I need to learn more about my profession. I need practical experience in a different phase of veterinary medicine."

She gave the matter a great deal of thought. Finally, she told Jeanne, "I've made up my mind. I'm going to lease out my practice and go to work for a while in a big city. I'm getting stale here. Everybody knows me and I know everybody. I need to go to a new place and learn new things."

She told the drug salesmen to pass the word along, and she also listed the practice for lease in several of the veterinary journals. Meanwhile, Dixie began to send out feelers, looking for new places to go, new fields through which to expand her knowledge.

She settled, at last, on the Albrech Veterinary Hospital, in Denver.

"If you've got to go away from here," Jeanne said, "why not go far away? Why not halfway across the country somewhere?"

"I don't know," Dixie told her. "I just don't know. I only know that I—well, I don't want to go too far away." Only to herself would she admit that possibly, just possibly, it was Jack Lycan that she didn't want to get too far away from.

The practice was leased to a Dr. Haller, and Dixie and her faithful Binx packed up and moved into an apartment in Denver. The following week she went to work at Albrech Veterinary Hospital.

Dixie found her new work very different. Even the people were different in this big city. Ranchers were intensely concerned about the health of their animals because the animals governed their economic welfare. City clients cared less about money, but were emotionally concerned about their pets.

For the first time in her professional life, Dixie had regular working hours. Office hours were nine A.M. until noon, and three to six P.M. Emergencies were handled outside office hours, of course, but on a rotating system. Night work was shared by all the veterinarians in the area. The group employed a telephone secretary who answered all night calls, decided which ones could safely wait until morning, and routed the rest to whichever doctor was on duty. Each veterinarian was on call for a week at a time, but since there were several, Dixie was on call only one week out of seven or eight.

Since, for once in her life, she could call her evenings her own, she gladly accepted dates with Jack Lycan, who—and she had hoped it would be that way—found it no hardship to drive to Denver. She found Jack an increasingly interesting companion, and increasingly fun to be with. "It's because I'm not on duty; it's because my conscience is clear that I enjoy myself so much with him," she rationalized.

Life was bright all around. She liked the challenge of having to do a different sort of work. Every day was an adventure.

The day started when she called, "Come on, Binx—time for a walk." She and the dog hiked fifteen blocks, rain or shine, each morning, because both of them were accustomed to fresh air and exercise. Then Dixie would set off for the hospital and the work she enjoyed so much.

As with large-animal medicine, there were certain tasks that could be categorized. In the laboratory, a routine urine analysis might unearth a kidney infection, or diabetes—a disease involving extra sugar in the blood, and causing hunger and loss of weight. For the latter—common in old dogs—Dixie prescribed orinase, the same oral drug given to human diabetics.

If, when she did a blood count, she found an elevation—clear evidence of infection—she prescribed antibiotics. And there was often surgery to be done. The surgery was often less difficult than catching the patient on which the operation was to be performed.

"Look at me," Dixie laughed, trying to hang onto a squirming, clawing bundle of fur. "This is ridiculous. It's safer to work on bulls!"

Dr. Albrech showed her the trick of handling the cat. He brought a bag of heavy cloth. "Put the cat in the cat bag before you try to give it anesthesia. Once it's asleep, you can take it out and operate." He held the cat by the scruff of the neck while Dixie slid the bag up over it.

The patient is often considerably larger than the doctor, but Dixie Cline has a way with animals and keeps them calm

Poodles, Dixie discovered, had an ailment all their own. Their thick hair kept moisture in, and light out, of their ears, producing the perfect medium for the growing of bacteria. Indicated procedure: Clean out the infection thoroughly and administer antibiotics.

Dixie, always interested in surgery, came in for her share. There were many emergency patients, victims of car accidents. Each time she saw a dog that had been hit, Dixie felt a particular sympathy for the owner, especially if it was a child. The memory of her dog Tiny under the teacher's car was still painfully vivid.

One such accident case was an eight-month-old Australian Shepherd puppy. The end of the femur, the long bone of the leg, was badly fractured. The head of the femur had broken off at the place where it fitted into the hip joint.

Dr. Dixie and Dr. Albrech went to work. As in human surgery, the greatest attention was given to the prevention of infection. The two veterinarians gave the puppy an anesthetic, then scrubbed and draped him. They scrubbed their hands, then donned sterile gowns and gloves. An incision was made and a piece of metal, called a "Steinman pin," was used to join the bone together permanently. It was a difficult operation, requiring three hours, but it enabled the dog to walk and run properly.

Dixie was proud of her performance, warmed by

As a child, Dixie was unseated by an occasional horse but the experience hasn't dimmed her genuine affection for them

the feeling of satisfaction brought on by a job well done. She told Jack about it the next time he came to see her.

Unexpectedly, "I love you when your eyes shine like that," he told her. After a moment he added, "I love you in all ways, at all times. Let's get married."

Caught off guard, Dixie whispered, "I love you, too."

That sounded like a happy ending, but instead, it was the start of trouble.

"But marriage for us would never work," Dixie went on, collecting her thoughts and reining in her emotions. "Our lives are too unlike. Your job and mine are too different."

Jack wasn't one to give up easily, and they argued far into the night. But nothing was resolved.

"All right," Jack said at least. "You win. I'm leaving—and I'm not coming back."

He did leave. And Dixie feared that he meant what he had said. . . .

The next morning, Dixie awoke to a terrible realization: Jack was gone—and she couldn't bear it!

The worst part of it was that she still didn't believe she and Jack could make a go of marriage. Their worlds were too far apart, their hopes and ambitions too different. Even if he would come back, what would be the use of it? It was hopeless.

Trying to ease her grief, Dixie threw herself into her work. Fortunately, there was a great deal to be done at the hospital. There was even a house call to be made, a rare thing among city veterinarians.

A distraught woman met Dixie at the front door and rushed her to the back yard. On the way she explained, "The dog was trying to jump a high wooden fence. His front leg got caught between two boards and he's just dangling there, yelping with pain."

Dixie didn't need this last piece of information—she could hear the unfortunate dog. He sounded more frightened than hurt, she decided.

In order to extricate him, she had to give him an anesthetic. Once he was free, she took him to the

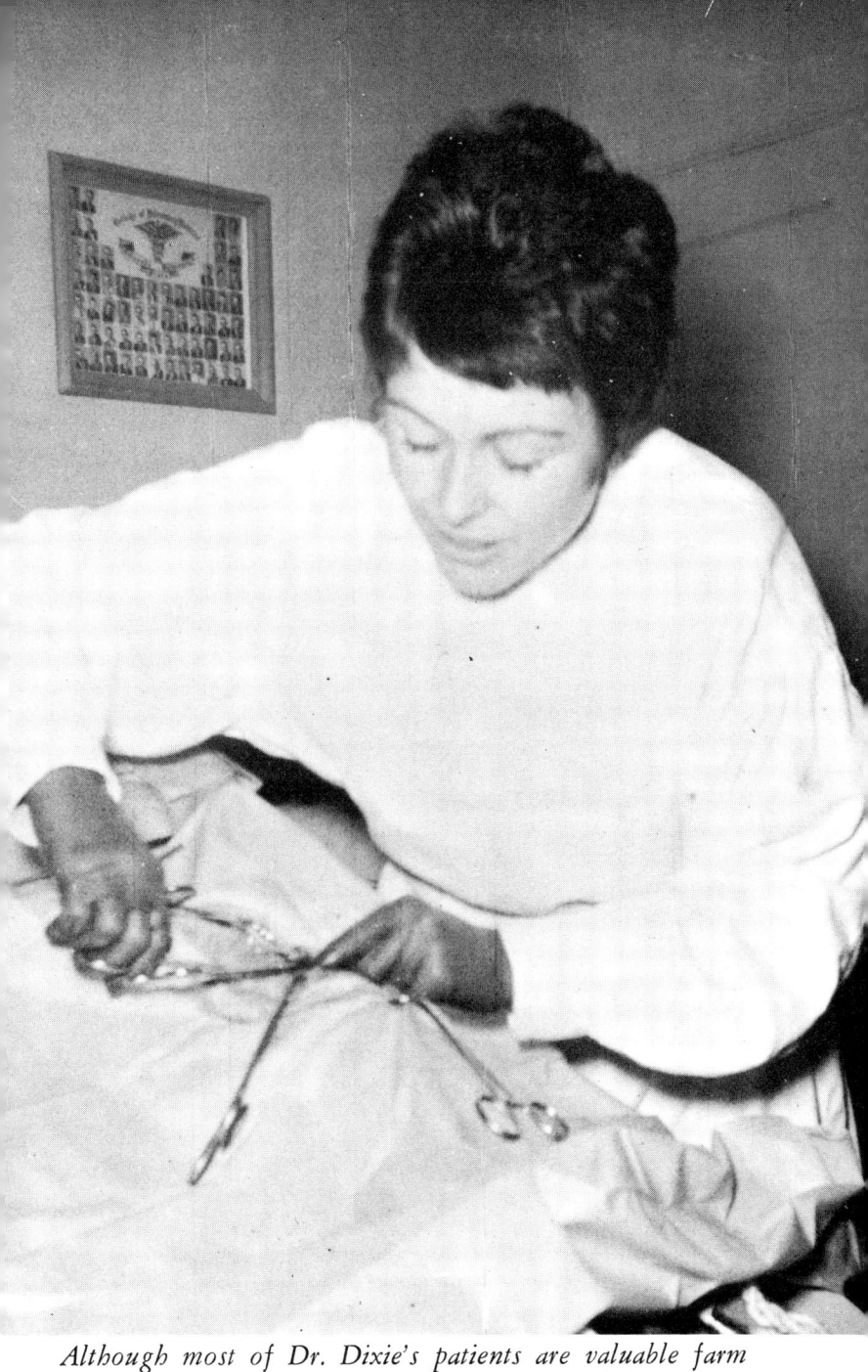

Although most of Dr. Dixie's patients are valuable farm animals, she never stints when operating on beloved pets

hospital, kept him under observation, then discharged him as none the worse for his harrowing experience.

Another pet owner telephoned the hospital, frantic. "The dog is having convulsions. What shall I do?"

Dixie managed to calm the woman enough to make sure the dog had been vaccinated against rabies. Satisfied that he had, she managed to ascertain that the woman had put out rat poison in the attic.

"Bring the dog in quickly," Dixie ordered. "Bring in the rat-poison container, too, so I can see what drugs are in it."

The poison was strychnine. Dixie administered phenobarbital, a sedative, to stop the convulsions, wishing that the dog had been brought to the hospital sooner so that she could have induced vomiting by injecting apomorphine. It was too late for that. She gave the dog a massive enema and washed out its stomach with such quantities of water that it sloshed out the dog's mouth.

It was a long fight to save the animal's life, but it was a successful one. The dog, in a state of collapse, was admitted as a patient, but recovered fully within days.

As long as Dixie could keep busy, she could postpone thinking about her personal problems. But she longed for Akron, where her nights were often busier than her days. Now, when she went home, a long, empty evening stretched ahead of her, and a

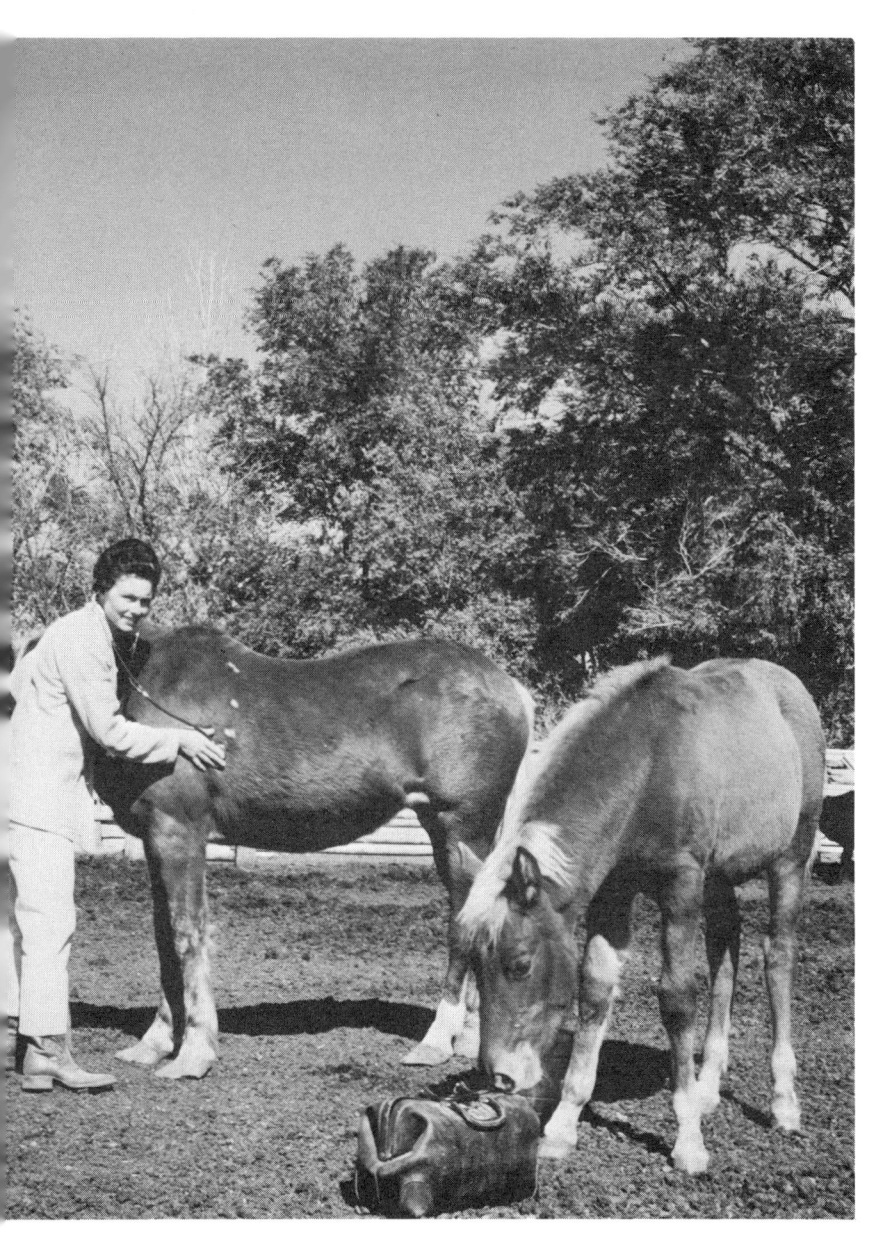

Listening, with a stethoscope, to the chest of an animal, Dixie can determine the presence of any lung congestion

night in which, she knew, she would sleep fitfully.

"What shall I do?" she asked herself. "What shall I do? I can't live with Jack and I can't live without him!"

The mailbox was always empty. Wouldn't he ever write again? And then she'd tell herself, "If you want to start it up again, why don't you write?" But she couldn't because, when it came to cold facts, nothing had changed. She still felt a marriage between two people whose interests and whose work were different couldn't possibly be a success. Better to suffer than to fail.

But Jack had more hope, or at least more tenacity, than she. One night, when she went home, there was the long-awaited letter.

"What we have is just too valuable to throw away," Jack wrote. "I still don't see why there has to be any conflict. Why can't I go on running the store and help you set up a practice here in Walsh? I wouldn't try to deprive you of your profession. I know how much it means to you. So what's the problem?"

Dixie sat with the letter in her lap, her eyes wet. What *was* the problem? Or—and this was the first time such a thought had occurred to her—was she making a problem when there really wasn't one?

"You can't change people," she told herself. "I'd be pretty angry if anyone tried to change me. I can

It is a big day in the life of many a youngster, when he holds his pet so Dr. Dixie can give immunization shots

regulate my own life, but I shouldn't try to regulate another person's.

"It boils down to this: Shall I marry Jack, whom I love and whom I *want* to marry? Or shall I sit here, perhaps for all the rest of my life, waiting for a veterinarian, just the *right* veterinarian, to come along? Can't I accept a man who's right for me in all ways except that one way, his line of work, and make that one way fit into the pattern of happiness? Can't I learn to give a little, instead of expecting to take? Can't I be a little less rigid, a little less demanding...?"

Getting up, Dixie went over to her desk. "Hurry back," she wrote. "All my love," she added.

Jack Lycan captured Dixie's heart; they were married in March, 19(

CHAPTER 9

A LONG WAY TO GO

Just before Christmas, Jack gave Dixie an engagement ring. They set a June wedding date.

Then, in January, Jeanne Bishop was married. Dixie went to Walsh to be a bridesmaid. Watching a wedding take place made Jack and Dixie decide that June was too far off. They moved the wedding date up to March 8.

Dixie resigned her job at Albrech Animal Hospital in the middle of February. Jack went to Denver with a pickup truck and moved her things to Walsh, while Dixie went back to Akron to get ready for the wedding.

A week before the momentous occasion, Dixie drove to Walsh to be the guest of honor at a shower given by Jack's relatives and friends. It was the largest shower the town had ever seen, held in the

Community Center, as this was the only place in town big enough to accommodate the crowd. Jack's mother and aunt helped to open the gifts, a project that took two and a half hours of steady unwrapping. When it was over, three cars were needed to carry the presents away.

Then Dixie went back to Akron. The time was close, now. Not much longer to wait.

March 8 came at last, and with it, a host of Dixie's good friends from college days, scattered far and wide, but gathered now to share Dixie's happiness.

The wedding took place in the First Baptist Church. Dixie wore floor-length white-lace gown, with a scalloped neckline and a tiered, bouffant skirt. Her veil, of illusion, was edged with matching lace. She carried a bouquet of roses.

On Mac Cline's arm she went up the aisle to place her hand in Jack's and repeat the lovely, solemn words. "I, Dixie, take thee, Jack..."

When the wedding ceremony and the reception that followed it were over, Mr. and Mrs. Jack Lycan went on a brief honeymoon. They drove to Denver and from there boarded a plane for Nevada—Dixie had never been there, but Jack had, and was anxious to show her the sights. They spent three wonderful, crowded days in Nevada, then flew to Los Angeles to visit an aunt and uncle of Jack's.

Finally, it was time to head back to Walsh and

get on with the important business of living happily ever after.

In Walsh, home was an apartment in a large, two-story house. In their absence, the Lycan relatives had moved in the furniture and set the place to rights.

Jack went back to work in the grocery store, four blocks away. Dixie set up a small-animal practice right at home, in the utility room of the building. She soon discovered that she was the only veterinarian within a radius of seventy miles. She was beseiged by calls from farmers and cattlemen.

But she had to turn them down. It wasn't a matter of not wanting to go back to large-animal practice—that was her real line of work, and she loved it. But she and Jack wanted to start a family soon. A pregnant woman simply couldn't do the heavy work required of a veterinarian caring for large animals.

She explained her reasons for refusing bluntly, for cattlemen could understand and accept such a worthwhile excuse. However, they continued to call her for advice, and that she gladly gave.

Because she had no assistant, Dixie set about training Jack to help her when help was needed. She saved her surgery for noon hours and evenings, when he was free. Occasionally, she had to call him to hurry over from the store when there was an emergency case.

Most of Dixie's practice, nowadays, was made up

Precise instructions are written out by the veterinarian so that her clients will know how to administer medications

of pet dogs and cats. There were the usual inoculations and vaccinations. Jack soon became an efficient helper and he was "promoted" to even more complicated work, such as assisting with accident cases or with exploratory laparotomies, in which a veterinarian opens the animal up with an abdominal incision in order to locate and diagnose a disease which can't be otherwise diagnosed.

"It's quite an experience," Jack said, "running a grocery store by day and playing doctor and nurse at night. Lucky for you, Dixie, I have a cast-iron stomach, even though I may not be the best assistant in the world."

"I have no complaints," Dixie told him.

Indeed, she had no complaints on any score. The obstacles she had once considered insurmountable had turned out to be very small indeed. Jack had his work and she had hers. They helped each other—Jack aiding Dixie in surgery, Dixie doing the bookkeeping for the grocery store. They were truly partners.

Among the unusual cases they handled together were Caesareans on chinchillas. Several people in the area raised the valuable little fur-bearing animals, which, for some unknown reason, had difficulty giving birth to their young.

One such case was referred to Dixie by Dr. Roger Troup, the local medical doctor. He and his wife had served in a missionary hospital in Africa before locating in Walsh. The Lycans and the Troups became good friends.

At one point, the Troups' sons caught four baby skunks. Dr. Troup sent them over to Dixie to be descented. She removed the scent bags successfully, but in the process the smell of skunk was transferred to Dixie, Jack, the office, and the whole apartment.

"Looks as if we're going to have plenty of fresh air the next few days," Jack said, throwing open every window in the place.

Dr. Troup offered Dixie an extraordinary opportunity to gain experience in a new area. "How would you feel about assisting me once in a while?" he asked.

Dixie jumped at the chance to assist with surgery on human patients. She observed an appendectomy, assisted with a tonsillectomy, then assisted with a second appendectomy. To her amazement—and embarrassment—she felt sick during that second appendectomy.

"I don't know what on earth happened," she apologized to Dr. Troup. "Why should I fold up at the sight of blood when I've done so much surgery myself?"

But, it turned out, there was a reason: Dixie was pregnant. She and Jack were delighted, and began at once to make plans for the arrival of their son. Both of them were certain that the baby would be a boy.

All was going too well, Dixie thought. Surely some kind of problem would arise, for nothing is ever perfect. And she was right. Dr. Haller, who leased Dixie's practice in Akron, notified her that he had decided to vacate. He and his wife wanted to live nearer the mountains.

It was a blow. This meant a serious loss of income to Dixie and Jack, unless someone could quickly be found to take over. Left vacant, the practice would go downhill rapidly. The thought of this was painful to Dixie; it would be a shame to see such an expenditure of time and effort go down the drain. Besides, she was sorry for the farmers and cattlemen, who would once again be left without a veterinarian.

But they had no luck in finding a replacement for Dr. Haller and, at the moment, there was nothing Dixie could do about it. They would have to wait until after the baby was born.

Jack stayed with his wife during her labor and even accompanied her to the delivery room. He stood by and, when necessary, gave her oxygen along with his moral support. The baby was born at three fifty-five A.M., March 14, 1965.

Dr. Troup held up a healthy infant for the father to see. "It's a fine girl," he said.

Jack gulped. "A girl. Are you—sure?"

But he was soon reconciled to the idea. The baby was named Bobbi Lea.

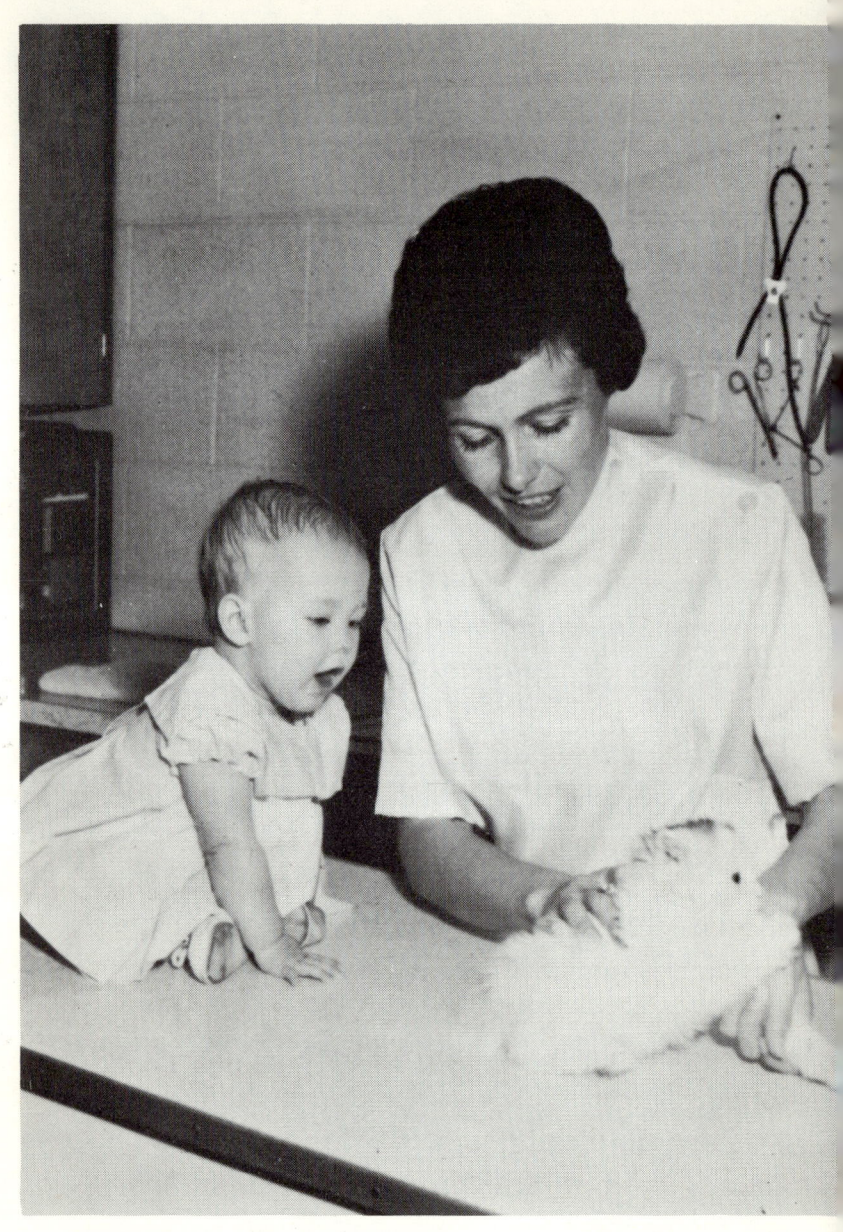

When both office and home demand attention, Dixie solves the problem by bringing Bobbi Lea to the office with her

Soon Dixie and the baby were back home, and she and Jack settled down to enjoy the pleasures of being parents. But now a new problem loomed—or, rather, the settling of a problem already too longstanding. The veterinary practice in Akron must be built up, so that it could again be leased. Dixie felt an obligation to her old friends, the farmers and cattlemen who had helped her get a start. Besides, the practice was an asset—too valuable a one to let go without an effort made to save it. Something had to be done about it.

And so, after much discussion, it was decided that Dixie must go back to Akron for a time. She would reopen the hospital, build up the practice again, then find a buyer for it when it was once more a going business. Bobbi Lea, of course, would have to go along. Dixie's mother would take care of her.

It was a lonely time—and, as she always had before, Dixie fought loneliness by throwing herself into her work. To ranchers who had known her before, and who had recently been without veterinary services nearby, she was a welcome sight. The calls began coming in. Once again Dr. Dixie was pulling calves, inoculating pigs against cholera, testing blood, performing surgery.

One particularly frantic call come from a rancher north of town. A bachelor, he lived with his brother and the brother's family, all of whom were away on a vacation trip, leaving him home to look after things.

"I was out mowing hay," he explained, "The kids' dog, Sox, was chasing rabbits. He ran in front of the mower and got himself chewed in the blades. You know how crazy the kids are about that dog—"

"Bring him in," Dixie directed. "Fast!"

While she waited for the patient to arrive, she set up for extensive surgery. One look at the rancher, who was covered with blood, showed that she had been wise, for the dog was seriously injured. Hastily she examined Sox. One back leg was nearly severed and one front leg was badly gashed.

The rancher held the dog while Dixie administered sodium pentothal to put him to sleep. Then she set about clipping away the hair from around the injuries and disinfecting the areas.

She scrubbed, donned a sterile gown and gloves, and went to work. She removed the injured back leg, amputating at the stifle—the kneelike joint in the hind leg. There was no possibility of saving that leg. Dixie's hope was that she could manage to save the animal's life.

When the amputation was finished and the stump dressed, Dixie went to work on the tricky job of suturing the front leg. When that was done, she put Sox into a cage to recover from the anesthesia.

"He'll do, I think," she told the rancher. "He'll be all right. Don't worry," she added.

Sox went home three days later. Within two weeks, he'd be out chasing rabbits again.

Dixie stood in the doorway of the Akron Animal Hospital, watching the car bearing Sox drive away. She had a deep feeling of satisfaction. How good it was to know how to do something worthwhile—how much better it was to be able to work at it! She loved her profession. She was endlessly delighted with the small miracles her hands could bring about.

Soon, she knew, she would be rejoining Jack. The thought filled her with joy. And yet she'd be sorry to leave Akron, to leave behind parents and friends and the business she had built up, the confidence in her and the miracles her hands could perform that she had slowly and painfully instilled in the farmers and cattlemen in this area.

But there was a challenge in the unknown that lay ahead, and Dixie had always been one to meet challenges head on. She'd have to work hard, Dixie knew —taking care of a family was a full-time job and so was veterinary medicine, and she'd have to combine them. But hard work had never bothered her. Only idleness did.

"I've proved I can do 'a man's work'," Dixie thought, smiling to herself. "Now I've got to prove I can do both at once, and do them well. I'll manage. I always have. It won't be easy—but life will never be dull, that's one thing for certain!"

Being wife-mother-veterinarian calls for a demanding daily schedule, but Dr. Dixie Cline Lycan seems to thrive on it

rec'd

Sands of the Desert

by
Stacy Chudwin

PublishAmerica
Baltimore

© 2003 by Stacy Chudwin.
All rights reserved. No part of this book may be reproduced, stored in a retrieval system, or transmitted in any form or by any means without the prior written permission of the publishers, except by a reviewer who may quote brief passages in a review to be printed in a newspaper, magazine, or journal.

First printing

ISBN: 1-4137-0486-7
PUBLISHED BY PUBLISHAMERICA, LLLP
www.publishamerica.com
Baltimore

Printed in the United States of America

Dedication

This book is dedicated to my parents, in thanks for all of their love, patience, and support.

For you, the city, thus I turn my back:
There is a world elsewhere.
-Shakespeare (Coriolanus)

Part One

The Sands Are Cast Away

Prologue

... In a land far away, a young prince sat at the feet of an old woman, gazing up at her in awe.

"What is it you wish, Your Highness?" the woman questioned, her voice sagacious and unchanging as an ancient oak tree.

"You are wise, far beyond anyone else in all the lands. If I am to be king someday, I should like to know all the wisdom in the world. I believe it is my fate."

"What do you desire to know, my young pupil?"

"Tell me of fates, wise woman," the young prince beseeched, and the woman began to speak.

"Our fates to choose are numbered as the sands of the desert. The golden, sun-kissed grains that swirl about the surface may tempt us, but the cooler, more obscure ones underneath may lead us truer. And some, young prince, never would have been found had we never chosen to dig at all..."

Chapter One

Serepta grasped a handful of sand and let it slowly sift back to the stone floor. She squinted around in the pale morning sun. It was a desolate place, the palace courtyard. The only sign of life in the rough pink gravel was a tiny purple flower that seemed to sprout from nowhere. It was a beautiful thing, standing as a proud shock of color against the dusty courtyard, but yet was so extraordinarily alone.

Serepta glared at the flower as it swayed in the breeze. "Don't you get lonely, standing there all by yourself? Don't you get mad, forced to live inside this place?!" She picked up another handful of sand and flung it sharply against the thick stone wall surrounding her.

"Temper, temper," a voice snickered from behind.

Serepta knew the voice without even having to turn around. It was impossible to forget the sound of the crackling of dead grass under foot, the howl of the wind through an empty night, the coldness of the frost that came creeping like a disease into a moonless desert.

"What do you want, Desmond?" Serepta snapped at her older cousin, leaping to her feet. Golden sand ran from her dress like rain.

"You simply must watch that tone of yours, princess. I just came to bring you some news," he replied, picking a bug off of his tunic. He examined it for a moment, and then he crushed the poor thing between his fingers. A crooked grin emerged from his sallow countenance as he flicked the broken life away.

Serepta gave a disgusted sigh. "I don't have time for this," she said, gazing ruefully at the purple flower she had abandoned.

"All right, I'll be frank then. I came to tell you that your father, Raghnall, has made his royal decision. Apparently you are old enough now to perform your marital duties to this kingdom, and the king has picked, well, a most excellent husband for you to rule over Shamar once he is *finally* gone." He leaned cockily against the stone wall, dark tunic clinging to his sinewy form, gray eyes laughing at her from beneath a pile of black hair.

Serepta stared at him blankly.

"You and I are to be married, dear cousin." Desmond's eyes hungrily took in the look of horror on her fair face, and his tongue slid across his lips like a moist snake. He then turned and strutted back through the heavy oak doors of the palace.

"What?!" Serepta cried. Her heart jolted violently. A quick flash of memory in her mind brought her back to a time when she was seven years old and had refused to help her cousin steal a pie. Desmond stood above her, bloody rock in hand, while Serepta lay below with a broken arm that he had shattered viciously into the dust...

Not only was she not ready to marry, but she would sooner marry a cobra than this vile man.

"Marry you? What is this *lie* of yours?" Serepta clutched her arm protectively and marched after him as best as she could in her ivory sandals. Her gold-threaded dress flipped rampantly about her legs as she hurried after him down the marble corridors, swerving in disgust to avoid a pile of dung in the middle of the hall.

"No lie, cousin," he replied coolly, not even turning around.

"Then my father has gone mad! All of the kingdom of Shamar has gone mad! Mad!!" Serepta shouted. The men and women bustling around the crowded palace stopped to stare at their princess, whose voice continued to rise in volume. She felt as though her life path had been changed, as though the flow of a great river had suddenly reversed and changed direction. Her insides melted with a sick dread.

Serepta and Desmond finally arrived at the elaborately guarded throne room. "Here, princess, why don't you ask your father yourself!" Desmond gripped her shoulder coldly and gestured into the chamber. Serepta jerked under his touch and ducked away.

The princess gazed down the long empty hall to her father's throne, gaudily decorated with gold and florid jewels. He seemed to be an eternity away, but then, he always did. She struggled to hold down the anger that was rising up inside her, but soon found it impossible.

"Father! Father, I pray you have an explanation for this *insanity*!" she declared as she hurried towards him. She still couldn't fathom the possibility of this idea, but it seemed to grow realer and realer with each passing moment, like a mirage looming nearer in the distance.

"Ah, I see you have heard the good news, my daughter." A cool smile slid across the otherwise expressionless face of the King of Shamar. His flustered daughter, although very angry, was still forced by custom to kneel before him.

"There *is* no good news. I will not marry Desmond," she replied, bringing herself up to her full height, daring herself to look into her father's eyes of black stone. The palace guards shifted on their feet and murmured amongst themselves, disturbed by her boldness.

King Raghnall's forehead twitched. His fist clenched tightly around the golden scepter beside his raised throne, but his voice was steady and monotone. "You dare to defy me, not realizing that at a whim I could take away your life as easily as I gave it to you. Your defiance means nothing to me. Desmond is a perfect choice: he is a prince of Shamar, and will make a fine king someday. You will marry him, or you will die."

Desmond smirked back at his uncle.

"He is a jackal! He is cowardly and cruel. And furthermore, he's my cousin, so what you ask is sinful!" Serepta snapped, the flames of her temper crackling and popping around the unchanging stone of her father's resolve. She was desperate now, fighting frantically for her future, but arguing with her father was like arguing with a stone wall.

"He is your cousin, so what I *demand* is perfect. He will keep the royal bloodlines pure," Raghnall began. His eyes glinted like the sheen of a twisting knife. "So not only do I order you to marry Desmond, but to start producing heirs as soon as possible. From now on, you and he will share a room, princess," he added insidiously.

After the initial shock of the comment wore off, Serepta's dark eyes flamed and she lunged forward. Before she could even go an inch, the palace guards had spears at her throat. Without a flinch, Raghnall casually ordered her away with a sweep of the hand.

The princess's lip trembled for a moment, but then she spun and fled from the room, away from that horrible place of cold iniquity.

Her cries of rage echoed throughout the palace.

Chapter Two

That night, Serepta sat in her chambers, poised by the open window. She sighed and gazed wistfully outside. Her seat was a pillowed bench beneath the windowsill. The princess could sit there for an eternity, simply breathing in the perfume of the desert. The window took up almost an entire wall, and it was one of the only features in the palace that didn't need to be decorated in fancy trappings and covers. The view looked like a portrait painted by the gods, the way it revealed the entire shimmering sands in all their glory before her. Palm trees waved silently in the breeze, and they seemed to swing their pale green leaves to bathe in the moonlight.

Ahh, nighttime. It was an illustrious cloth spun with inky black wool and silver thread, comforting Serepta, soothing her, wrapping her up in such a way that it almost made her forget... but no. She was still betrothed to her cousin, still held under customary lock and key by her father, still choked within the realm of her own kingdom, and still heart-wrenchingly alone, like the purple flower in the courtyard.

"If only my mother were here...she would...she would...no," the princess sighed. Serepta had no idea what her mother would have done. She had died when Serepta was only a baby, perhaps of a broken heart from being forced to marry the tyrannical king Raghnall. The princess's breath caught in her throat when she realized she might suffer the same fate with Desmond as the future monarchs of Shamar.

Tears rose hot to her eyes, but Serepta fought them back. Raghnall always said that crying was the squalling of the weak. He punished her severely as a child at even the slightest whimper. Serepta never cried now, not since she was very little, but tears were threatening to spill down her face as she gripped the windowsill tightly.

"Isn't there anyone out there?" she cried, her voice wavering as she beseeched the night sky. Serepta began to pace back and forth across the cold stone floor like the tigress in the king's menagerie.

"I need someone...anyone! I just feel so lonely sometimes, it's as though I can't even bear it anymore! It's choking me!" Serepta cried. The kingdom was filled with people, overflowing with people, reeking with so many people that it made her head spin. But these people were as inaccessible as blank walls. Her weakened plea soon turned into rage, and she slammed her fist against the windowsill.

The thought of marrying Desmond made her heart sick with grief. It was a sentence to a life without love, and the only release would be death. Love...the one emotion Serepta was forbidden to feel. Anger, jealousy, misery, and fear, but not love, never love. It cried to her, beckoned to her, pulled her from within and from without, and adventure called to her soul.

She reached her arms as far as they could go out the beloved window. Somewhere, past the horizon where the gods drew the sun forth from the earth, there were other lands and other people and another life. But the window could only let her go so far.

"Serepta?"

The princess whirled around to find her grandmother sitting on the bed. "Saba!" she cried, leaping onto the covers next to her. The sight of the woman made her temporarily forget her plight. "I haven't seen you in so long! You've been up in that Tower again, with all your musty old scrolls and herbs. I see you've rejoined the rest of the world!"

"Yes, and just in time to hear the awful news. I can't believe your father is forcing you to marry that vile grandson of mine," Saba replied, gazing at her granddaughter with deep, sympathetic brown eyes. Serepta saw her reflection in the dark pools as she looked back at her lovingly. The old woman always peculiarly seemed to know when Serepta needed her most. Perhaps this was what a mother was for, but the princess would not know of such things.

"I fear all of Shamar will know soon. Perhaps it is better if they do. Maybe they will realize my sacrifice and take pity upon their princess," Serepta said bitterly, putting her head onto the softly clothed lap of her closest and only friend.

"Pity? My dear girl, to have pity on you is an impossibility! You are leagues above anyone I have ever met. Never let it be said that all you strive for is to be pitied by others," Saba said firmly, stroking Serepta's long dark hair.

"Strive for? I have no right to strive for anything but to serve my father. I have had no other rights since I was born."

Saba sat there for a moment, her forehead wrinkling in thought. Sometimes the old woman would do that, and Serepta could almost see tiny enigmas working themselves out in her mind.

"Since you were born... you used to be so happy when you were little. There is much to learn from the child within, who sees the world and knows the world and loves it," Saba said. She turned to the window thoughtfully, commanding a look of a perfect longing.

"Do you see that whole wide world out there? Have you ever just sat and tried to comprehend the fact that beyond the walls of this palace there are other lands, and lives, and hopes? Shamar is a dungeon. No one comes in, and no one goes out. It has always been this way. But there is a whole other world out there! I have only seen them in my dreams, but you, child, you are special. You have been delivered a different fate by the gods."

Serepta looked up at her, puzzled.

"Your name, Serepta, means peaceful, yet you never seem to be. That is only one of the lessons you must learn. Another is that you never ought to surrender until all options have been spent," Saba continued, a wry smile sliding across her face. Almost never did a smile come to Saba's withered face. She had seen too much, felt too much, borne too much to ever be amused by the world that had treated her so harshly.

Serepta sat up. "Are you saying...are you saying that there is some way you can get me out of this?"

"I will deliver you from this curse if it takes the last breath in my body. Meet me at midnight in my Tower. That's all I can say for now. Oh, Desmond will be coming over here later tonight, after the party."

"The party!" Serepta interrupted. She had forgotten about the festival her father had planned. It would be another night of bitter wine and overly rich foods, of raucous men and bawdy songs.

"Desmond will come to your room late tonight, if only to stir up trouble. You can turn him away, but it will do you no good to be executed because of that quick temper of yours. Take care, and I will see you later tonight."

Saba was out the door before Serepta could even open her mouth in amazement at the way the river of her life seemed to pick up speed once more.

The lanterns shone like sickly clots of light over the outdoor promenade of the palace. They cast a faint glimmer of light over the red stone floors. The princess stepped tentatively out into their milky glow, her nerves drawing back with a sudden sensory overload.

The place stank. It reeked of cheap wine, of greasy food, and of perfume clinging to the sweat of dirty bodies. The heat of the desert night held the aroma in its grasp and would not let it go.

Serepta stood hidden behind the doorway, watching. Its old wooden beams were all that separated the young woman from foreign frenzy that came with these parties. The princess hated this. She hated the bubble between what was comfort and what was not, what was safe and what was not. Serepta finally forced herself to look again, shoving down her insecurities as her hands trembled against the doorpost.

A whirlpool of bodies flooded around the dance floor. They were the best of the best in Shamar. Dark skinned men with golden breastplates swung wine goblets about in time to the pounding music of the drums. Their women, dressed in little more than carefully placed strips of cloth, panted after them, laughing aloud. These people, these rag dolls, these swine stuffed with alcohol, swirled like stew in a cauldron about the raised throne of Raghnall.

The king sat high above the crowds, dark eyes glittering from holes in a leaden face. He enjoyed his position there, a smug faced sun with wild palm trees gyrating before him. Serepta refused to meet his gaze. Desmond would probably be somewhere nearby, and at that chilling thought, Serepta wished she could become as invisible as the slick night air.

The princess stared all around, and she smoothed her gold dress down. The constant movement made her nervous. Serepta did not know what she would do if Desmond were to approach her then. The princess darted her eyes all about, searching for the telltale black hair and white skin among the squirming masses of gaudy cloth.

She didn't even know why she was there. She hated this place, this event, these people. But she always felt the press of obligation, and there was always the hope that she might find someone worth her time. A new song kicked up, and the puddle of people was stirred up once more.

The drums were beating loud and hard. The very vibrations of this song seemed to offend the jeweled night sky. The people danced below in an abomination of brightly colored clothes, cloying perfume, and the sound of bare feet slapping against stone. Serepta saw an anonymous hairy arm reach to grab her into the mix, and she recoiled in disgust.

The princess stumbled about, dazed by the party as the circle of dancers seemed to expand. The kaleidoscope of colors whirled in the damp heat, burgeoning like a fat balloon. In the more obscure corners of the stone enclosure, Serepta could see men dragging women off into the darkness. Their pathetic whines of protest made the princess shake.

My gods, is this all there is for me? her heart cried over the dirge of the drums. With that, a calabash of beer sloshed onto her dress. The cold stink of it permeated her nose, causing her to reel about in disgust. Finally, eyes stinging, the princess let out a cry of frustration and fled over to the stone wall of the palace. Frantically, she hauled herself on top of it, panting loudly.

There. That was better. Serepta sat poised on the edge of the cold stone, chest heaving, the chaos of the party behind her. And ahead lay the shimmering desert. She stopped, and breathed.

A sound then came flowing slowly over the sands, a lone cry, like milk being poured over bread. It rolled off the dunes and caused Serepta to close her eyes in quiet appreciation. A wolf was howling in the distance.

The princess's throat rumbled in recognition. Wherever the creature was, it probably knew what it was like to be free. And soon Serepta would, too. With that reassuring notion, she turned and went back inside the palace.

Until midnight, there was nothing left to do but rest. The princess sighed and snuggled into the purple satin sheets on her bed. Her hands trembled with excitement at the idea that she could finally leave this horrendous place. There had to be more to the world than this rotting kingdom in the desert, and she wanted to see it all. The thought of Raghnall's fury when he found out her insolence made a sly smile slide across her face.

Serepta was eager for midnight, yet exhausted beyond belief, and the luxurious covers wrapped her up like a baby bird in a nest. By and by, the subtle hands of sleep had her in their grasp.

Sometime later, perhaps minutes or perhaps hours, a dark form slid into bed next to her. Instinctively, Serepta cuddled up to the warmth.

Suddenly, a hand began to slide up her thigh. Serepta's eyes snapped open in full alertness.

"*Desmond*! What do you think you're doing?"

The young prince beside her gave his trademark crooked grin. "I am simply following the King's orders that you and I should begin making him heirs. And never before have I received such wonderful orders, cousin," he leaned in closer, and his hands continued to roam. Then he hauled his heavy body on top of hers.

Serepta's skin crawled at his touch as though a million sticky flies were beating their wings against her. She jerked wildly and struggled and tried to wriggle away, but the satin sheets that had once comforted her were now smothering her.

"Stop it now, you jackal, or I'll scream!"

"That's what all the beautiful women of Shamar say until they spend just one night with me," he murmured, gray eyes wide with excitement. "And as your future husband, I demand that you do as I say."

As he spoke, a drop of his spittle landed on Serepta's cheek. It burned away at her skin like a red-hot iron, like a mosquito whining next to her ear in the darkness, like an itch she couldn't quite scratch. She remembered the way he had squelched the bug in the courtyard, and her muscles tightened, ready to attack him, ready to tear the filthy flesh off his body, ready to crush his skull and murder him in cold blood.

Serepta brutally raked her fingernails down his back. As he arched backward in pain, Serepta deftly reached behind the bed coverings and drew forth a tiny golden dagger. She had the tip pointed at Desmond's throat before he even knew what had happened.

"Get out of my bed, get out of my room, and get out of my life, or you will not live to harm any more of the women of Shamar."

Desmond's features fell in an expression of pure shock and defeat. The prince slowly removed himself from the bed, and then he gave Serepta a look of unadulterated hatred. His gray eyes narrowed to slits, his jaws clenched tightly together, and his face twisted with fury. Serepta could see blood dripping down his back from where she scratched him, and it pooled on the floor like the crimson embodiment of his rage.

The muscles in the prince's face then began to slowly relax, like a balled piece of parchment crackling and unfolding.

"I will leave for now. But once your father finds out about this insult, he will kill you. And if he doesn't, I will," he stated calmly in a voice that sent an involuntary shudder down the princess's spine. Then he was out the door as quickly as he had arrived.

Serepta sighed and swung herself out of bed. She glanced out the window at the moon and figured it was about midnight. Pulling a feathered cloak about her, she was off to meet her grandmother in the Tower.

The Tower, also known as the Eye of Shamar, rose so greatly and smoothly out of the desert that it appeared as though a tremendous hand had thrust it forth from the bowels of the earth. The sheer pink granite was so ancient that not even the eldest scroll keepers of Shamar knew how it got there. Because it offered a magnificent view of the entire kingdom, the Eye used to be used as a guard tower. Now, however, there was no one to guard against. The surrounding kingdoms had fallen one by one, decaying in their own cesspools of moral corruption and squalor. The desert was taking back what was rightfully its own, and Shamar would eventually be next.

Saba had moved herself into the room on top of the Eye and used it to store old books and herbs. The superstitious Shamarrim thought the king's mother-in-law to be a witch, and they stayed far away from the Tower, muttering prayers to the gods of protection whenever they passed by the place.

Serepta crept quietly up to the old timber door. The night was silent and inky black, and she felt as though every shadow were concealing a spirit or murderer, or even worse, Desmond. The memory of his cold touch sent a chill down her spine, and she reached to her hip to make sure her golden dagger was still there.

The princess sighed and steadied herself. It was time to meet her grandmother. Ready to begin the adventure she had been waiting for her entire lifetime, Serepta swung open the rotting old door and began to scale the formidable stone staircase.

Chapter Three

When the princess finally arrived at the top of the stairs, her nose was blanketed in a thick cloud of fragrance. Jasmine, sandalwood, and something else unidentifiable burned and smoked together in the stuffy room atop the Tower, tingling in Serepta's nose and warming her completely. It felt as though a soft, heated, fuzzy blanket was slowly being pulled through her insides. She gave a heavy sigh, and her tensed muscles finally began to relax.

Through the haze, the princess saw Saba by the window. She held an ancient text in one withered arm and a small black pot in the other. Serepta squinted curiously at the pot; the substance inside seemed to be neither solid, nor liquid, nor even a gas, but something else entirely, and trying to comprehend it made her head feel numb. In fact, her head was beginning to feel numb already.

"Welcome, Serepta. Just lie down for a moment and breathe deeply. Relax," Saba cooed, stirring the pot skillfully.

The princess opened her mouth to speak, but she found her tongue hanging swollen and useless inside. She tried to move it, but her mouth was paralyzed. Her eyes widened and she began to panic. Above anything, Serepta hated feeling helpless, and the warmth of the aroma in the air was beginning to weigh her down, pulling on her muscles like thick chains. Her neck began to quiver. The princess's head felt heavy as a boulder...and then a mountain...and then as heavy as the entire earth. Her legs buckled, and she crashed to the floor, unable to resist anymore.

"Sleep, Serepta, sleeeep...." Saba urged softly. The princess's head lifted up in a last defiance, but then dropped to the ground once more. The warm cloud took her completely under its downy wing, and then she knew no more.

Something moved in Serepta's mind, in the dark recesses of the chamber way deep down that knows without reason and perceives without seeing. It was the flicker in a flame, the twitch of a wing in flight, the light breath of the wind that she felt waft through that darkly pleasing abyss.

"Sereeeeepta..." the voice of Saba flowed through the chamber inside her mind. "I have crumbled the walls into the dust...the doors have been flung open to the heavens...now you may look and see as you never have before...these are the roads you are destined to take...."

And then Serepta felt as though a great eyelid inside the yawning black chamber had been pulled back to reveal another world within. Serepta could see wisps of other lands far beyond her, around her, and inside of her. Lands dark and misgiving, sunlit and peaceful, lands that had not yet come to be, and lands that had long since crumbled into the dust. It was chaos, yet it made the most perfect sense in the world. She felt a freedom she had never known before this awesome sensation, as if her eyes had been opened for the very first time.

Golden sands of the desert sprinkled in front of her, sparkling in the light from some unknown source. They were beautiful, natural, infinite, and she felt a powerful connection to them. The sand had some deeper meaning for her. One grain in particular, one that was buried deeply underneath the rest, began to inflate to a monstrous size. As it grew, Serepta saw an engraving of crags and mars within its surface, and the top rose into a jagged peak. A mountain. And soon, from each crag grew a forest of trees; huge timbers with endless arrays of emerald leaves that reached towards the sky. The single grain of sand had become an enormous, forested gray mountain in the distance whose pinnacle was shrouded in fog.

"Where am I?" the edge of Serepta's soul pressed in a question.

"You will go to Mount Morad...." the voice of her grandmother flowed.

In Serepta's mind, she slowly focused in upon a single leaf of a single branch of a single tree on that tremendous mountain. She knew its life story, could feel its leathery texture, and could see every wrinkle and vein that flowed beneath the dark green skin and a silver droplet of water that dribbled from the tip. Cold water... no, warm water, sticky water.

Humid. The air was humid and wet all around the princess, and she felt smothered by its thick heat. The leaf had transformed into a large, fluorescent pink flower, and the vibrant color from its floppy petals nearly blinded her. The great canopy of a rainforest hung above. The water droplet fell from the petal and joined a great rushing river below, rushing, flowing, always moving, quickly taking all that was good and bad along with it. The hot air off the river brought the perfume of the flower's blossom to Serepta's nose, and she drank it in.

"The Stream of Jimakana...." Saba's voice came again.

Serepta barely heard her, she was so entranced by the scent of the flower. It was so young...so alive...it caressed her skin like a soft breeze...and then it was a soft breeze. And there was more wind to cool her moist face, and sand again. The stream was gone, and the princess stood on a cliff overlooking a vast, barren desert. In the far distance rose a great pyramid, its ancient peak pointing towards the midday sun, stones bathing in the warm glow. It stood there firmly, stable, unmoving, and as steady as the very sentiments of peace and knowledge that radiated from it. It was not an impediment on the desert around it, but a great testament to the underlying power of the wisdom of nature. Serepta knew without a doubt that within those golden walls was a greater place of divine knowledge than anywhere else in the world.

There was no name for it.

A stone at the very tip of the pyramid began to waver and tremble in the burning sunlight, and then it came off altogether. It flew at Serepta, and she shielded her head from the blow. Feeling nothing, she removed her arms. And saw blue. A great blue sky hung above her that made her heart swell with joy. Her gaze fell, and she saw a young child who had playfully thrown the stone. He ran off with a group of friends through the streets, laughing and laughing. It was a city in an oasis. Merry green foliage wound itself around craggy hills and structures, and people busily milled about in the sunlight that filtered through the fragrant trees above. She took in a quick breath when she noticed an entire garden of tiny purple flowers, just like the one growing in her courtyard. An air of peace and joy hung over the oasis, and the princess felt so happy, so instinctively loving towards the people there.

Suddenly, the clatter of horse hooves shattered the image into a thousand pieces. Serepta felt as though she were being jolted violently from the abyss within, and her mind screamed in agony. Images and colors tried to weave a web around her, but kept bursting apart into wispy little threads. Her heart fluttered rapidly within her breast, and cold sweat ran down her forehead. The princess's eyes were forced apart, and they darted crazily around the room at the top of the Eye of Shamar.

"Serepta! Serepta, are you all right? It's a wonder you weren't killed, being thrust from the spell so suddenly!" Saba exclaimed, and nervously clambered over to the window.

Still unable to speak, not wanting to pollute that incredible sense of understanding she had felt moments before, Serepta staggered to her feet. She was surprised to find it was approaching sunrise already, but what shocked her even more was seeing a band of armed horsemen coming swiftly towards the Eye of Shamar. By their silver weaponry and formation, she could see they were the king's private cavalry: Raghnall's Riders.

"Desmond must have found out I was here! He sent them to punish me!" the princess cried, finding her voice again.

"Then we have to hurry!" her grandmother exclaimed, turning around to an old wooden table with a waterproof sack. Saba quickly emptied the sack's contents onto the table. "You will bring this with you on your journey. There are two jugs of water, a couple pounds of dried meat, and some dried fruit to last you a little while...."

"Wait! Journey? What journey? Where am I going?" Serepta interrupted, still dazed by the dream. As far as she knew, she was never in her life going to leave the gates surrounding the desert kingdom of Shamar.

"The dream, child, the dream! All those places...you *will* go there! It is a tremendous journey, and the place you saw at the end is where you shall come to live out the rest of your days, assuming you make it there."

"Make it there?"

Saba then looked very old. Her forehead stiffened, and her eyes darkened as she gazed at her granddaughter. "You have this choice now, to stay or to leave. You will live for certain if you stay, and just as certainly, love never. This is truly a great journey, across foreign lands many men have never seen. It is great in danger, yet is your only savior. It is great in difficulty, yet will give you all the wisdom in the world. It is great in fear, yet great in love as well. It is the greatest task you will ever undertake in your life, because for once, it is your own life to lead."

And Serepta accepted the task with all her heart.

Saba turned once more to the materials on the table. "Most importantly, there is this," she said, and pulled from the sack a necklace.

A brilliant piece of amber tiger's eye stone dangled on a leather thong. Within the stone, black, brown, and a tinge of orange flickered together, like the subtleties in Serepta's own eyes. The necklace was certainly not the gold and silver baubles the princess was used to. Her father would have scoffed at the piece, deeming it a cheap trifle. But it had a natural beauty all its own, one that intrigued Serepta deeply.

"This pendant will aid your inner sight. It will keep you focused on what is important and reveal great powers deep within yourself. Keep it with you and remember what I have taught you always," Saba instructed, lovingly tying the pendant around her granddaughter's neck.

Serepta let out a sigh and swung the sack onto her shoulder. "Anything else before I leave?"

Saba smiled, her ancient face folding with delight. "I certainly can't let you travel alone, now can I? Behold, your new Companion," she said, and stepped aside to reveal a sight that Serepta was destined to remember for the rest of her life.

Desmond rode forth at the head of the Riders, waving his silver sword high in the air. He spurred his stallion onwards toward the Eye of Shamar, bitterly fueled by rage and humiliation. It was there his betrothed waited, and it was there that she would die.

Death awaited Serepta in the Tower, and wove a dark web around that quiet moment before the sun could even begin to glance out over the horizon. Death shifted in the cold blankness of the sky. Death gleamed in the shadowed steel of Desmond's sword. Death pounded in the mad dance of the horse hooves, and shone in the empty blackness of the fur that rippled across the muscles of the prince's stallion, racing to bring him ever and ever nearer to the Eye of Shamar.

The Tower stood in front of the Riders, waiting there in silence, waiting for fate to come and dance within its hallowed stones.

Saba stepped aside with a simple yet meaningful flourish. Serepta peered into the shadows, taking a step back in surprise.

From the darkness emerged a large, lean male wolf. It moved powerfully towards her with the grace of a king. The wolf's muscles rippled underneath its gleaming coat, which in the light transformed from a smoldering ebony to a shining silver. Serepta had never seen such a powerful, magnificent strength before, and it seemed to radiate from this creature. She now could recall a howl, the sound of this wolf's voice, comforting her last night at the party.

"Is he...is he real?" she asked in disbelief, crouching down to examine the wolf.

"His name is Rafe," Saba said with a grin. She watched her granddaughter admire him, and her wrinkled forehead moved as something in her mind seemed to make sense.

"He's incredible..." Serepta breathed, gazing into the wolf's eyes. They were the blue of the sky on a chilled spring morning, and flecks of gold within them caught her eye. Suddenly, she had the sensation of someone kissing her hand. She fell back onto the floor in shock.

Saba laughed. "Of course, Rafe can't talk, but he has other ways of communicating. He will be your Companion on this journey, and he shall help you find the way. You can trust him."

And Serepta did, without a doubt. She was tempted to touch the wolf, but the proud look in his eyes made her hold back. It wasn't proper; he was to be her Companion, not her pet.

Saba glanced nervously out the window. "Serepta, the Riders are coming closer. You have to leave now."

For the first time, the reality of this journey seemed to wash over the princess. She was leaving home and could never return again. Quietly, Saba caught her up in her arms.

Serepta's chest heaved, but she did not cry. The princess never cried. What was left for her in this place anyway? There was a father who had never loved her, palace nannies who looked at her and saw gold coins, and walls thicker than any prisoner could ever hope to burrow through.

Saba pulled away, and she took in a breath. "Go now; take what you have learned and don't look back. I will try and hold them off as long as I can. I have one last thing to tell you, and I pray, dear child, that you will remember it. Rafe is, and always will be, your Sole Companion."

"My Sole Companion…" she murmured under her breath. The sound of horse-hooves brought her back to alertness, and without looking back, Serepta ran to the door. Together, she and Rafe fled down the stairs, and outside to the world that awaited them in the moments before the coming of dawn.

Together, wolf and princess raced across the open desert toward the city gates. Rafe's silver body rocketed powerfully alongside Serepta, sand flying up with each stride. They ran there together, and as the sun began to slowly rise over the horizon, it cast their shadows on the ground and molded them as one. Raghnall's Riders were dangerously near, but the princess knew they would make it; she knew it with the very heart that trembled within her chest. Outside the city gates there was a hope, a dream, a life, and for her life Serepta burst through the gates that were flung open wide to deliver her into the world.

Chapter Four

Saba heaved a sigh of relief, one that came from deep within her bones, one that had been building up since the day Serepta was born. She knelt on the dusty floor beside the window and clasped her hands together in gratefulness to the gods that had brought the princess forth into the world outside the gates. It was a world that she had always been destined to be a part of.

Suddenly, the door burst open, and Desmond strode in at the head of a score of armed soldiers. His narrow chest puffed arrogantly at the sight of his old grandmother kneeling on the floor, and he slammed his sword hilt down on the table. Dust from the ancient furniture clouded into the air and seemed to bathe the prince in a shadowy haze.

"Where is Serepta?" Desmond barked, his gray eyes challenging the dark ones of Saba.

The old woman pulled herself up to her feet, shaky as they were, and she met her grandson's gaze. "You will never find her now."

"Where is Serepta? She and I are to be married, and without her I can *never* legally become king. Where is Serepta?!" he repeated, face shaking as he tried to hold back his rage and humiliation at being defied in this manner in front of his troops. Each moment that the old woman stalled, the princess was getting farther away.

Saba looked up at his towering form, and she seemed to look down on him as well. "Desmond, I don't believe your poor mother would approve of you behaving in this way," she commented ruefully.

Something in the prince's face seemed to twist violently. He shuddered, and the grip on his sword tightened. "You leave my mother out of this."

"Your mother was my daughter. And you, you poor, twisted young man, seem to have forgotten her completely."

Desmond's features began to tremble. He grimaced and bent over slightly as if doubled up in pain. "My mother is dead," he said through clenched teeth. "She has nothing to do with this. And I swear in front of all these men, to every single god above, if you don't tell me where Serepta ran away to, you will die right here and now."

A look of blessed acceptance spread across Saba's features. "So be it, grandson."

At those words, at that condescending calmness, Desmond flew into a cold fury. In a fit of rage, he slammed the hilt of his sword down on her shoulder, and she crumpled to the floor.

The prince's eyes quivered for a moment, almost remorseful, but not enough to check the fury and guilt that bubbled and frothed from within. His grip retightened on the sword, and he used the flat of the blade to ruthlessly pummel his grandmother on the floor, pushing her down, pushing her down in an attempt to push down the wrenching emotions he felt at the mention of his mother. The soldiers watched silently with tightened lips.

Exhausted, Desmond finally stopped, seeing the old woman lying there bloody and battered.

"You...you *made* me do this! It's your fault for being so *stupid*. Don't make me kill you! Tell me where Serepta is. I will hunt her to the ends of the earth, whether you tell me or not, so you might as well just tell me now. Where is she?!"

And Saba did not answer.

A pained expression came to Desmond's face. "Cut off her head, Ratinka, and be done with it!" he ordered one of his soldiers, not daring to look into his grandmother's eyes.

The soldier came forth with his silver sword raised high. With perfect obedience, he swung to cut off the old woman's head. Just in time, with a swiftness not of her years, Saba managed to duck out of the way.

Although her skin was purpled and crimsoned with blood, although her bones were crumpled with age, although her poor muscles screamed in pain and desired to rest, they performed their final task. Saba staggered to her feet and forced Desmond to meet her powerful gaze.

"You will never find my granddaughter." And with one of those perfect smiles that seemed to come far too rarely to her face, Saba flung herself out the window, to return to the sands of the desert from which she came.

When Saba died, a great hush fell over the land. The babble in the marketplace sharpened and then grew quiet, and not even the creatures of the desert dared to utter a sound. The sun solemnly continued its journey into the cold blue sky, and a slight breeze danced eastwards. All of nature seemed to be mourning for the woman who had worshipped all the beauty there was in the world.

Serepta laughed and skipped gaily across the open desert, giddy at her own sense of freedom. Rafe danced at her side, large paws slipping and sliding on the precarious sand. He was so strong, yet so gentle at the same time, as he raced her to the top of a dune. The princess blithely swung her sack around and tossed it onto the ground.

A light breeze coming westward from Shamar ruffled her long dark hair. She smiled appreciatively, but then her face suddenly dropped. Something was different...a feel in the air...a taste...the fur on the back of Rafe's neck stood on end as he felt it, too.

Serepta began to stumble about atop the dune. There was a peculiar tingling in her hands. She cast them about in the breeze, searching for something that wasn't quite there, something that was missing...Serepta's hand instinctively grabbed at the tiger's eye now around her neck, and then she could see everything.

Rafe gave a cry when the princess suddenly dropped to her knees in the sand. The wolf's ears picked up and he leaned forward, head cocked to one side, trying desperately to figure out the look of blank horror pasted upon her face.

She had seen her grandmother's death in the tiger's eye, carried to her on the wind.

The argument between Saba and Desmond... the nauseating mixture of impatience and rage and guilt etched into his features... the hideous slap of metal upon skin... all of this, carried to her on the wind.

And Serepta didn't want to see anymore.

She grabbed the sack, swung it over her shoulder, and took off running. Her legs stretched and flew, wanting only to keep moving, keep moving so she wouldn't have to think or see anymore. Rafe struggled to match her incredible pace as they fled across the ground. Serepta's muscles embraced this task; the sun, the winds, and the sand all seemed to be supporting her and lifting her up, with the sole purpose of taking her away from the place that had taken away her beloved grandmother.

Chapter Five

Raghnall's Riders congregated outside the Eye of Shamar, waiting for their prince to come down. Finally, Desmond staggered down the stone staircase.

"Your Highness, how may we serve you now?" Sanjay, Captain of the Riders questioned, grabbing the reins of his auburn stallion.

The prince let out a sigh. He reached his arm behind him to lightly touch a pink scar that had begun to form on his back. Serepta's nails had made the cuts as crooked as his smile.

"We go east. We will hunt down the princess and bring her back here," Desmond finally replied bitterly.

"Because you need her to become king," another soldier, Ratinka, nodded appreciatively at the prince's cunning.

Desmond dug his sword point into the sand.

"Yes, she is my betrothed. And as a Prince of Shamar, I hereby hold her responsible for the death of our grandmother, Saba."

The Riders began to murmur amongst themselves.

"Your Highness, how is that so?" the captain Sanjay came forward, a troubled look upon his fair features.

"Because I say it is! How dare you contradict me? It is *Serepta's* fault, because if she hadn't run away, none of this would have happened. Now I say we ride east and hunt her down. I will not stop until I have brought her back to Shamar. We *will* be wed, I *will* become king, and then she *will* be punished for the death so clearly on her hands," Desmond said firmly.

Raghnall's Riders were obliged to obey their prince. Eastward, they went.

When night descended upon the land that day, Serepta and Rafe were forced to finally collapse at the edge of a thick forest. The princess's breath came in ragged jolts, and she grabbed for the water jug. She and Rafe had run the entire day across the desert in the midday sun and now into this forest. It was a trip that should have taken three days, but they finished it in just one, and both were exhausted. Rafe's coat was torn and filthy, and his paws weary, but the wolf crouched loyally by the princess's side in the cool shade under a tree.

Serepta gulped down some water, and the coldness of it numbed her teeth and shocked her throat. Good. Pain was good. She deserved pain. It took her mind off other things...faster and faster she dumped the water down her throat, trying desperately to drown and smother the memories and emotions beginning to fight their way up, because if she were to realize that the only person in the entire world who ever loved her was gone, it would kill her right then and there.

The princess gave a strangled sob. Gone. Saba was gone, and Serepta suddenly felt very alone. Her stomach retched with the thought of it, her hands shook, and her entire body began to shake and heave. Serepta emitted a cry like a wounded animal and began to claw at the rotting forest floor, eyes blurring with tears that just wouldn't fall.

Her hand reached up to grab the cold golden collar around her neck. She violently ripped off the only remaining symbol of her former life and flung it sharply into the trees. Why, why did this have to happen? Why did Saba have to give her life for Serepta?

I'm not worth it... she cringed. It was true. *I'm just not worth it...* the words rolled painfully through her mind, and she felt very tiny and alone huddled at the edge of that great forest in the darkness of the night. All she had behind her was the death of her grandmother and a band of soldiers hunting her like an animal. All she had before her was a seemingly impossible journey. And all she had beside her was a wolf. The wolf....

Rafe stared back at her, deeply into her eyes. He looked so tired, so tired and so in pain. But in his eyes there was a calm ferocity that softened Serepta's misery, if only for one sweet moment.

"No!" the princess bellowed. She had no right to feel better, not when she owed everything she ever had and ever done and ever was to Saba. Bitterness rose like a wave deep inside her, and then receded from her throat. Up it came again, and a sob threatened to burst forth from her body. But no, she couldn't cry. Serepta never cried, and crying wouldn't do justice to one iota of the pain she felt.

Please, Serepta beseeched the wolf with her eyes. She wasn't sure how to ask him for help, or why, but he was all she had left. *Please, show me how to mourn for a woman who meant all the earth, the sun, and the stars to me...*

Rafe let a great breath escape from his massive chest, and he staggered to his feet, rising up proud to his full height. Then the wolf threw his head back and pointed his nose at the pearly, opalescent moon. From his jaws erupted a tremendous, ethereal howl. Liquid poetry it was, and it rent the sky like a knife. All of his aches, pains, and bitter thoughts flew out the wolf's jaws and up to the moon, fully released and never to return again.

Serepta watched this wolf do what he seemed born to do. She closed her eyes and savored the notes of his song, quieting as the knots inside of her began to loosen. He was helping her then, just as his cry had helped her at the party.

The princess felt overwhelmed with pride at knowing such a creature. He was so strong, yet so vulnerable, and hauntingly beautiful all at once as his blue eyes squinted with emotion. Rafe was revealing his soul to her in that moment, and she loved him for it, and wanted only to join him in that song of mourning.

Serepta hesitated for a moment, gazing up at the full moon through the criss-crossing black branches of a tree. Then she joined Rafe at his side, stood up tall with a straightened spine, and threw back her head. She howled, she sang, she cried. A tuneless, wordless song erupted from her throat and carried all her desperation and guilt and pain up into the night sky. Her body shook with it, thrilled with the howl. Her eyes fluttered shut and her throat tightened with the song. Higher, lower, quickly, steadily; each note sang in perfect rhythm with the aching she felt within. Then, exhausted beyond belief, Serepta finally collapsed to the forest floor.

The great white moon above took every bit of her tremendous pain and absorbed it into the night sky, returning only soft, loving moonlight to the jarring soul beneath. It fed her the strength she would surely need in the weeks and months to come.

Part Two

Up a Mountain

Chapter Six

The warm sun soon replaced the moon, and the golden rays it cast served to rouse the princess from a deep slumber. She stirred, slowly sitting up, taking a moment to realize where she was. The wolf awoke soon after, and he clumsily pulled himself off the forest floor to get a bite of meat.

The princess yawned wide. Her jaw ached with it. She felt so...clean. So empty. So immaculate. It was as if every emotion she had ever had had been wiped away. Saba came to her mind, and besides a tiny pull at her heart, Serepta felt nothing but emptiness. It was a good sort of emptiness though, like the calm after a furious storm, and she felt re-energized with it.

She was braver, stronger, and more at peace with herself and with the world than she had ever been before. And older, she felt older. For the first time, Serepta noticed a tremendous forested mountain looming in the distance. Something in her mind stirred with recognition, causing her to clutch at the pendant around her neck.

The touch of the tiger's eye made her tingle as it seemed to open the third eye within herself. Then she knew it was Mount Morad that awaited her there in the morning fog.

The sun rose in all its brilliant glory, ready to begin a new day, and Serepta was finally ready to begin it, too. Saba would want her to go on. She was ready to take on the mountain.

Serepta packed up their supplies and started off into the woods with Rafe, and all that was left to show they had ever been there was a broken golden collar that glinted peculiarly in the foliage...

The princess and the wolf had run the first leg of the journey out of love and compassion; Desmond and his Riders ran out of hate and forced loyalty, so it took them twice the time. Finally, they managed to cross the desert and reach the great forest.

Sanjay, Captain of the Riders, led his auburn stallion to a nearby stream for a drink. Both man and horse were tired and sore from the long journey, but they hid it well from the others. Sanjay, pushing a lock of dark blonde hair away from his sweating brow, gazed about the thick forest all around him. The exquisite trees were adorned with rich black bark and emerald and champagne colored leaves. Warm sunlight filtered through the canopy of treetops above to paint a pattern of soft black shadows on the ground below. It was so beautiful, and peaceful.

"Hello, Captain," a cool voice came from nowhere.

Startled, Sanjay whirled around to find the soldier Ratinka behind him. He was unnerved that he had managed to sneak up on him despite the numerous twigs and dry leaves that littered the forest floor.

"Hello, soldier," Sanjay replied.

"So sorry to intrude, but my horse needs a drink," Ratinka added with a hint of sarcasm. He began to water the scrawny horse. The black creature had the same sinewy build of its owner, and its eyes darted this way and that as it lowered its head into the stream.

Sanjay patted his stallion again, relaxing into the quiet sounds of the forest. The Captain was wary whenever Ratinka was nearby. The cold sharpness of the soldier's personality did not mix well with Sanjay's quiet warmth. He closed his eyes and tried to draw patience from the environment around him.

Ratinka let out a sigh. "I do hope we find the princess soon. My horse and I detest these filthy trees," he said with an annoyed grunt.

Sanjay took in a deep breath and didn't reply.

"Once we return to Shamar after capturing the princess, I am going to have a big leg of roasted goat and praise the gods that I'm home."

Patience... the captain reminded himself, trying to hold his temper in check.

"That wretched woman doesn't stand a chance, with us hunting her down. I can't wait to see what Desmond does when he catches her!" Ratinka chortled to himself.

Sanjay felt pained within his heart. The great floodgates inside were let down, and his anger came pouring out.

"Do you possess even a single scrap of honor? Doesn't it bother you that we're hunting the princess like an animal? I will follow my orders, but I do not approve of this at all. *Serepta* isn't the one responsible for Saba's death; it's Desmond that is!" he erupted, bluntly stating what all the Riders knew but dared not say.

Ratinka raised an eyebrow. "Are you doubting the prince? That's treason, my dear captain," he challenged, green eyes flaring. His horse lifted its dripping head from the water and stared at Sanjay as if accusing him, too.

Sanjay's gaze was steady. "I do not doubt my loyalty to Shamar and its rulers. I just think Desmond has been acting strangely of late. He is far too quiet, and paces about, touching the scar on his back that Serepta gave him. I sense a change in him," he said thoughtfully.

"If there is a change, it is for the better. I think the prince is brilliant. And cunning. He knows exactly what he wants and how to get it," Ratinka huffed. Suddenly, something caught his eye. He scurried off into the trees, and emerged, quite pleased, with a golden collar in his hand. Sanjay's heart stopped when he saw it because he knew then that it was a death sentence for Serepta.

"Ah, look what I found! The princess has been this way after all!" Ratinka declared and started off towards camp. After a few strides he stopped in his tracks and turned around.

"Desmond will most certainly reward me for this. You better hang on tight to your captaincy," he said ominously, and once again took off through the forest, leaving Sanjay with an even darker look upon his troubled countenance.

Desmond paced nervously about the campsite, chewing on a fingernail. There was no sign of Serepta anywhere, and it would be easy to lose track of someone in a forest like this. If they didn't find her soon, the Riders might not be as willing to carry on. The thought of Serepta getting away, the thought of never becoming king, the thought of her *winning*, made him scowl with rage.

"Your Highness, see what I have brought you!" Ratinka declared, coming from the woods. His green eyes flickered excitedly at the prince as he grasped the collar between his bony fingers. His wretched horse shifted back and forth, mimicking its owner's anticipation.

Desmond strode over to the soldier, pushing his flowing cape aside with an anxious sweep of the arm. "What is that you have in your hand?"

Ratinka held out the collar, which Desmond instantly snatched away. The prince held it up to examine it, and he shuddered with recognition.

"Serepta," he whispered coldly. The entire forest seemed to quiet with that word.

Desmond lifted the collar and dragged its cold metal across his nose. He breathed deeply, inhaling Serepta's perfume, a crooked grin emerging on his sallow face.

"Ahhhh," he let out his breath. "Cousin, you are somewhere

nearby...somewhere just waiting for me to come find you." His gray eyes darted across the forest, unaware of the soldiers who were beginning to gather around him. He stared at the air in front of him as though Serepta was right there.

"This necklace is yours...I can still see it on your bare throat...that beautiful throat...such soft skin..." his eyes fluttered shut, imagining the night he had slipped into Serepta's bed. Sharply, a molten rage shot up inside of him. It was the night that she had thrown him away.

"No!" he suddenly roared, and he reached at the scar on his shoulder blade. The scab ripped off, and dark blood began to flood freely from the marks of Serepta's nails, the crimson seeping across the back of Desmond's dark tunic like a disease.

He violently flung the golden collar to the ground. The sharp metallic thump quickly caught the attention of all the Riders, and they watched him begin to pace furiously around the clearing.

"Serepta! Where are you, cousin? Always turning your back on me? Am I not good enough for you, cousin? Not good enough to be your king?!" he bellowed, questioning the quivering air in front of him. "Your king!! I am supposed to be KING! I am supposed to rule Shamar, and *you*, cousin, are supposed to be home in my *bed*!" he began to laugh at the irony of it all. Veins bulged on his forehead, and he felt dizzy with the rush of hot blood to his face.

Lightheaded, Desmond stumbled about for a moment as if drunk. After a moment of furious thought, he tore the black hair away from his eyes and glared up at the darkening sky.

"I swear to every god above that I will hunt you down Serepta! You will pay for what you are *doing* to me! Look at me. Look at me!" he stared at his quivering hands, shoulders heaving, oblivious to everything around him. "I will *have* you, cousin. I will have you in my bed, have you as my queen, and once I do, I will KILL you!" he roared at the top of his lungs.

He stabbed his sword point into the dirt and knelt upon the ground. "I swear it upon my mother's grave!" Desmond whispered to himself, and he gave a quiet sob.

Raghnall's Riders watched in silence as the icy claws of obsession began to tear away at their prince.

Day by day, Serepta and Rafe began to climb Mount Morad like shaky newborn deer. The slopes were unpredictable and treacherous, scaled with thick brush and loose rocks. One of the only thoughts that encouraged Serepta was that she knew that others had made it safely over the mountain before her.

"If they could do it, I can," the princess muttered firmly to herself, staring up at the peak shrouded in fog. Rafe padded silently alongside her.

As each day went on, however, the princess began to suffer. She had never experienced land like this before in the desert. Climbing this mountain was not exactly as exciting as she had thought it would be. The very soil under her feet felt unsteady to the touch, and even the air had a foreign taste to it. Each step taken was quite possibly a step farther to fall.

The higher she went, the more that the cold, wet fog of Morad tried to wrap itself around her and strangle out the sunlight. Serepta had never felt this kind of cold before; it clung tightly around her bones to the point where she could no longer walk. Finally, one ice-bitten, moonless night, she collapsed to the frozen ground.

Serepta's body was racked with violent shivers, and each time she moved it felt as though a little bit of her was giving up and dying. Goosebumps prickled painfully across her bared skin, and the hard-packed ground beneath seemed to press sharply against the places that ached the most. There was no moon to howl at, no sun to draw warmth from, no stars to see by, and no desire to go on.

A cold breeze came slinking through the barren trees, causing Serepta to shudder. She was ashamed to find that her heart ached with an overwhelming desire to be found by Desmond and taken home. At least it was warm there, and she wouldn't have to keep going. Her stomach crackled and growled with hunger. Extravagant four course meals had been replaced with meager scraps of dried food, and her belly was twisting up inside. Serepta was losing precious body fat to keep her warm, and her muscles barely even had enough energy to curl her into a ball. The princess took in a deep breath, felt the raggedness of the clammy air, and she knew she was going to die if she could not withstand this cold. She hated how weak she was.

I'm going to die and it's all my fault, a voice in her head cried. Serepta gave a desperate look at her Companion, face bleak and weary.

Something in the wolf's eyes seemed to break when he saw her curled up like that. Forgetting his instinctive pride, he flowed into her arms and wrapped himself around her shivering body.

Serepta almost cried at this selfless gesture, but the princess never cried. Instead, she relaxed into the safe warmth of Rafe's fur and the powerful heartbeat within his chest.

Home... the pitiful voice in her head cried. *What am I doing here, starving and freezing on this filthy ground? I'm so foolish! I should be home in bed!*

Home was with Saba, in her chambers by her window. Home was with the little purple flower, dreaming in the courtyard under the gentle sun. Her heart broke when she remembered the poor blossom, and she felt torn with guilt at leaving it behind.

I want to go back...

But her dark eyes hardened when she realized what would happen if Desmond were to ever really find her. And she looked around in the darkness at the barren, wind-swept trees, at a lizard that crept silently into its hole, and at the crumbling black soil just inches from her face, and Serepta did not want to die yet, or even worse, return to Shamar. Not when there was so much life around her; not when there was so much she had yet to see and to know.

"No!" Serepta suddenly cried, sitting straight up. Startled, Rafe leaped aside. "No!" she shouted again, stronger this time. "If Desmond finds me, he will bring me back to Shamar to become his queen and then *kill* me."

She slammed her fist into the dirt with all the strength she could muster. "I will never go back to that pitiful land in the desert! I will never go back to that rotting pile of filth!" Serepta cried. The heat of her resolve seemed to liquefy the ice around her bones, and her heart began to beat again. "I will never go back to Shamar!" She staggered to her feet, warmed and strong now.

"Saba *died* so I would never have to see that place again," her voice cracked. "I made my choice, I accepted this journey, and I will finish it or I will certainly die trying!" her attention suddenly turned towards the blank, moonless night sky, and her dark eyes flamed ferociously.

"Go ahead, do your worst! Block out the light, freeze my bones, send all of Shamar after me, and it still won't matter! I *will* keep going!" she roared at the sky. Serepta stumbled about for a moment until her fist wearily unclenched. Satisfied finally, and exhausted, she curled up on the ground beside Rafe.

The young wolf's eyes glowed warmly, and if he could have smiled, he certainly would have.

Chapter Seven

Two nights, two days up Morad's slopes the Princess and Wolf will fly,
Beware the peak that is shrouded in fog; this is where the danger lies.
Mountains loom and walls will leap, the Princess will find the mirrors
  sly;
With visions untrue and feet pinned down, to kill her the crags will try.
If brave of heart and strong in mind, then she will start to see why
The power of her very soul lies in the tiger's eye...

Serepta stirred in dark sleep, moved by the haunting tune in her head. It felt as though melted honey was being poured into her ears by the night. The princess grinned slowly and snuggled down into the leaves on the ground, only wanting to hear more of that voice...it sounded almost like Saba's, yet was different, perhaps even wiser and more comforting. Serepta felt like a tiny baby when she heard the song...

Her eyelids fluttered for a moment, and she awoke to find it was morning. Grayish sunlight fell upon her through a blanket of clouds and caused her skin to tingle with a faint warmth. She sat up straight, startled by the quick passage of time. It felt as though only moments had gone by. Even more startling was that Serepta found that no matter how hard she tried, she could not remember the words to the song from her dream. The princess tried again and again to reclaim the words with her senses, but they were nowhere to be found. The melodic tune kept eluding her grasp, slipping away like oil before she could recognize it fully.

Serepta looked over at Rafe. From the bewildered look upon his face, she figured that he had heard the song in his dreams, too. He looked at her intently and moved his jaw, as if trying to tell her something. It pained Serepta to see her Companion struggle within the confines of his body, and she couldn't fathom why the wolf thought he could even talk in the first place.

Serepta put a hand on his head and stared up at the mountain peak, which was now much closer to her than before. It loomed in front of her like the scarred face of a blackened god fallen to earth. A chill ran down her spine for some incomprehensible reason, and she felt without a doubt that something was waiting for her at the top: something cold, something cruel, something powerful.

"Well, whatever you are, you are standing in my way," Serepta announced. She swung the pack onto her shoulder, gestured to Rafe without a word, and the two were off.

All was quiet that morning in the small, makeshift camp of the Riders. The powerful horses tethered to the trees closed their eyes in fatigue and did not utter a sound. Each soldier was curled up on the ground, dreams drifting in and out of their silent heads. Even Desmond was quiet, sleeping in a tent, mouth curled with a joke that only made sense to him.

One soldier, however sat on a rock, green eyes wide open with the alertness of a hawk. Ratinka was quiet, yet the grindstone turning in his mind, sharpening his plans, would have awakened the entire forest had it not been kept inside his dark head. He gazed almost wistfully at the sleeping form of Sanjay. Why was this man so respected? Anyone would agree that Ratinka was far more clever, and resourceful, and ambitious.

I must be the most underrated soldier in all of Shamar. Someday, someday soon, these fools will all look upon me and realize the brilliance I have had all along, and then they will be sorry, Ratinka's thoughts grumbled. He turned up his nose as he squinted down at Sanjay again.

The Captain of the Riders emanated strength and power even while he slept. There was a quiet warmth about him, an unshakeable integrity, that served to infuriate those who did not possess it.

Ratinka did not possess it.

He is a weakling, the mental grindstone screeched. *He is a slave to his emotions and is more concerned about what is "right" than about what makes logical sense. He is not fit to be Captain of the most elite soldiers in all of Shamar...*

The green eyes intensified their gaze upon the sleeping man. The captain was handsome, with honest, open features. He was the type of man who everyone couldn't help but to love. Ratinka stared at the man's throat. Dark blonde stubble lightly sprinkled the smooth skin like a soft sandpaper. It would be so easy to murder Sanjay after the way the captain had treated him. He could slit that bare throat and hide him in the woods. The others would think he had deserted.

No, Ratinka thought. *The time is not ripe, and to hurry it would be foolish. I will soon become Captain, and Sanjay will soon die for his insults. Once I am Captain, and Desmond is King, I will become his most trusted advisor. With no heirs yet to speak of, I will be made King of Shamar if Desmond were to have a, well, rather unfortunate accident,* the grindstone picked up speed. Then, with a mental slap of cold discipline, Ratinka stopped this train of thought.

All in good time. All in good time. But at least, I can start right now.

Temporarily, the grindstone screeched to a halt. It was time to act.

The first sound emitted into that early morning was a quick snap of a twig. The young soldier named Admael's eyes opened alertly. He saw Ratinka's leather boot right by his face.

"Ratinka, what are you doing?" he murmured, yawning wide.

Ratinka looked at him as if startled. "Oh, nothing, nothing at all. I wouldn't want to bore you with the worries of an old soldier like myself. No, no, you are young, you need your sleep," he cooed and continued pacing nervously about.

Admael sat up indignantly. "Just because I am the youngest of the Riders doesn't mean I can't handle any news about what's going on. I am eighteen years old, *not* a little boy. I demand you tell me what is troubling you!"

Ratinka was a little surprised at the soldier's mettle, but he masked it well with a patronizing smile. "Of course you're not a little boy! I would never call you that. In fact...well, no, never mind," he stopped himself, masterfully faking a blush.

"No! Do tell me!" Admael cried.

"Well," he began. "If I may say so, I have always felt that you remind me of myself at your age. You are so skilled, and intelligent, and brave! I suppose if I were to tell anyone what's bothering me, I would trust you the most," Ratinka said. He nearly laughed out loud at the way Admael's eyes lit up. "Let's walk," the soldier commanded, tugging on the young man's tunic.

Admael pulled himself up and stealthily moved into the woods with Ratinka. The young soldier was amazed at the way Ratinka could move so silently through the trees. It didn't even occur to him that there was no way Ratinka could have accidentally snapped that twig by his head earlier...

"So what is it that's troubling you?" Admael asked.

"It's our captain, Sanjay. I have been suspecting it for some time, and now my worst fears have been confirmed."

"Fears? About what?" Admael's face grew wide and white, like a lump of dough rising.

"Treason!" Ratinka suddenly cried passionately, causing Admael to take a step back in surprise. "Treason, young soldier! I heard Sanjay confess it to my own ears...oh, how I wish it weren't so! He told me that he thinks *Desmond* is responsible for Saba's death, and that he no longer wanted to follow his orders!"

Admael looked shocked.

"And, I hate to admit this to anyone, but I'm afraid. Terrified, in fact. Sanjay is just the sort of man to murder Desmond and take command of us all. I've seen the mark of an evil ambition in his eyes."

"You think he is capable of such treachery? Why, I always thought he was such a kind man…"

"Open your eyes, soldier! Underneath those locks of golden hair lies the mind of a mutinous schemer."

"But... but we have to do something!"

"Ahh, I agree. But no matter how brave and quick you are, we must not act in haste. First, we have to alert the other Riders and tell them what is going on before we can make any moves."

"But what can I do now?"

"Now? Right now, you can swear absolute loyalty to me, and in doing so, reaffirm your allegiance to the kingdom of Shamar!"

"I swear it!" Admael cried proudly.

"Now there's a good boy," Ratinka's lips curled in a smile.

Throughout the next two days, as Ratinka began to build up a conspiracy against Sanjay, Serepta and Rafe made their way up the last stretch of mountain. Finally, the two collapsed at the top of Morad, at the top of everything they had been striving for throughout the past few days. Serepta fell to her knees in the rocky soil and clasped her hands in gratitude for having made it.

She climbed up on top of a boulder and looked down below at how far she had traveled, how far she had come and conquered since her rebirth outside the gates of Shamar. Serepta had in time adapted to the coldness of Morad and no longer pined for the heat of the desert. The mountain felt solid under her feet, the breeze of cool air blew her dark hair wildly about, and for once,

Serepta felt her chest swell with an overwhelming joy at pursuing her dream. If anything were to happen to her now, at least she had made it farther than any princess of Shamar before her. At least she was free.

Rafe let the breeze ruffle his fur, and his nose picked up at the scent of a rabbit. Serepta laughed.

"Go ahead, big hunter. We could use more meat. I'm going to explore."

Rafe darted off, and she began to meander her way around the mountaintop. There was a swagger to her step, a coolness in her smile, and pride in her heart. She felt invincible, walking about the peak of Mount Morad, her conquered land. Serepta had battled the mountain and won.

The land at the peak was strewn with rocks and foliage. It had been ravaged by the winds of the ages, and all that was left was that which could withstand such a beating. The croppings of rocks were battered by the elements, their craggy faces twisted open in a moan. The plants were wiry, tough, and bare.

Strange, fat, black trees sprouted up from the soil all around Serepta. The branches were so wispy and numerous that they looked like roots, as if a great hand had plucked the trees from the soil and turned them upside down. Some trees were a lot larger than others, and some were just beginning to sprout.

How awkward, the princess thought to herself.

Suddenly, she realized that she had wandered into a circle of large boulders. It was as if she was just coming out of a dream, and she noticed them for the first time. The magnificent stones were so peculiar looking...the princess stepped farther inside the ring to examine them closer.

The boulders had millions of facets that caught the light and gave off a multi-colored, crystalline shimmer. Even the ground she trod upon was made of the stone. The walls of rock directly around her were perfectly smooth, shiny, and far more reflective than any looking glass Serepta had ever seen. Everywhere, all around her, above her and below her, she saw in the stone the reflected image of herself.

At first Serepta did not want to look. She was ashamed at the possibility of seeing herself dirty and unkempt. In Shamar, a look in the mirror always meant her father wanted her to fix something. To him there was always something that just wasn't quite right, something that caused those piercing eyes of his to glow with disapproval. The princess tried to look away, but everywhere she turned there was another mirror. It was as though the stones had gathered themselves around her. She couldn't even find the place where she had entered the ring of boulders, and soon gave up trying.

Serepta finally turned to a mirror-rock in front of her, ready to accept the feeling of shame. But what she saw was so far from what she expected that she nearly stepped back in surprise. She looked so different...so beautiful, so exquisite...as though she were a glorified portrait painted by the king's artists in Shamar! Serepta turned this way and that in a blushing awe, mesmerized by the magnificent image in front of her.

The journey had carved away any excess fat, its unforgiving hands had sculpted muscles upon her body, and the warm sun had baked her once fair skin to a golden brown. Serepta began to admire the way her gold tunic clung to her curves, rejoicing in everything, including the way her feet poised upon her ivory sandals and helped her to move with the grace of a lioness. Her hair flowed long and black down her shoulders and was as silky as a panther's fur.

Serepta almost laughed in disbelief, but instead her open mouth caught her eye. Her lips were full and dark as they opened to laugh, and her eyes lit up. Her eyes...they sparkled like twin dark jewels above cheeks that stood like sculpted mountains.

Serepta's mouth curled in a smile. "I am a goddess," she murmured, and she felt as though she could spend a lifetime just admiring herself within that quiet circle of stone.

Time passed there...perhaps minutes, perhaps hours.

"Look at me...I could live here forever, feeding upon nothing but my beauty and drinking nothing but my glory...." Serepta whispered, barely recognizing the words that sprang from her perfect lips.

The princess stepped closer to the rock and touched a finger lightly to its dry, icy surface. Her mind swooned with fantasies of men who would cross the entire earth for but the sound of her voice, for but one smell of her perfume. Finally, Serepta felt the love she had longed for all her life. She was overwhelmed with joy, and she felt as though her great journey was at long last complete.

Rafe suddenly sprang into the circle of stone. The wolf had spent the past hour trying to track down Serepta. His eyes lit up at finding the princess, but the hair on the back of his neck stood on end when he saw the way she was staring at the boulder in front of her. She was turning all around and running her fingers through her hair as if she were standing in front of a mirror. He leaned forward, trying to figure out why his Companion was so intently admiring nothing but a blank stone wall.

Something was wrong. Something was very wrong within that queer little circle of stones, and Rafe felt as though the woman in front of him wasn't even Serepta anymore. He sprang forward and nipped at her calf, but the princess didn't notice. Terrified, the wolf bit her again, and he even drew blood this time. Still, Serepta didn't move. The princess vaguely felt a touch on her leg.

"Ha ha ha!" she laughed merrily. It was the hand of a lover on her perfectly smooth skin.

Rafe heard her mad laughter and began to frantically pace about. This all was very wrong. He had to speak to her; he had to cry out. But no, of course, the wolf couldn't speak. It was then that he remembered the song, that strange song that he and Serepta had both heard in their dreams two days before. It was as though a switch had been flipped in his head. He didn't know why it was a good idea, but the song had come from within her mind, and perhaps it could bring her mind back again.

Rafe tried hard to hum the tune, but wolves are not meant to hum. It scratched against his throat and made his eyes water. Frustrated, Rafe realized there was only one way to bring Serepta back to him. He sat back on his haunches and threw his head way back. Then, the wolf began to howl with all his heart. Rafe's eyes squinted and his throat tightened as he prayed that this idea would work. The haunting melody of the dream-song knifed through the air and echoed off the stone walls, slowly rising in speed and volume as Rafe desperately tried to reach through to his Companion.

The song seemed to pierce the fog within Serepta's mind. It stirred up some recognition deep within her and began to move her from the intense spell the mountain had spun. Finally, Serepta could remember the words from her dream that had been bothering her for so long, and they were revealed to her in this most desperate hour:

Two nights, two days up Morad's slopes the Princess and Wolf will fly,
Beware the peak that is shrouded in fog; this is where the danger lies.
Mountains loom and walls will leap, the Princess will find the mirrors sly;
With visions untrue and feet pinned down, to kill her the crags will try.
If brave of heart and strong in mind, then she will start to see why
The power of her very soul lies in the tiger's eye...

That soothing voice called to her, joined with her to help struggle against the spell of the mountain. Serepta's mind fought and kicked and clawed ferociously to free itself, and she tried with all her might to tear her eyes away from the tantalizing image of herself. But no, now she didn't want to. She couldn't see the real, dirty, imperfect Serepta...she couldn't bear to think that other women were more beautiful or that men didn't adore her....

But it's all an illusion! the real Serepta cried from inside.

The princess's mind screamed in agony as the mountain fought to keep its hold on her. Suddenly, the picture in the mirror rippled and morphed to show an image of Serepta as a hideous rotting corpse. Her flesh was mangled and green, her eyes were half eaten by maggots, and she could almost feel their fat wet bodies flopping across her skin. Serepta let out a shriek.

Rafe saw his Companion's gaze reaffix itself in horror upon the stone wall, and he howled even harder. His throat burned with it and tears ran hot down his face...he had to help her, he had to save her. The wolf pushed his head hard against her hand, begging her, pleading her, willing her to move.

And then, finally, as slowly as the moon moving through a darkened sky, Serepta's hand began to rise. *The power of her very soul lies in the tiger's eye...* The words came back to Rafe and he knew then what it was she had to do. The princess's hand rose higher and higher, until finally, her trembling fingers touched the necklace that was a last gift from Saba.

And then, with a slight stumble backwards, Serepta was free. Free from the curse, free from the mountain, free from the vanity that had threatened to consume her. Morad was strong, but Serepta was stronger, and she had won. The princess stared at the precious tiger's eye in her hand, and in its shiny surface she could see a reflection of herself. It was the real her, untainted by perfection.

Serepta gazed gratefully at Rafe, and her eyes were enough to convince the wolf that he had saved her. Together, they fled from that quiet, cold circle of stone.

Chapter Eight

Hearts heavy and soaked with the weight of exhaustion, the two took a brief respite in the cool mountain air. Serepta leaned against a rock face, wearily running a hand through her hair. Rafe sat solemnly at her side.

All of a sudden, a new sound replaced the heaving of their breaths. It was the sound of pounding hooves on hard soil, of the clashing joints of cold metal armor, and of the beating hearts of men eager for blood. Another danger had come forth now, one that had taken place in Serepta's nightmares many times before. Over the reddened crest of the horizon, Desmond and the Riders had finally joined them at the top of Morad.

The stallions began to thunder nearer and nearer across the mountaintop. Each hoof beat tolled out a rampant clatter of impending doom, and the beasts shrieked aloud excitedly with all the passion of a great storm let loose. The horses were thrilled with this new open land, and they galloped towards Serepta with Desmond at the lead. The prince's gray eyes squinted hauntingly in the light of the blood red sunset, and he swung a weighted net high in the air, ready to throw it down hard upon his long awaited quarry.

The princess's eyes widened in horror and she felt a nauseating, gripping fear across her insides. All her muscles tensed tightly, as if trying to keep her heart from dribbling from her breast. The color leaked away from her face and her hands began to tremble when she saw the cold look of hatred in Desmond's eyes, a look that evoked the primal, destroying fear she felt as a child when he had shattered her arm with the rock.

"Enough...enough already...." Serepta moaned. But she had begged for this, begged for the gods and fates to show her their worst. And somehow she had the feeling that this was only one black wisp of a great and terrible storm to come.

Rafe saw something break in Serepta's eyes, a snap like a great oak under the force of a powerful wind. She was exhausted from her ordeal within the stone circle, and this new threat was too much for her to bear. She dropped to her knees in the soil, smothered with an apathy borne of a life of resistance, finally unwilling to resist anymore.

Rafe saw her danger and leaped in front of her to shield her with his own body. Desmond came pounding forward and furiously cast the net at both of them. Luckily, the wolf managed to shove Serepta out of the way just in time, and the prince's momentum carried him away.

Serepta fell hard to the rocky ground, and the clatter seemed to finally jolt her out of her stupor. Mind sharpened, yet still in a cloud, she sat up straight and saw that between Desmond and a dozen armed Riders, she was horribly outnumbered. It was only a matter of moments until Desmond would turn around and come back with the net.

Well, this is it, Serepta. Stubbornness gets you so far, but even you can break and topple to the ground, the princess thought to herself. Surrender seemed exquisite, a glowing paradise compared to the risk of facing the coldness of those terrible eyes ever again.

Then, Saba's words from long ago came to her mind: *Your name, Serepta, means peaceful, yet you never seem to be. That is only one of the lessons you must learn. Another is that you never ought to surrender until all options have been spent...*

And suddenly, Serepta was peaceful for the first time in her life. The babble of despairing thoughts finally ceased. Her mind quieted to the hushed sound of the moment just before sunrise when the fate of a new day hangs in the balance. Time for her seemed to stand still as Desmond pounded closer with his net, as Rafe stood poised to lay his life down in defense of her, and as her mind sat quietly, waiting for an idea to come.

More words of Saba came flooding back to her: *This pendant will aid your inner sight. It will keep you focused on what is important and reveal great powers deep within yourself. Keep it with you and remember what I have taught you always...*

The tiger's eye, her soul! It had helped her before, and it was all that Serepta had time to rely upon. The princess grabbed the pendant and braced herself for whatever was about to happen, whether it be death or salvation.

When she touched the necklace, her heart flooded and seemed to swell with a love and joy that she couldn't even comprehend. It was a love for her Companion who stood cool and composed before the threat of a painful death. It was a love for the warm tingle the tiger's eye sent through her body. And most of all, it was a love for the woman who had given it to her so long ago. The powerful surge of this love crackled through her hands, elating her and lifting her to her feet.

Desmond was but feet away now, and there was no time left in the world.

"STOP!" Serepta cried and held out one hand in front of her while the other one trembled as it clutched the amber necklace.

As if slamming into a mountain, Desmond's oncoming steed screeched to a halt, its face a mask of surprise and bewilderment at the force that had stopped it so suddenly and so completely. A hush fell over the mountaintop as Raghnall's Riders stumbled back in shock.

Spinning dizzily at this new power surging through her fingertips, Serepta turned around towards the other soldiers. The sheer downpour of her emotions seemed to cloud her vision, and a great howling wind began to pick up atop the mountain.

"STOP! All of you! I command you with the power of this stone, and with the power that is inside myself! I fight with love, I fight with light, I fight with all the goodness that is inside my heart, and because of that, I will always be protected!" she roared, barely recognizing the words that flew from her mouth.

Before Serepta could take another breath, the wind blasted with all the strength of the heavens. She watched with a pacified intensity as the forms of the stallions and Riders were suddenly swept up into the sky by the storm and hurled back down the mountain, wriggling and screaming in horror. The sounds of weapons clattering down the rocky slopes rang like demented bells.

The princess let the tiger's eye drop, and she fainted weakly away to the ground.

The night sky grew purple and mottled like the bruises forming across Desmond's face. When he finally awoke at the foot of the mountain, darkness had claimed his view. Cold crept through every space around and inside of his body. The prince gave a violent shudder.

Am I dead? he questioned himself. *Am I in the Land of the Dark Gods?* He blinked hard, bugging his eyes out wide to see in the blackness all around him. *Finally, I am to suffer for my sins...*

He felt a perverted longing for self-punishment, a cry for eternity, one to drive away the ever-lingering guilt that had owned his soul since the day he was born.

Suddenly, a torch flamed in the darkness. It was Ratinka, slightly bruised and battered, casting the eerie glow of reddish orange into the forest. "To me, soldiers, to me!" he cried. The loud shock of his words drew Desmond back to the world of the living, drew him back from the sullen downward spirals of thought.

Slowly, the Riders crumpled on the ground seemed to unfold and stagger over to the light. Desmond touched a hand to his bruised cheek and felt that he was quite alive. He was alive, and angry now. Indignant, the prince leaped up and snatched the torch away from Ratinka.

"You see, my men? You see the devilry and witchcraft that is Serepta, the dark poison that flies from the serpent's mouth? You have felt first hand the evil of her black magic!" Desmond cried.

The Riders began to shout in agreement. They were from Shamar, and superstition was their birthright.

"The prince is right!" one cried.

"We have to kill the witch!"

"Slay the wolf, too!"

The soldiers began to find their horses and pick up weapons and torches. They were injured and angry, and they no longer doubted the judgment of their prince. Curses and oaths of vengeance began to ripple throughout the dark forest at the base of the great mountain.

Suddenly, quite another sound was heard. "Riders! I think I injured my side on a rock. Come to me!" a familiar voice called, strung tightly with pain. The torchlight flickered to reveal the Captain Sanjay lying beneath a great oak tree. He was propped up on one arm, and there was a great deal of dark blood in a pool around him. His blue eyes were warm and steady, but his face was etched with pain.

Ratinka drew a dagger out of his belt and slid over to Sanjay's fallen form. He stared down at him contemptuously. "Ha! See how the mighty have fallen to their knees," Ratinka spat.

Sanjay's eyes widened in surprise. "Ratinka, friend, help me!" he cried, immediately sensing the inappropriateness of his gesture.

With a look of disgust at the kindly word, Ratinka tightly gripped his arm and yanked him sharply to his feet.

Desmond and the other Riders moved over to the oak tree. "Ratinka, your lack of loyalty towards the Captain is disturbing," the prince accused.

Suddenly, Admael came into the circle, excited by all the action. "Lack of loyalty? Lack of loyalty you say? Ratinka is the most loyal soldier you have! It's *Sanjay* that's the backstabber!" the young man cried, passionately defending his new master, proudly stirring up trouble with one flick of his softened hand.

Sanjay let out a cry of shock and stepped backwards against the tree, clutching his wounded side. Flickers of excitement spread through the forest. The Riders knew now that the time had finally come to reveal the rumors of treason that had been creeping through the group like little snakes slithering in the darkness.

"Sanjay? Backstabbing? What are you talking about?" Desmond demanded.

Ratinka's green eyes brightened with excitement. His nerves screeched with ecstasy as he realized his plans were coming to fruition of their own accord. Now was the time to play the hand fate had dealt him with all the strength and cunning he possessed.

"Your Highness, *Sanjay*, all along, has been plotting to kill you and take over all of us!"

Desmond's eyes widened in surprise. Sanjay looked around the circle of his men, and he saw in the firelight that their faces were filled with anger and carnal delight. These were his men, the men he had lived with, the men he had fought alongside of, the men he had led for years.... his heart felt sick to see that they completely believed in Ratinka's lies.

"Captain, is this true?" the prince demanded.

"No! Your Highness, no! Of course not!" Sanjay cried, still in shock at this turn of events.

"LIAR!" Ratinka roared. His eyes glittered passionately, and soon he even believed the wicked stories spun in his head. "Sanjay, did you not tell me in the woods that you thought the prince was acting strangely?" he asked slyly.

The Captain's insides twisted. To live and to lie, or to stay true and to die? "Yes. But I didn't mean..."

"And did you not tell me that you did not like the orders the prince was giving?" Ratinka interrupted.

"Yes, but..."

"And did you not say that it was *Desmond* responsible for Saba's death, and not Serepta?"

When Sanjay muttered a "yes" to this last question, a hush fell over the group. No one had dared to even mention the possibility of this in the presence of the prince before. They watched as Desmond's face twisted with a mix of hatred and anxiety. If he had any doubts of Ratinka's accusations, they now had completely dropped from his mind.

"FOOL!" Desmond roared at Sanjay. "How *dare* you!! You are a treacherous liar, and not fit to be Captain! You are not fit to live!" Desmond condemned, drawing his sword, fueled by humiliation.

Sanjay's world began to spin about him. He was weak from the loss of blood, and the Riders gathering in a circle around him looked like dancing demons in the flickering torchlight.

"Kill Sanjay!"

"Kill the Captain!" the soldiers began to shout, entranced by the spell Ratinka had spun.

"No, but I didn't..." Sanjay weakly began to protest.

"The traitor will die for his sins!" Ratinka roared, and the circle lunged closer towards the tree.

Sanjay fought back the dizzying nausea rising in his stomach and drew himself up to look at all the Riders. His voice cracked with emotion. "Soldiers, brothers! Your betrayal stabs my heart far more deeply than any blade possibly could. You have all fallen like sheep under the staff of Ratinka," he cried, turning to look him in the eye. Ratinka stepped back a bit, unnerved by the look in Sanjay's eyes.

"Ratinka! That name itself reeks foulness from my lips! I warn you, brothers, do not believe the lies this filthy spider weaves!"

The Riders drew their blades and began to press even closer around the Captain. Sanjay saw that the end was near for him. He drew his own sword, but did not point it at any of the soldiers, not even at Ratinka.

"I swore my allegiance to the Kingdom of Shamar, and will never draw a blade against any of my own men. However, I will *not* die dishonorably because of the manipulations of one of my own soldiers!" Sanjay lifted the sword and pointed the blade inward towards his body. The Riders took in a breath when they saw what he was about to do.

The Captain lifted one last glance at Ratinka. "I swear to you, you black-hearted jackal, that I will have my revenge. I will have my revenge, no matter what, even if I must wait until you join me in the afterlife. You will pay for what you have done!" he cried, and he plunged his sword deeply into his cloak. Sanjay, Captain of Shamar, crumpled to the ground. Evil had won this time, the evidence borne in the final breaking of a great and righteous man.

Desmond looked down contemptuously upon the body and then turned to face his troops. "Now you see what happens to traitors! Sanjay is dead, and we will leave his body to waste away here in the forest that is as black as his lies. Now raise your swords and salute your new Captain, Ratinka!" the prince cried.

Ratinka's lips triumphantly curled in a grin, and shouts of joy echoed throughout the forest.

Chapter Nine

The Princess is beginning to understand the measure of her own great power,
Evil in its darkest form has been sent beneath her to cower.
The Companions will journey down the slopes of the rocky mountain tower
And play as children in the fields, where there will come a tragic hour.
When the petals of beauty and innocence begin to wilt from the youthful flower,
Bear in mind, O Princess strong, that the eyes do tend to shower....

    Serepta awoke with a start, banging her head on a low hanging rock. She noted through hazy rimmed eyes that the sky was a grimy dark blue; it was night, but morning would soon come. Rafe was already awake, with the same bewildered look he had last time the princess heard the voice.

    Ahh, that voice. If wisdom and truth and an aching beauty could speak together as one, they would sing aloud proudly in that voice.

    "Where did it come from? Who is the old woman? How could she possibly know what is happening in my life?" Serepta whispered in confusion.

    The princess leaped to her feet and looked around the mountaintop, half expecting to find the soothsayer crouched in a shadowed crag. Instead, she found angry hoof prints of horses and sword blades glinting in the faint starlight, littering the ground like garbage. Everything from earlier that night came flooding back to her.

    Her eyes wide, she lightly touched the amber pendant around her neck. It was cool and stone-like; she never could have possibly suspected the tremendous, raging power that lay within its confines. Serepta went over to the edge of the cliff and looked down.

In the darkness, she couldn't see anything but the leafy green treetops, but she knew there was a small army of men way down below. An army of men that she might have killed, sending them crashing down the mountain. Filled with the press of remorse, she opened her mouth to cry out to anyone alive below, but Rafe nudged her leg sharply.

Clearly, in his eyes she saw that he had not forgotten that they had almost died earlier that night.

"I guess you're right...I don't think they're dead. They can't be dead. But even if they are, the fault is theirs anyways," Serepta stated firmly to herself, and couldn't help but to nudge Rafe back. Startled, the big wolf fell backwards onto his bottom.

Serepta laughed aloud at the look of indignation on his face. He leaped up to his paws and bumped her leg with his shoulder, and she fell to the ground beside him. Rafe's jaws opened wide in a toothy grin. Their eyes twinkled merrily and laughter filled the air as the two Companions wrestled there for a moment.

Finally, her face flushed pink, Serepta hefted their belongings onto her shoulder. "Come on, wolf. Let's go see what's on the other side of this mountain!"

Underneath the canopy of trees that the princess had gazed remorsefully upon, a dark figure moved ever so slightly. It was a twitch, a breath, a beating of a heart that seemed so small and insignificant, yet glowed wanly with vitality. Throughout the night, throughout the darkness, it had struggled relentlessly just to reclaim that first breath of precious life. It had fought, and it had won.

Sanjay's blue eyes fluttered open weakly, blinking the dirt and grime away. He hurt everywhere...it was such an intense pain that the man closed his eyes tight and with tears of joy thanked the gods that he had the chance to even feel such a pain. He was alive, and that was all that mattered.

As the first beams of the light of the new day began to glow from behind the mountain, Sanjay saw a glint of metal beside him. It was his sword, cloven in two. The top must have broken off during his fall down the mountain, and it was some hard rock on Morad's slopes that had saved the man's life. The broken edge had not been sharp enough to stab him, and instead served as a battering ram upon his wound. The immense pain had caused him to faint to the ground in shock.

Sanjay found himself wondering what god, what glorious fate, had intervened in such a way to let the soldier live.

His wound...there was so much blood around him, so much. His body was surrounded by a dark crimson pool that soaked everything in its path. It was a miracle that anything could survive after losing so much blood. But Sanjay was alive, and that was all that mattered.

The man carefully lifted himself up to lean against the great oak tree behind him. The black oak supported him, gave him much needed strength, and Sanjay bathed in the nourishing gold of the sun. He picked up the two pieces of his broken sword and knew that the blade now held two purposes that he must carry out until the end: to hunt down and kill Ratinka, and to protect the princess Serepta with all his might. He knew this in his heart to be right.

Sanjay gazed steadily at the horizon in front of him. He was no longer a Captain loyal to Shamar; he was a Warrior, pledged only to justice and righteousness. And with that new title, as the sun of the new day burst gloriously over the land, Sanjay swore to the gods that he would carry out his two tasks until the end.

Chapter Ten

The world was a brightened stage of blue and green. As Serepta and Rafe came over the edge of the mountain, all there seemed to be in the world was the great blueness of the open sky and the rich green grass blanketing the ground. This side of Morad seemed to be the complete opposite of the other; its gentle slopes were warm and welcome and wonderfully open. Serepta was awed at the realization that if she had quit on the other side of the mountain just before reaching the top, she never would have seen such profound beauty.

The princess remembered a story from her childhood about the first day the world was created by the gods. In wonder she thought, *This place must be what the world looked like on that first beautiful day!*

Rafe gave a joyous bark and took off down the hill. His body stretched gloriously with the freedom of the land as he danced among the grassy tussocks. Serepta laughed as his proud exterior was melted away in the warm sun, and she felt the same change in herself.

"Wait for me!" she cried and started down the hill. She flapped her arms out wide and thought if she ran any faster, she would surely start to fly. Serepta laughed aloud and chased after the wolf. He was faster, but he slowed his pace to let her to catch up. The princess leaped upon him, and the two began to roll down the mountain slopes, gaining speed.

Finally, in a tangle of dark hair and silver fur, they fell in a clump down below. Dizzy and giddy, Serepta lifted her arm to smell the earthy sweetness of the grass stains on her skin. Her friend lay panting beside her, large paws in the air.

The princess gave a great sigh and stretched her arms up towards the jolly cerulean sky. "This place is so big!" she cried. "Who would have known such lands existed back in Shamar?"

Serepta rolled onto her stomach and found that she was surrounded by patches of tiny purple flowers. They looked just like the ones back at the palace courtyard...the place where this adventure had all began. Instead of the normal twinge of guilt the princess felt when reminded of the lonely blossom, she felt contentment instead. The flower would have wanted her to be happy in a place like this. Serepta plucked one lavender blossom from the ground and took a playful bite. The juice of its petals was wonderfully sweet in her mouth.

They spent the day like that, laying in the fields halfway down the mountain slopes. Serepta set out a frugal picnic of leftover fruit and meat. She and Rafe ate while lazily staring up at the expanse of blue above and watching the clouds float by.

"I could never have been this happy back in Shamar...." the princess murmured. The wolf gave a short grunt in agreement, and Serepta thought for a moment.

"I wish I knew where you came from...do you have a home? A family? Do wolves have families?" Serepta questioned.

Rafe quietly rose to his feet and began to pace across the grass. The wolf's old icy pride seemed to have returned once more. His head and tail hung low to the ground, gait shifting with an internal conflict, yet made obvious to any who were to observe him.

Serepta leaped up and started after him. There was that same look in his eye, that same pained expression of someone being held back somehow. His face was taut, and his eyes glowed with urgency. The princess felt guilty and knelt beside him.

"I'm...I'm sorry. I was just curious. But no, I don't want anything to ever ruin this day! This place feels magical. I haven't been so happy since I was a child!"

All of a sudden, the bush nearby began to rustle and shake. All frivolity was swept aside now, and Serepta instinctively drew her golden dagger from her hip, whirling around to face the danger. Rafe put himself between her and the bush in a matter of moments.

The leaves continued to quiver, as if something inside was trying to get out. Rafe leaned forward and sniffed at it tentatively. He stepped back, a puzzled expression on his face. The scent seemed so familiar...

Serepta's brow furrowed, and she cautiously poked at the bush. Finally, its branches began to part. The princess suddenly stumbled back upon seeing the most shocking sight of her life.

A little girl emerged from the bush with long, curling black hair. Her lively dark eyes sparkled up at Serepta, and a grin spread across her face. The girl lifted a tiny arm to touch her own dark curls, and there was a pinkish scar where the arm had been recently broken by a rock....

The little girl was Serepta, aged seven.

Desmond and Ratinka sat in silence, chewing thoughtfully on their supper in the commanders' tent. The Riders had traveled fiercely all day through harsh terrain and were now about halfway up Morad. The sun was beginning to set, and milky yellow light gleamed through the holes in the burlap tent, casting a blurry glow upon everything inside.

Desmond's eyes slid up from his leg of goat. Ratinka sat across from him in silence, and he returned his gaze with a curt nod.

There is something amiss with that one, the prince thought to himself as little ants of suspicion marched through his mind. *A thickness to him, a feeling of layers that I've never sensed before... I barely even had time to think before Sanjay was dead. I shouldn't have acted so impulsively!* Desmond cursed under his breath, agitated. He was annoyed with the way he had been acting lately. Where was the strategy? Where was the control?

Grab hold of yourself and don't let go again, Desmond. Stop. Think. Then act. The prince looked up again at Ratinka, whose green eyes were darting everywhere about the tent.

Ratinka's mind was moving too quickly to be concerned with the platter of food before him. His sharp eyes picked up every miniscule detail inside the enclosed area, from the dribble of wax from an ivory candle, to the pattern on the richly woven rug holding the prince's riding equipment, to the arrangement of Desmond's bed sheets.

The new Captain gave a sly glance at his dining partner. Desmond's gray eyes seemed clouded over in stormy thought.

I wonder if he knows that he'll be dead soon, Ratinka thought. He mused on this for a moment, trying to picture what Desmond would look like as a corpse. *All he is and ever was is destined to be but a memory...* Ratinka thought. He sat back with a contented sigh, patting his belly. *And so goes life.*

Desmond didn't like the way the Captain was staring at him. He felt as though he were a tiny insect under scrutinization before being stepped upon. Briefly, the prince was reminded of a time long ago in the palace courtyard when he had squashed a bug between his fingers with great pleasure.

Be the hand, Desmond. Not the bug, the prince mused, biting off a large hunk of meat. *There is something lurking beneath the surface of this one... he is most certainly plotting something, and it should be revealed all in good time,* a voice spoke in Desmond's mind.

Most men are born with a voice within that speaks of good conscience, of love and of trust and of faith. Not so with these two.

Look at him sitting there, Ratinka thought. *As though he is a god, and we are but made in his image!* The Captain watched with keen eyes as Desmond precisely cut his vegetables. *He always has to feel like he's in control. Ha! I seem to be the only one in the entire world who realizes that arrogance leads to destruction. That's why I am meant to be King of Shamar,* Ratinka smiled. *All in good time.*

All in good time, Desmond's thoughts chimed with Ratinka's, as one, in that little tent resting upon the great big mountain of Morad.

Chapter Eleven

The stars came out that night to twinkle like sparkles of magic above the fairer side of the mountain. The very air seemed to be woven with tension and excitement, as though all the world held its breath for the little girl that climbed out of the bush.

Serepta's jaw quivered and she stepped back. Her hand trembled and shook as she silently put the golden dagger back at her hip, unable to tear her eyes away from the child. Rafe sat back on the ground, all the color and expression drained from his features.

The child took a step closer. There was a regal air about her, a fierce grace that would have been apparent even if she were clothed in rags. The girl was like a little spout of flame.

"Who are you?" Serepta whispered, not daring to believe what the answer might be. She felt as though she were talking to a dream.

"I'm Sera," the child whispered back. Their eyes met quietly then; brown melted with brown as the two princesses stared at each other, stared through the mirror of time itself.

Sera…my gods… that's what Saba used to call me when I was young… Serepta realized in awe, discovering she had forgotten the nickname long ago. She had forgotten this child, forgotten this beautiful little girl that had been hidden somewhere deep inside of her for a lost eternity. The princess could have cried for all the remorse she felt.

"Do you...do you mind if I touch you? It's been so long since I've seen you," the princess breathed, afraid that at any moment the child would return to the land of memories lost.

Sera laughed aloud as Serepta reached out tentatively. The princess carefully touched a finger to the girl's cheek, and it felt quite solid. Feeling the cool smoothness of the child's skin, *her* skin, Serepta couldn't help but to wrap the little girl in her arms. The princess could almost feel a shiver of sensation on her own. She held the delicate frame tightly, and their hearts beat together as one.

This child was real, as real as the stars that danced in the sky. What god, what fate had spun such magic? Serepta buried her nose in the soft black hair, and she trembled with the familiar scents. Sera smelled of hallways burning with incense, of stones warmed in the desert sun, and of little purple flowers growing in the courtyard. Such pain, such joy, such memories these smells evoked...Serepta wanted to cry, but of course, the princess never cried.

"How did you get here?" she finally asked, staring deeply into the little girl's eyes.

"I dunno, I took a nap, and I was in that bush when I waked up," Sera smiled wide, and a dimple came to her left cheek.

My dimple... Serepta thought.

Sera's attention wandered and she suddenly reached out a tiny hand to pet Rafe's head. Serepta lunged to stop her, but the wolf seemed to allow this contact. His blue eyes filled with wonder, and he lifted his head to meet her touch.

"Is he real?" the little girl peeped, asking the same question in the same voice Serepta had used when she met Rafe for the first time.

Serepta dizzily ran a hand through her hair, and she suddenly felt as though the very earth had moved beneath her feet. Completely overwhelmed, she dropped to the ground, and fainted clean away upon the hill under those stars that seemed to twinkle with a wide-eyed magic.

Desmond sharply blew out his candle and wrapped the bed sheets tightly about him. It was time for sleep. His body ached with the knowledge of this, but his mind could not seem to rest. It crackled with a nervous, chattering energy that would not subside.

Strange birdcalls echoed in the night, and the burlap walls of the tent seemed far too thin. It felt odd to be there on that foreign mountain, so far away from the palace of Shamar, so far away from home.

The prince curled up in a ball on his side and bunched the sheets about his chin. That was better; he felt less vulnerable that way. Desmond nuzzled his head into his satin pillow, feeling just as secure as he always had as a child in the palace. As a child...something in the air faintly rippled with childhood...some note that chimed playfully in the night. Finally, sleep came to silence the pressing thoughts in Desmond's mind.

... "Desmond! Come join me on the balcony. It's beautiful today!" a woman's soft voice called.

The little prince's laughter bubbled joyfully as he toddled outside to join his mother on her balcony. In his excitement, he stumbled and fell hard onto the sunny, marble floor. His face crinkled up in hurt, and the little boy began to wail.

"Awww...Desmond...come here, baby boy!" the mother cooed and gathered him tenderly into her arms. Her soft silky dress smelled like warm incense.

The little prince's cries finally subsided. Pacified, he looked out over the desert from his mother's lap. He reached out a tiny hand, and he imagined grasping the whole kingdom in his fingers. From way up high on the balcony, it fit so perfectly into his white little palm.

And he fit so perfectly in his mother's lap. The boy bunched the fabric of her dress about his chin and nuzzled his dark head into her. She was safe and warm. She would never hurt him. The little prince didn't know what he would do if she ever were to hurt him, but he was safe with her for now...

Desmond grinned widely within the inky depths of sleep, and he finally relaxed his tightened grip on the bed sheets. They fell like a white halo all around the prince's peaceful face.

Alarmed at her sudden fall, Rafe nudged at Serepta. Her skin was soft and warm, and she seemed to be just asleep, curled in a ball on the grassy hill. The wolf let out a sigh and decided to let her rest. Rest...that sounded delicious. Rafe's muscles groaned as he prepared to flop down beside his Companion. Suddenly, Sera popped up in his face.

"Play with me!" she cried, staring at him with delight.

Rafe rolled his eyes. He was exhausted, and he gave her an icy glare, but the little girl still would not go away. The wolf emitted a low growl and bared his fangs.

Sera growled back and wrinkled her mouth in a mock ferociousness, revealing her perfectly tiny white teeth. "Play with me!" she demanded.

I don't know how to play, Rafe grumbled in his mind.

"Everybody knows how to play! You probably just forgotted how," Sera stated matter-of-factly.

Rafe mused on this for a moment, and he suddenly realized that she had heard him thinking. He leaped up with a start. The little girl was staring at him, her dark eyes practically welling over with innocence.

How could she possibly read his mind? Rafe marveled at the thought. Who was this strange little girl that looked so much like Serepta? Did she have some sort of power? There had to be some key, some trick he could not quite grasp yet. It wasn't as though the real Serepta could read his mind...except for the time they first met. In his mind, he had kissed her hand, and she had felt it. And she had stared back at him with the most beautiful expression of awe, of wonder, with those same innocent dark eyes that were looking at him now.

And that was it. A shiver of magic ran through the wolf, and he inhaled the night air deeply. Rafe threw his head back to feel the starlight on his face, and he reveled in the universe that suddenly seemed to make sense in the most perfect way. Sera could listen to his thoughts and understand him because no one had ever told her it wasn't possible. In those innocent wide eyes, anything was possible, and that was the magic of the child. Sera, *Serepta,* believed in him, and Rafe had never felt so happy in all his life.

"You're not like other doggies. Not like the ones daddy has at the palace," the little girl said, patting his silvery fur.

Of course not. I'm a wolf, Rafe replied, wanting to dance at this new sense of freedom. It was as though a colossal burden had been removed from his shoulders.

Sera looked at him peculiarly. "No...that's not it. There's something different about you."

The wolf let out a sigh. *If only you knew how true that was...*

Sera leaped up again, face lit up with joy. "Come on! Play with me!" she cried, tugging on his ear. The child took off running clumsily through the dewy grass, chubby hands flailing in the air.

It was impossible to resist. Rafe's jaws widened in a grin, and he tore off after her, causing a cloud of sparkling mist and tiny buzzing flies to burst into the cool air. Together, the child and the wolf danced across the slopes under the moon and the stars. Sera's giggles chimed like a bell into the night air.

The grass felt cool and soft under the light step of Rafe's big paws. The earth smelled of childhood, and the air smelled of spring. The wolf reveled in this wide open freedom, this land where all that mattered was the rippling field of bluish grass and the inky black dome that stretched out to reach for the horizons at the ends of the earth. Finally, after what seemed like an eternity of this boundless play, the two made their way leaping back to Serepta's sleeping form.

Rafe flopped to the ground, chest heaving with delight. The stars twinkled down at them like little droplets of water, and the only sounds were the chirping of crickets and the sound of each other's breath. It was perfect.

Almost asleep, Rafe saw out of the corner of his eye that Sera's attention wavered once more. Her lively dark eyes fixed upon Serepta's still face, made pale and smooth in the moonlight. The child smiled and lightly touched the princess's hair.

"I grow up to be pretty," she whispered, yawning wide.

Rafe stared down at Serepta, a warmth in his heart.

You grow up to be beautiful...

Chapter Twelve

"Up, Riders, up! Hurry to your horses and prepare them to leave! Today is the day we will reclaim the mountain top for Shamar," Desmond announced to the campsite. The men sensed a change in their prince; there was a more peaceable, confident air about him that morning. Savoring it until his next change of moods, they hastened to pack up their belongings.

Ratinka had been awake and alert since sunrise. Sleep bothered him entirely; it felt like a lulling lick of death. It was nothingness, and not knowing of the nothingness; it was helplessness, and comfort in that helplessness; it was exerting no effort, and requiring eternal rest for that effort. Sleep was a microcosm of the world that awaited the dead. Plus, early morning was the best time for planning and observing.

And it seems as though the universe has bent entirely to my will once more, the Captain grinned, eyes rolling back with contentment. He stood up and stretched, straining his sinewy arms as far as they could go in every direction. Then Ratinka sheathed his sword and watched the Riders scurry about the campsite. They were dirty, disorganized, and completely helpless.

The Captain's lip curled in disgust. He shivered with frustration. Who were these bumbling morons? Who were these besotted idiots content to stay in the same pit hole of mediocrity their entire lives? They fooled and joked around as though nothing else in the world mattered.

Ambition is the key to glory, Ratinka imagined himself dictating the words to his legions of future followers once he was king.

He had a loathing contempt for this collection of soldiers before him and could almost see the puppet strings attached to their limbs. Ratinka observed the men down below as they stumbled around like simple beasts of the forest, content only to follow orders to survive. But what sort of survival was this?

The answer was none. Or if any, it was completely inferior. That was not the question; the question was what to do when one found oneself confronted with such creatures. Tolerate their maddening ways and risk going insane? Reach out with a fist of iron and obliterate them completely? No, that wouldn't do as long as they had other uses. While these beasts joked and pawed around, Ratinka would just have to take complete and ultimate advantage of them.

If they were foolish enough to sleep their way through life, then Ratinka would always be the one awake instead.

All of life is a mindless dream, if one is not willing to scrape and to scheme....

The men were finally falling into order. Desmond lifted his sword high in the air and cried, "Onward, Riders! Onward to the top!"

And of course, they obeyed.

Serepta awoke to find a warm breath tickling her arm. The sleeping child was curled at her side, and the princess gazed down at her, beaming with pride.

Sera was beautiful. Her perfectly smooth face, unblemished by the wear and tear of time, was poised in a cherubic expression, and her long dark eyelashes fanned above the white skin. The child's tiny frame rose and fell delicately with each breath, yet Serepta knew there was nothing delicate about her.

Finally, Sera's eyes fluttered open. "Hello," she whispered.

"Hello," Serepta replied, her voice unnoticeably deeper.

"I waked up."

"I know."

Rafe stirred, and the wolf pulled himself onto his feet. Serepta watched him move and sensed a change, a lightness in his step. He stretched and sat down calmly at her side. The two remained there for a moment, feeling the warmth of the new sun on their faces.

Suddenly, Sera jumped up and began to twirl about in the grass. She hummed an off-key tune and held her arms out in front of her, spinning around in mock gracefulness.

"What are you doing?" the princess asked, slowly opening her eyes, savoring the sunlight.

Sera curtsied low. "I'm dancing at the royal palace!" she replied. Her face lit up with delight, and she continued twirling.

Serepta gave the child a strange look, and then a great laugh escaped her lips. She couldn't remember a time when she was able to entertain herself in this way. Rafe leaped up and began to gracefully step around the child.

"And who might you be dancing with, princess?" Serepta asked.

"I am dancing with my husband, the prince, of course!" Sera curtsied clumsily at Rafe.

For a moment, the game was soured by the devastating flash of Desmond's eyes. Serepta consciously shook it off, and she rose to join the child.

"Rafe...Rafe doesn't look very much like royalty to me. I'll have to fix that!" Serepta grinned. She sat back down in the grass, and began to pluck some of the lacy white flowers that sprouted all around. Soon, she had deftly woven them into a crown.

"There you are, Your Highness," Serepta said, placing the crown on Rafe's head. "You truly are a prince among wolves."

Rafe stopped dancing for a moment and stared at the princess peculiarly. A strange look in his eye, he finally lifted his head to accept the crown of white flowers.

"I wanna know how to do that!" Sera cried, feeling neglected.

Serepta put a hand on her shoulder, and she felt a tingle of a shadow on her own. "You'll learn someday. Believe me, I would know."

The frown on Sera's face brightened into a smile. "Dance with me!" she cried, grabbing Serepta's hand tightly. The child spun her around and around, bubbling over with laughter. Her dark eyes twinkled above soft pillows of white cheeks. They twirled and bobbed in the grass, until finally collapsing dizzily to the ground.

Sera, Serepta, and Rafe spent the entire day playing in the warm sun. They sang nonsensical tunes, played ridiculous games, and watched the clouds float by over the slopes of Morad. It was a breathless perfection, a warmth and joy that replaced any fears or doubts the travel-worn Companions had. It was refreshing, it was pure, and it was a day spent in the most delightful way Serepta had ever known.

"Tell me a story," Sera ordered as the sun began to grow heavy in the late afternoon. It hung like an over-ripe peach, past its prime, ready to plunge into nighttime. Exhausted, the three settled down in the cool grass.

"No. You tell me a story. Tell me about what you do at the palace," Serepta said. She wanted to know everything, everything about this life of hers that was buried in forgotten memories. The princess now had a chance to regain those memories. She was reminded of the words that Saba had spoken to her long ago:...*You used to be so happy when you were a girl. There is much to learn from the child within, who sees the world and knows the world and loves it.* It was true, so true.

"Let's see," Sera began, putting a tiny hand under her chin. Her brow furrowed in an expression that mirrored Serepta's perfectly. "I live in the palace. And I have a big window in my room that I like to look out. And Saba teaches me how to cook. Except yesterday I burned my…"

"Elbow," Serepta completed the sentence. The two lifted their arms, and saw identical pink scars.

Sera giggled and went on. "And sometimes daddy is nice, but mostly he's grouchy." Then the girl put on a mock frown and shouted gruffly, "Serepta! Clean your room! Put on something presentable! You will make a disgraceful queen one day!"

The princess laughed with delight. "Yes, father sounds like that."

Sera's little face suddenly grew solemn. "When he gets grouchy like that, I wish I had a mommy." The girl stared off across the field. "My mommy wouldn't never be mean to me. She would play with me, just like you. You aren't ever going to leave me, are you?" the child asked, grabbing Serepta's hand.

Serepta and Rafe exchanged desperate glances. Suddenly, something else caught the wolf's eye and he turned around to face the mountain. The princess squinted in the hazy light of the sunset, and to her horror she saw the gleam of metal.

The Riders were alive, and they were at the top of the mountain.

"Oh no….no!" Serepta cried aloud. How could this happen? They were supposed to be dead at the bottom on the other side! Rafe began to pace about, growling low with rage. To match his fury, thick clouds began to slide in from above and rumbled ominously with thunder.

"We have to get out of here now! They must have spotted us in this open land here at the bottom," Serepta babbled, frantically gathering up their supplies. She couldn't believe they had wasted the whole day like that. Rafe grumbled a quick agreement and continued pacing.

"Where are you going?" Sera asked with wide eyes.

Serepta turned to face her, and her forehead stiffened. The princess dropped her bags to the ground, and then her heart dropped just as low, thudding to the grass with a hollow ring. She and Rafe exchanged a glance, and each knew what the other was thinking without a word.

"Sera…we have to go now. The bad men are coming," she murmured to the child.

"Are you leaving me?" she asked quietly.

A thick drop of rain from above fell hard upon Serepta's cheek. She paused for a moment. "I...I don't think there's any other way," she began to pace across the grass, thoughtfully running a hand through her hair. "I mean, you would slow us down if you came…" the princess began. But she looked at Sera and knew that it would tear her heart out if she were to ever leave the child behind.

"Oh, come on! You'll have to hurry though!" Serepta cried, holding out her hand. More drops of rain began to fall.

Sera looked up at her silently for a moment. Then, she shook her head no.

"What do you mean, no? We have to leave now!"

"I can't leave this place," Sera whispered.

Serepta cringed, and the world seemed to lurch beneath her feet. *No*... Her mind reeled in silent agony with it. She knew it was true deep down, knew that there was no way this child could possibly go with them.

There was no way she could go with them, and grow old with Serepta, because she was Serepta, and she wasn't real.

The clump of horses and metal drew nearer down the mountain. The sky opened up, and the rain began to pour down.

No, no, no... Agitated, Serepta wrung her hands. The Riders were coming closer, Rafe was growing anxious, and Sera was standing alone in the cold rain.

"I have to go now."

"Why are you leaving me?" the child wailed. Her hair hung in limp, wet ringlets.

"Sera, we have to go now!"

The child stamped her foot. "You're leaving me! You're leaving me here all alone..." she cried, hugging her arms tightly and shivering. Her face crinkled up with hurt as she shrank under the freezing rain.

Serepta felt her pain like a cold hand around her heart. She wanted to hold the child and soothe her and never let her be abandoned again....

"I'm...I'm sorry."

Sera began to cry then, her helpless wail piercing through the rain. It was a foreign sound to Serepta. She hadn't cried since...since she was a child. And the princess felt torn apart with an agony she never knew could exist.

The rain began to come faster now; it was a cold, driving downpour. The sun sank lower in the sky, and the pack of Riders drew closer. The princess could almost make out the individual men now.

Rafe whined at Serepta, urging her to follow him.

"I can't...!" Serepta cried. She hated the wolf for pulling her away. Her heart was ripping apart, tearing apart. She wanted to fall to the ground, wanted to fall down and die, never ever wanted to feel this pain, but mostly just wanted to cry…

And with that agonizing thought, the words of the dream song came pouring into her mind, pouring like the freezing rain:

The Princess is beginning to understand the measure of her own great power,
Evil in its darkest form has been sent beneath her to cower.
The Companions will journey down the slopes of the rocky mountain tower
And play as children in the fields, where there will come a tragic hour.
When the petals of beauty and innocence begin to wilt from the youthful flower,
Bear in mind, O Princess strong, that the eyes do tend to shower....

Sera sobbed, and the princess took her into her arms.

The child's breath was ragged as her chest heaved against Serepta's. Her tears were wet upon the princess's bare shoulders, and Serepta squeezed her so tightly, it was as though their bodies were one. Their bodies were one, though Serepta's heart felt torn in two.

"Stay with me...please…" Sera begged, her face stretched with pain. The pain looked so real...but no, this *girl* wasn't real...she couldn't be real.

Serepta pulled away, tore herself away, and stared at the child with quivering eyes that welled over with hurt.

"It's time for me to go now. I cannot tell you why. Just know always that I love you, I love you, and goodbye...."

Suddenly, a tremendous shock of thunder exploded through the air. The sheet of rain grew so thick, that for a moment, Serepta could no longer see the child. And when the rain finally lessened, the little girl was gone. Vanished, as quickly as she had come.

Serepta stared about the empty field in shock. All that remained was mud and grass that was swollen with rain, and more kept pouring down all around her.

"What have I *done?!*" the princess howled, falling to her knees in a numb shock. A cold dagger tore at her heart and made wretched pain spread like fire and ice through her limbs. Tears sprang to her eyes, begging to fall, aching to fall.

Bear in mind, O Princess strong, that the eyes do tend to shower...

And with that, Serepta's body gave a great heave, a shudder, and the tears that had been waiting to fall for years were finally let free, free after all that time. She cried for her mother, she cried for Saba, and she cried for the lost piece of her that was the little girl, lost somewhere out in the cold, cold rain. She ached with it, wretched with it, died and died again with it.... Serepta sobbed and sobbed until she thought her very chest would crack in two.

Rafe watched her, his heart paining at the sight. After some time, the princess bleakly held out a hand to him, shaking, and he supported her quietly as she struggled to her feet. The princess let out a tremendous shudder, and she turned weakly away from the mountain.

Serepta knew she wouldn't find the child there. She wouldn't find her anywhere, for that matter. The girl was inside her now, and she had helped her to crack the wall around her soul. And Serepta knew then in her heart that as long as she could let those tears fall, the child would be with her for all of time.

Part Three

Down A Stream

Chapter Thirteen

The rain began to abate, but the clouds remained to gray the night. Desmond shielded his eyes with a hand and glared down the sloping fields. There, towards the bottom, were three small figures...no, now two. The princess and the wolf.

"After them! After them! They're heading for the trees!" he roared, pointing a finger like an arrow of the gods. The Riders, exhausted from a full day of travel, stared back at him bleakly, not even having the energy to complain.

"NOW!" Desmond commanded, seeing that the black spots were moving again. "They're at the bottom! Do you not remember the curse of the witch's black magic? Strength, soldiers, strength! Honor! Capture the witch! Kill the wolf! Do this and you will be remembered in Shamar for all of time!"

Inspired by this speech, the Riders let out lusty battle cries and tore off down the mountain. The possibility of glory had refilled their hollow shells for the time being.

Quickly, Desmond turned to Ratinka. "Captain, if they make it to the trees, it will be almost impossible to find them again," he growled under his breath.

The prince hated needing Ratinka's help, but all he could think about was capturing his cousin once and for all. All he could think about was how it would feel to hold her body in his arms, to feel it tremble with absolute fear, hearing her beg for mercy from the terrible fury that now coursed through his hands, threatening to consume him, as they clenched and clenched again.

Ratinka whirled around and threw his sword out straight, stopping a Rider dead in his tracks. "Here!" he cried, thrusting a torch at the man, mind shivering with a quick idea. "You must ride swifter than ever before! You must ride as though the black demon gods themselves are nipping at your heels! Hurry, hurry down to the trees at the bottom and set them ablaze. If you do this, we will smoke out the witch, and your name will be known through all of Shamar!"

The Rider saluted the Captain and was off. As the stallion galloped onward, sparks from the torch flew to the grass. Great columns of flame leaped up all around, casting an eerie orange glow in the darkness.

Ratinka let out a caustic laugh. "This will work, if that buffoon doesn't burn us all to a crisp first," he muttered.

But Desmond was already away, flying down the mountain with the volume and fury of a blackened tornado in the night.

Darkness won out over day, and for the princess, the only light was that of the wildfires that burst forth in a scythe-like pattern all down the mountain. She did not need light, though; she had the gleam of Rafe's silver fur and absolute trust in the direction the hunter was traveling.

The lonely two reached the brimming edge of a dark forest, a mass of trees and moist earth that radiated with the thick scent of life and death. Rafe's eyes darted around for a moment to seek out the most suitable path. Serepta's heart fluttered in her breast, beating to the quickening rhythm of the flurry of horse hooves behind.

She turned to find that the entirety of the tremendous mountainside, those fair slopes that had once echoed with innocence and joy, had now burst into furious flame. The grass sent up thick arms of waving smoke. It seemed as though the fresher and greener the blades had been, the blacker the smoke they burnt. An acrid, choking smell replaced the scent of warmth and sun, and Serepta knew that her precious side of Morad now existed only in her memories.

Rafe gave a stout whine, urging her onwards. She leaped to join him and was nearly thrown back by a fortress of heat as the trees in front of her burst into flame. Through the smoke she could just barely make out the image of a torch-wielding Rider returning back up the slopes.

"Rafe, where do we go now?" she cried, eyes searching for the wolf and coming up empty. All she could see everywhere was a bewildering mass of orange and green and black and brown. A sick feeling of panic spread through her insides like melting glue. He was abandoning her in this mess....

There, was that a flash of silver in the trees? She blindly took off after it, eyes shut against the crackling burning air.

But the wolf was nowhere to be found. The heat of the growing fire was overwhelming now; filthy air drooped heavily in Serepta's lungs, and she felt as though her skin was tingling and popping. The thick smoke all around grew so intense that the princess was forced to drop to her knees. Flames licked and burned all around. They danced and waved about like the king's concubines back at the palace; luring, tempting, yet with the guised promise of death.

"Rafe, where are you?" she screamed. In a fit of coughing, she reached for her chest and clutched at the cool stone of the tiger's eye.

Wait, her heart quickened. *Is that him over there?* Serepta took off crawling through the trees, slithering through the dirt like a snake with the supply sack leaving a thick trench as it dragged behind her. The ground was moist with rotting half-life and dense with a fortress of twigs and branches. Serepta wanted to either collapse in disgust or take off running like a madwoman through the trees, tearing her hair out and yelling at the top of her lungs. Where was she going in this hellish labyrinth of a forest, this maddening inferno of countless paths to take?

Finally, the princess stopped moving.

"He left me here...."

The princess sat trembling on the ground, dumbfounded at this turn of fate. She huddled there, bewildered and alone, shoulders shaking. Serepta couldn't believe he had done this to her. She should have known it would have only been a matter of time before Rafe betrayed her trust, too. The wolf had been too good to be true.

A tongue of flame crackled by Serepta's head as it devoured a dry tree branch. As the wood went up in a conflagration, the bitter sadness Serepta felt leaped up into rage. She would never forgive the wolf after this, never forgive him for going off on his own and leaving her there. This fury and humiliation empowered her, and gave her the energy to keep plowing through the foliage.

After blindly crawling through moss and fern, twig and leaf, splinter and spike, Serepta suddenly sensed water nearby. Water, the one element that dared to challenge fire. The princess was drawn to it like a starving man to a feast.

And there it was. Glittering like a brilliant gem under the light of star and moon and flame was a great rushing stream. The princess, with her hand still on the tiger's eye, took comfort in recognizing this place from the dream Saba had given her so long ago. Standing before her, as a welcome escape from the hardships of the mountain and the betrayal of her only remaining friend, was the great Stream of Jimakana.

Serepta bundled up the supply sack and took one last look at the lands behind her, where the mountain slopes were now turned to quiet ash and columns of flame leaped up to bid her adieu. There was nothing left for her in this place.

Without another thought, the princess dove headlong into the stream.

Desmond grabbed locks of his hair tightly and pulled with all his might, feeling the yank of the tension throughout his entire head. His breath came in jerky movements, and his eyes narrowed to slits as he ground his teeth together. Desmond didn't know what he would do if he didn't see Serepta's white skin and dark hair and trembling eyes soon...the prince sat upon his horse in this manner, waiting in a gnawing silence for the Riders to return with news.

Finally, the one with the torch came cantering towards him. "Your Highness...I came to inform you that...ah...the trees were set aflame as ordered."

Desmond gave a crooked grin. "Yes? And where is she?"

"Ah, it seems as though the princess has escaped," the soldier reported, face sinking in a grimace of fright. He shrank in anticipation of the prince's fury.

Instead, Desmond stared at him blankly for a moment, and then he let out a wild laugh. He paused for a moment, and then ran a hand through his dark hair in disbelief. Desmond thought for a moment, waves of words bobbing and chattering through his mind. Then the prince looked up at the sky and shook a finger at it.

"Ha! Ha ha ha! Good one, gods above! Comic geniuses, O fates that be! Once again, you have made a complete *fool* out of me!"

The soldier reined his stallion to a halt and watched with tightened lips as the prince began to pace queerly about, mouth open in laughter at the stars in the sky. Desmond shook his head back and forth with a broken look.

"No, no matter, that Serepta is a *witch* and a whore. No, dear gods, do give me more! More fighting, more heartache, more humiliation and pain! In fact, make it so in Shamar that I *never* shall reign!!!" Desmond roared, voice rising in volume. A tiny part of the prince felt ashamed of his outburst in the presence of the soldier, but that embarrassment was simply fuel for his leaping flames of rage, feeding them to the point of a blinding light and heat. He shook with fury and exhaustion, and he could no longer hold back the words that dribbled from his mouth like sewage.

"I will never forget these insults! I will never forget this humiliation as long as I have breath in my body! Run, Serepta! Run! Keep running, dear cousin, because when I finally catch up, you will get down on your *knees* and pray to the stars above that time will run backwards and that you never had been born!!!"

Desmond turned his back on the sky in disgust and huddled under his stallion. He buried himself deep within his black cloak, deep within the dark woolen cloth that allowed him to curl up in a seething aloneness.

Serepta felt the first graceful touch of the waters as she dove in. The stream puckered in readiness to receive her aching body, and the princess gasped at the refreshing coolness that surrounded every inch of her. She stretched out her limbs as far as they could go into the water, not even realizing until now how confined she had felt before, how trapped she had felt within her own self. The heated tension and dirt finally seemed to dissolve and wash away.

Serepta treaded in the water for a moment, using her supply sack to support her, and she let the cool waves lap gently around her body. She realized that the rushing stream was pulling her farther and farther away from where she dove in, but she simply didn't care. A newfound peace came over her, a tranquility, and a sense of independence. She didn't need Rafe.

Serepta threw her head back and the water soaked it up to her hairline. The coldness and weight of it refreshed her to the core. All above there was a canopy of broad leaves waving gently in the breeze. Through the pattern of fronds, Serepta could make out the soft black sky and twinkling points of starlight. They sparkled, shining down at her in a way that seemed so familiar....

Rafe. She was reminded of Rafe's eyes, and the way he looked up at her, and seemed to look down on her as well. Serepta realized that she never wanted to find the wolf ever again. He had torn her away from Sera. He had abandoned her in the trees. Yes, he had helped her, too, but there was an indignity in that help. She was doing perfectly fine on her own, and for once took comfort in her own presence. Serepta let out a frustrated sigh. She didn't *need* Rafe anymore. Or even want him.

The princess grinned sleepily and continued wading through the dark waters, her mind swimming with the boldness of this new feeling. Wouldn't it be far more glorious to complete this journey on her own? Wouldn't it mean so much more to make it to the end without help from anyone but herself? When poets and scholars wrote about her marvelous journey, one that no other princess had ever dared to take, she wanted it to be about *her*. Not about her and the wolf.

Serepta turned her head to run a hand through the heavy dark coils of hair, and the bright color of silver caught her eye. Rafe stood up ahead of her on the muddy embankment, and the grateful look in his pale blue eyes told Serepta that he could never abandon her, even if he tried. He had never meant to leave her behind; it must have been an accident. This realization made her burn with guilt.

The princess furrowed her brow in frustration and jerkily clambered out of the water. Serepta clawed angrily at the mud as she crawled to her feet. No, no, of course, her idea would never work. She wanted to go off on her own now, but she couldn't help but to feel obligated to the wolf. He had saved her life before, and she supposed she owed it to him to stay by his side. But her heart ached to explore what lay beyond the edge of the river bend...

Rafe squinted and stepped back as water from Serepta dribbled onto his head. He gave a disapproving grunt, and then he took off running through the forest, body long and lean in the moonlight.

"Rafe, stop! Where are you going?" the princess asked, wincing as she sharply wrung out her hair.

The wolf didn't even turn around, and he kept on plowing through the foliage.

"I said stop! You're going the wrong way!" Serepta shouted.

Finally, Rafe turned around and stared at her as though she were crazy. He glanced at the stream, and then at the path through the woods, and then back at the princess.

"Yes, yes, I know. Your way seems easier. But if we go in the water, it'll be much faster! And far more exciting! There's so much more to see," Serepta said, taking in a deep breath of the fresh air off the stream, intoxicated by its beauty.

Rafe stared at her for a moment in disgust and then bared his teeth a little. A low growl escaped from his throat.

"I'm not afraid of you," the princess responded calmly. "And I'm not going to back down." Finally, an excuse had presented itself.

"You go your way, I'll go mine."

The wolf's face softened, and he stepped back in surprise. His Companion was staring at him in a way that made his breath catch in his throat. Rafe's tail lowered a bit as he cocked his head at her, trying to figure out if there was some joke he didn't quite get.

Serepta ignored him. The stream was calling to her.

"I know it wasn't supposed to be this way...but I think it's better for the both of us. This is something I just need to do on my own," she murmured.

Something in Rafe's eyes broke, but he hid it with a quick sweep of the head. He whirled around and began to saunter off, sending dirt flying towards her as he stumbled back into the woods. Soon, all the princess could see was the tip of his tail as it disappeared into the trees.

"Goodbye to you too, wolf!" Serepta hollered indignantly. Then she turned, alone at last, and plunged back into the stream.

Chapter Fourteen

Desmond threw his cloak away from his head, and he was surprised to find that he had been sleeping. The prince shook his head to clear the fuzz that the night had quietly wrapped around his brain.

The Riders had set up a makeshift camp for the night surrounding the prince on the ground at the base of the mountain. Desmond could barely make out their forms in the dim mixture of grimy smoke and early morning fog. Many were sleeping, and the rest were working to put out the remaining fires all around.

Finally, these idiots do something right. Desmond yawned. He bundled himself up in his cloak once more. Dawn would not come for some time, and he was sick of hearing his own thoughts. They slipped through his mind like a chattering river of oil that would not cease. The only escape from them would be either death or sleep...

...The young prince squinted up at the burning sun, and he flapped at his tunic to relieve some of the heat. A blast of sticky warmth rolled off his body and into his face.

All he could see was an ocean of legs and hips in the crowded marketplace as the commoners stumbled about the dilapidated buildings to buy their goods. The prince felt very small, and he didn't like it one bit.

A little girl sat in an unoccupied corner, crouched in the sand and scratching at it with a stick.

"Serepta!" the boy shouted at his cousin.

She looked up at him fiercely. "My name is Sera."

"I don't care. I'm bored. Now help me steal that pie," the prince ordered, pointing a sharp finger at a boarded up window with a cool apple pie on the ledge. It looked so moist…and cold…and juicy…and soon it would be all his.

"No."

Desmond whirled around. "No? What do you mean, no?" he snapped at her.

"It's bad to steal stuff," Sera replied, and coolly continued digging at the sand. The prince ran up to her.

"You're not allowed to say no to me! No one is! Now get up there and help me steal that pie!" the boy sneered. Sera stood up to meet his gaze.

"I said no."

In his sleep, Desmond broke out in a cold sweat. His brow knitted in fury, and his hand gave a sharp jerk under the black cloak.

...A jagged rock on the ground caught the boy's eye. He picked it up and hefted it in his hand, delighting in the weight of his new power. "I'll give you one last chance."

"No. No, no, no!" Sera cried back at him. The words rang around and around in his head…

Suddenly, Desmond flew at her in a cold rage and pinned her little body to the ground. She squirmed and cried and fought, but the prince was stronger.

Her left arm lay to his side, white against the gold of the sand. It looked so whole, so pure, and so defiant.

No, no, no… the words howled and cackled like the taunting of demons. He felt as though it would never leave his head as long as he lived. Desmond frantically raised his rock high above and slammed it down onto the little arm, slammed it to rip apart that perfect wholeness.

Sera let out a tremendous howl, and she curled up in pain as the arm cracked and gushed with blood. She cried and cried, rolled in a ball beneath him.

The little boy gave a crooked grin and let the rock fall to the sand. She would never say no to him after this. And if she did, he would just have to hurt her again and again and again...

Serepta waded for hours through the dark waters, allowing the stream's flow to pull her eastward. She was exhilarated by the drops of cold water that landed tingling upon her face, and she felt as though all her senses were heightened with this new found independence.

The princess's eyes took in the surroundings that flooded by with a new clarity. She inhaled deeply and relaxed into her own body, relaxed into the intricate tapestry of scenery all around her. Puffs of dark tree branches lined the jungle banks, and the broad fanning leaves seemed to reach high up as far as they possibly could into the velvety humid night sky.

Serepta floated on her back and lifted her head out of the water. Her ears were flooded with a myriad of new sounds. The princess could hear the jarring calls of strange birds in the night. Her sharp ears could now detect even the slightest rustle in the woody grass surrounding the banks, though it was nearly drowned out by the roar of the rushing stream all around her.

And the smell...there was a scent of freshness, of newness, and of youth that seemed to rise like warm incense off the stream. The jungle all around radiated with the musk of flourishing plant life, and the floppy pink petals of scattered giant flowers released an intoxicating floral aroma in thick clouds. Serepta breathed it all deep into her body, her nose swimming with delight to capture all the new smells. For a moment, she felt as though she could even take in the pure, silvery scent of the stars in the sky.

The princess flipped over onto her front side and grasped the floating supply sack tightly between her arms. For the first time in her entire life, she was alone. There were no palace nannies, no gawking commoners, no domineering father, no watchful Saba, and no wolf within sight. She was alone, with herself, with her thoughts, drifting along that dark stream in the middle of the night. Each lapping wave of the water was bringing her closer and closer to the freedom that awaited at the end of her adventure. And with that thought, Serepta pulled over to the side of the stream and fell asleep; asleep in a jungle somewhere between the land she had come from and the land she desired to go to with all her heart at the end of this great journey.

Chapter Fifteen

The two Companions have been severed, a move that seems quite bold
The answer to whether this was wise or not, only time shall hold
The Princess will travel down the Stream to a land of young and old
Where the tempter shall arise from the mud and stinking mold…
Keep in mind, impulsive one, for every action there is a toll,
And in the end, are you prepared to pay it with your soul?

Serepta stirred under the heavy net of sleep. A light breeze picked up, and the trees swayed, allowing a beam of sunlight to puncture the thick canopy. The princess's eyes fluttered open, and she sat up slowly.

"My head...." she murmured, touching a finger to it tenderly. It felt as though a ram inside was trying to pound its way out.

Then she realized that the song had come once again in her dreams. The remembrance of the soft melody brought wakefulness to her body, and Serepta stretched, feeling the sensation spread gracefully through her limbs. This time, the princess didn't even bother to try to remember the words to the song. It was a waste of time; she knew now that they would be revealed to her again when she needed them most.

The stream and surrounding jungle looked different in the morning light. Now she could see the hundreds of shades of green and brown and black and blue all around. They wove together subtly, with different textures and shades, all with amazingly clear detail. For the first time, Serepta felt as though she were an active, present part of the world instead of just some dull spectator of it all.

The princess hoisted up her sack of supplies and meandered her way along the banks. Tremendous, ancient trees thick with years rose up all around. Their massive roots dunked thirstily into the jungle mud. Farther down, the stream picked up speed and frothy white waves burst along its length. It would be so fast to travel in it now...but dangerous, too. She had to find some way to navigate it safely.

Serepta scanned the area like a hawk, looking for anything to use as a raft or a boat. There was an old log that floated in the water...but no, it would probably roll around in any rapids. There were twigs...and leaves...far too small. Finally, the princess's eyes were drawn to a clump of giant lily pads along the bank. The lily pads were a vibrant emerald green, and their tremendous sides reached up, poised perfectly in the shape of a boat. In the middle of each was an immaculate white flower.

Serepta took in a sharp breath when she saw the flowers. Their perfectly white petals cupped innocently and openly upward to take in the precious sunlight. They appeared so clean, so pure, so poised in the vast rotting quagmire all around. And they were enough of an omen to make up the princess's mind for her.

Serepta tied the supply sack to her back and precariously put one foot onto the closest lily pad. It rocked a bit and shivered on top of the waves, but held her weight. Serepta muttered a quick prayer, and, cringing, she slid the rest of her body onto the pad. Some cold stream water licked at her foot, but the plant remained gracefully afloat.

"Ha ha!" the princess cried, snapping a thick reed off the banks. She dug its woody tip into the mud and used it to lever the pad out into the stream. Soon she was off down the rushing waters, breathing the fresh air deeply as it blew her hair back, an illuminating smile spread brightly across her face.

Ratinka let a shallow breath release from his closed mouth. The lips, sealed by the dirt and grime of the night, burst apart with a thick pop to let the air escape. The captain flinched a bit and rolled over on his side.

Ahh...this was much better. He was facing the darkened forest and could feel its cool shade replace the heat of the rising sun. Yes...facing the jungle was nice...scattered black shadows and shapes flickered peacefully in the early morning breeze.

Ratinka opened his eyes a crack and squinted into the foliage. Dark limbs waved in the light wind, and tiny birds fluttered their wings.

Suddenly, a dark form moved silently through the trees, with long, purposeful strides. It disappeared behind a massive oak and then reappeared on the other side. Something about its movements by that oak seemed so familiar.... the captain closed his eyes again and felt his forehead tingle with a cold sweat. Who was that shadow in the woods?

"Pardon me, Captain. The prince says we have to get on the move now. Sir, wake up!" a Rider urged.

"What?" Ratinka sat up, startled. "Was I sleeping?"

The soldier looked at him queerly. "Ah, yes, sir."

Ratinka silently cursed for allowing himself to fall asleep. He mumbled to himself for a moment, trying to grab hold of the dream that had felt so real. "So, so you didn't see that shape in the woods then?" he implored.

"Ah...no, sir."

"Good, good," Ratinka murmured to himself, forehead twitching. He felt the eyes of the Rider, and he quickly snapped back to alertness. "What are you staring at, soldier? Let's get on the move then!"

"Yes, sir!" he saluted, and scurried back to the main campsite.

Ratinka staggered to his feet and shook his head to clear it of any doubts. There was no shadow in the woods. There was only a fleeing princess whose imminent capture would deliver him complete and utter control over Shamar.

Serepta dug the woody reed down into the mud and poled herself through the waves. Soon, the strong current took her into the thick of the stream, and the princess easily discarded the staff into the all-consuming waters.

The stream was moving quite steadily now. It rippled gently and with purpose, and the top flickered with soft waves, concealing the swollen blue-green beneath it. Huge trees bearing sweet fruit hung lazily over the river as the princess drifted by. Hot sunlight filtered through the broad leaves and twinkled merrily on the water's surface, casting a golden glow upon everything around it. The downy lily pad cupped supportively underneath her as she floated along, and she light-heartedly ran her fingers through the silky white petals of the lily.

"Life is good," Serepta breathed, grinning wide.

The princess could never have imagined a few weeks ago that she would be gliding down the Stream of Jimakana on a giant lily pad. It seemed...unreal. She felt a sense of magic, and it was pulling at her...she didn't know what she was looking for, but the stream was tempting her onward and onward with a breathless excitement, a quiet joy that made her hands quiver....

A bend in the stream appeared up ahead. The princess squinted through the sunlight, but thick patches of trees guarded her view of the dark blue elbow that veered so suddenly to the left. The lily pad drifted nearer and nearer to the grove of trees, and their shade cast a shadow upon her white flower. Tangles of branches reached out to block Serepta's way and darken the grayish stagnant waters that pooled around the thick roots.

The princess grabbed tightly to a spindly branch to bring the pad to a stop. She had to get through this blockage of brush somehow. She fiercely refused to have to get out and walk the rest of the way. If Rafe ever saw her along the banks, she would never get over the humiliation. The thought of this reaffirmed her annoyance at the wolf, and her desire to never have to put up with him and his logical ways again.

Serepta grunted in frustration and clawed at the foliage. She used the back of her hand to wipe away the sweat that had formed from the heat of the jungle. The princess's face began to brighten again, though, as her curiosity bounded and leaped. What were these trees trying to hide? A swelling of excitement arose in the princess. There was something important in the fork of stream beyond their branches, something she was meant to see. Serepta didn't know why she felt this way, but there was a stirring deep within that drove her on, drove her hands to snap and tear and pull at the roots and leaves guarding the way.

Finally, a path was cleared through the shady waters. Serepta peeked hesitantly around the bend, but she still could not see anything.

"Well, I suppose there's only one way to find out," she murmured, and pulled her pad through the gap in the trees. She didn't even notice when a gnarled branch tore her lily from the plant, causing its white petals to flutter down into the dirty stream.

Serepta pulled away one last scraggly tree limb and shielded her eyes from the sudden flood of sunlight. She blinked hard to focus her eyes, but when she finally did, the sight took her breath away.

The princess's face opened in wonder as her gaze fell upon the small pond that lay before her. With a trembling hand, she paddled her way farther inside.

A magnificent waterfall stood directly across from her, feeding the pond with bright sapphire water. The droplets of falling froth formed a sparkling white wall as it thundered in the background. All around the falls, tropical trees with thick emerald leaves sprang up. Their sleek branches rippled in the breeze and mesmerized Serepta, beckoning her closer and closer towards them. Her eyes swept all around the beautiful enclosure, greedily drinking in the brilliance as her hand slid through the cool waters.

The lily pad glided easily over the glassy water as it moved into the center of the pond. The princess reached up to pluck a ruby-red fruit from the outstretched branch of a tree, and she took a bite. Its succulent flesh sent sweet juice dribbling down her chin.

This place is wonderful... she thought to herself between swallows. The waters gleamed with the golden light of a thousand coins, and the rich, fanning trees released the tantalizing smell of spices into the hot air. Alluring red flowers sat poised on their branches, making Serepta's fallen lily seem quite plain in comparison. This place was a masterpiece....

Desmond would go crazy if he ever found this paradise. He would claim it for Shamar, camp his men there, and it would be destroyed in a matter of days. Or Rafe! If Rafe found it, he would probably insist on leaving just in case there was any danger.

"No!" Serepta cried aloud, causing a glittering frog to hop into a tree. "This place is mine! All mine!"

The princess stared greedily around the gleaming jungle pond that seemed to literally throb with riches. Everywhere she turned she saw an abundance of diamond water, silky bright petals, and rich ebony bark. She wanted to hold it somehow, to be able to wrap it up in her arms and show it off to all the world. This was how she had been trained in the palace, to see beautiful treasures and to want them. They were glittering, they were glamorous, they were temptation, and now they would be only hers.

The princess threw herself into the cool waters with a splash and began to pour it down her throat. She waded frantically around the pond, plucking bright fruits and leaves and shoving them roughly into her supply sack. Serepta had to preserve this youthful beauty somehow...she had to find a real souvenir worth keeping, one to prove of her own riches and value.

She pulled herself along the slick banks, eyes searching for something better and more beautiful than she had ever seen before, something that she knew in her heart existed somewhere. She wasn't content with what had been shown to her before. The palace baubles of Shamar had been paltry compared to these throbbing natural treasures all around.... A family of regal peacocks, with feathers of a thousand sparkling colors, flocked around the water to get a drink. Thick bushes with leaves like sheets of silk bloomed by the dozen all around her.

But they still weren't good enough. Serepta felt a stirring within her, an arrogance, and an indignation. This glorious place had made her proud. How dare the gods offer her such trifles? She was a princess, she had made it this far, and she deserved even better.

She came at last to a thick puddle of mud. It puckered as a rotting brown mass in the banks along the pond. Serepta nearly laughed aloud at the audacity of the gods to offend her sight with such an eyesore. It was old, it was death, it didn't belong in a place of flourishing life like this. The princess turned away from the ugliness in disgust. She was about to leap back into the pond when a glittering light caught her eye. A small golden hump began to emerge from the bubbling brown mud. It started out tiny, but it kept growing in size and splendor, gleaming with the light of a gilded mountain. Serepta's eyes widened when she suddenly realized that it was a tremendous snake that arose from the quaking mud!

Serepta slid back in awe as the magnificent serpent rose to its full height before her. The stinking mud and mold shed easily from its sleek wet body to reveal glassy scales that were made entirely of precious gems! Thick bands of diamond, emerald, and sapphire wrapped around its body, and glittering black onyx eyes looked down upon her from a face of solid gold. It stared at her, haughty, and a taunting ruby tongue flicked down at her.

Serepta felt the stirring within her much stronger now, and her lips curled in a grin. This glorious creature was what she had been looking for all along. *It* was a treasure fit for a woman such as herself. She wanted the snake so badly.... her fingers ached with desire to touch the sleek scales, and her eyes burned with the glitter of the gems.

The snake's mouth parted in a sly grin and it wrinkled its golden forehead conceitedly. It knew it was temptation incarnate, and it dared her to touch it....

Serepta slowly began to reach out with a hand, quivering with desire, but then she pulled it back. Something about this felt wrong...what was it? Saba had always warned her about serpents. They squirmed in the filth of the ground and spent their lives trying to destroy those who walked above them. But this was definitely no ordinary snake.

"Serpent...." the princess whispered, reaching her fingers towards it tentatively.

"Sereptaaa," the snake hissed back at her, its voice cloying and soft.

"Serpent...." she murmured sleepily, mesmerized by its slow, dancing movements.

"Sereptaaa," it replied, moving towards her lazily, and then drawing back again.

The words blended together now, and the serpent and Serepta were one. The princess' brow furrowed in concentration as she reached trembling fingers towards the bejeweled snake. Soon it would all be hers....

Suddenly, the serpent shot forward with the speed of a golden lightning bolt. There was the clicking sound of teeth on a smooth surface, and Serepta felt a jolt as the leather thong around her neck snapped. Before she could even comprehend what had happened, the snake was off into the brush, taking her precious tiger's eye stone with it.

"Aaaah!" Serepta let out a wild cry. She lunged forward, but the slippery tail had already disappeared into the shadowy undergrowth. The princess collapsed to her knees in the mud. "My heart!" she groaned, face contorted with pain as she grabbed for the empty spot at her throat.

But it was no use. The tiger's eye was gone.

Chapter Sixteen

Desmond and the Riders clambered through the thick jungle, panting and sweating with exertion. They were only marching along the first leg of the stream and were already weary and impatient. Their horses were no better. The stallions staggered through the trees, stopping often to steal a mouthful of leaves along the way.

Desmond ran at the front to hack a way through the dripping plants with his silver sword. His face burned red and gleamed with sweat, but the prince didn't seem to notice. He didn't even turn around once until one of the horses finally collapsed to the ground.

The great beast dropped into the mud, chest heaving wildly. The Riders fell all around it, using this as an excuse for some rest. Desmond flung his thick cape aside and lunged forward, ready to reprimand his men, but Ratinka stood in his way.

"Your Highness, the men do have to rest. And the horses simply cannot go on this way through the mud and trees," the Captain panted matter-of-factly.

Desmond wiped away sweat from his brow and puffed up to his full height. "So what exactly do you suggest, *soldier?*" he sneered.

Ratinka thought for a moment, green eyes darting around the jungle. "Well we can't leave the stallions behind. They're all we have. No, we have to build rafts and have them swim alongside us."

"But that could take hours!" Desmond cried, impatiently checking the position of the sun through the canopy of leaves.

"I don't see any other way than my idea," Ratinka replied coolly, removing some mud from his boot.

The prince heaved a sigh of disgust. "All right, Captain, but you better pray to the gods that your idea works." He turned then to address the Riders. "Men, I see that you all have grown weary. After a brief rest, we are going to build rafts and float our way downstream."

The men grumbled and fell wearily to the ground, some slamming their fists down in frustration. One remained standing, a young man named Justinian.

"Your Highness," he began, jaw quivering with purpose. "We are exhausted. The horses are half dead. We're running out of food, and we don't even know where we are anymore. We have sworn an oath to serve you and the kingdom, but these foreign lands are far beyond the borders of Shamar. I don't understand what more you can expect from us," Justinian declared, raising the fighting spirits of the other Riders. They began to babble in agreement and indignation.

Desmond sighed and shook his head. He stared at the sky, the jungle, and back at his men. Anger began to rise up inside his chest. Didn't these men understand that he had to capture Serepta to punish her for her treachery? Didn't they understand the rewards they stood to gain if he was finally made king? Well if not, he was going to have to remind them. Greed could inspire men to even walk through fire for a few gold coins.

The Riders watched tentatively as Desmond remained silent. He blinked a few times, and then he reached up to pluck a reddish fruit from a tree.

"Soldiers," he began. "Have you ever seen this kind of fruit before?"

The men glowered back at him, and they slowly shook their heads no.

"That's because it doesn't grow in the desert. Have you ever seen these vines, this sap, or this wood? No? That's because they don't exist in Shamar!"

The soldiers looked around in confusion. What was he getting at?

"You!" Desmond suddenly cried, pointing a finger at the man Justinian who had spoken before. "You! Try a bite of this fruit!" the prince ordered, tossing it at him.

Justinian examined it carefully for some trap, and sniffed at it cautiously.

"EAT IT!" Desmond roared. The man took a bite, and his eyes lit up as juice dribbled down his chin.

"Is it good?" the prince asked.

"It's delicious!" Justinian cried, taking another bite of the refreshing fruit.

Desmond whirled to face his men. "Do you realize that this stinking, muddy, hell-hole of a jungle is a gold mine? Do you realize how much money any intelligent man could make by selling these raw materials back in Shamar?"

The faces of the Riders lit up, and they stared around the jungle with new, greedy eyes.

"Stay with me, men! Stay with me, find the princess, and make me your king! You will be rewarded far beyond your wildest dreams! Stay with me, and I will make you all governors of the new colonies we will establish on this journey! Adventures, taxes, slaves, goods, treasures; they will all be yours for the taking!"

The Riders looked around at each other, chattering with excitement. The prince intended on claiming all these new lands for Shamar! Their kingdom would spread into these eastern lands of Morad and Jimakana and take over everything in its path, and they would be at the front of it all.

"Long live the King!" Justinian cried, pumping a fist at Desmond.

"Long live the King!" the other men roared in agreement.

As the Riders began to devour the rich fruits all around and refresh themselves in the stream, Ratinka gave a sly gaze at the prince. Perhaps Desmond wasn't such an idiot after all. Perhaps he would even be an opponent worthy of boasting about when all of this was over.

Serepta whirled around and around dizzily, desperately trying to find some idea of what to do. The serpent was long gone by now and had taken with it the only thing Serepta had left with her in the world. The princess reached again and again at her throat, half expecting to find her precious tiger's eye returned, but all her fingers grasped were empty air and cold skin. Her eyes welled up with hurt, and she found it hard to breathe.

"It's all my fault!" she cried, slamming her fist into the water, watching as filth clouded up around it. All she could think about was the proud look in Saba's eyes when she had given her the pendant: *"Keep it with you and remember what I have taught you always..."*

Serepta cringed at the feeling of her grandmother's love. What now? Would she forget Saba, the only person who had ever loved her? Would she forget herself, without the stone to remind her who she was? Would she forget what she stood for, what she was even fighting for in the first place? Serepta let out a cry of anguish and tore at her hair. She clawed at her face, trying to rid herself of the vile feeling of guilt that crawled over her skin like leeches.

And she felt ripped open. It was as though she were no longer connected to her body, and her emotions all rang hollow somehow. Where was her soul? It was nowhere to be found; the snake had stolen it and taken it far away from her without even a second thought. The princess could never get it back. She was angry and miserable and alone but she was the only one to blame for it.

"Rafe...." she let out a tiny sob. But she had lost the wolf, too.

Serepta leaped to her feet and plunged back into the water. Chest heaving, she hauled herself back onto the lily pad and began to paddle her way out of the cursed lagoon. The princess was nauseated by the place now, and the setting sun cast a sickly yellow glow on the water. The cloying smell of the flowers made her stomach turn, but not nearly as much as the sight of her own reflection in the glassy pond.

I'm a horrible person... a voice wailed inside. *I don't deserve to live...*

She began to paddle more furiously now, and she burst through the trees that had guarded her on the way in. Why hadn't she heeded their sign? Why? Serepta violently tore a branch off a tree and used it to lever her way into the middle of the stream. She wanted the danger, wanted the rapids, and wanted to die because there was nothing left to live for anymore.

Serepta sat shaking on her lily pad, hugging her supply sack tightly as she flew down the stream. Her hair was blown back by the thick air as she began to gain speed. Faster and faster the scenery flew by, all reduced to green and brown blurs. Suddenly, there was a sharp drop, and Serepta was nearly flung into the rushing waters. She shuddered with a quick fright, but embraced any pain or fear she might feel with a cold grimace. She was empty now, anyways. What did it matter?

The lily pad took a quick turn, and the princess found herself hurtling sideways down the stream. Serepta trembled a bit and squirmed to turn it around again, but the pool of water flooding at her feet made her stop. She couldn't risk moving anymore, not at these speeds. Serepta used her big toe to desperately flick some of the water out, but more kept splashing in.

Something felt wrong, and vulnerable, as she flew faster and faster down the stream.

I'll sink if this doesn't slow down soon! Serepta realized with horror. But what did she care? Why did she want to live anyway?

And suddenly she knew then that it was Rafe. It was all Rafe, only her dear friend Rafe. The princess could finally feel some spark of emotion in her hollowed body, and it was an aching to see her Companion one last time, to feel the warm gaze in his eyes, to admit for once in her lifetime that she had been wrong. But Serepta didn't even have that choice anymore. She would die and the wolf would never even know....

The princess's eyes darted wildly about, looking for an escape as bursts of white froth sprang up all around. She owed it to Rafe to live. The wolf had given her so much, and all she wanted now was to spend her life making it up to her friend and never see the look of hurt in his eyes again. Her entire body was tensed to stay balanced, and she didn't even dare turn her head. She sat quivering in a ball, arms hugged around her supply sack. The lily pad took a sharp dip once more. Serepta jerked and dug her fingernails deep into the leaf. Water oozed around her wrinkling fingertips.... there was too much water...water, everywhere. Serepta grew nauseous with it, shaking, as though each fluid in her body was moving with the flow of the stream.

The princess was a speck of an island in the middle of the great stream, which was now growing faster, rougher, and broader in width. Serepta realized in terror that she now had absolutely no control over what was to happen to her. If she were to fall into the water, she didn't know if she would ever make it out again. She was a princess of the desert and had never experienced the utter force of water like this before.

Looks like you ruined everything now, Serepta. It's your fault if you die and let Rafe down yet again.

She clenched her teeth and held tightly to the lily pad. Her hair clung stickily to her shoulder and her muscles were beginning to cramp up. All she wanted was to move, but that was the one impossible thing.

Enough... enough already.... she moaned, without daring to utter a word. Her stomach tightened and her heart continued to race. At any moment, she could be tossed into the wild stream, and her life would end. Was this her last thought? Or this? This morbid notion made her feel hollow with fear.

Serepta careened around another bend, and the lily pad somehow stayed afloat. This new stretch of the river was more densely wooded.

Rafe... she cried. *Rafe, help me, you were right, you were so right...*

Suddenly, a small figure swooped down from up above, whooshing by Serepta's head. She let out a wild shriek and whirled around to see what it was, causing the lily pad to rock dangerously.

The princess barely had time to regain her balance when two more small furry forms swung past her face from the other side. It took a moment for the image to register in her frantic brain, but she finally realized that she was being set upon by tiny monkeys.

More and more began to plunge down rapidly now, digging their little claws into the thick vines that spanned across the stream. They chattered and shrieked with one another as if fighting over who got to destroy the princess first.

"Go away! Let me be! I have nothing left to give you!" Serepta sobbed. The monkeys leaped from tree to tree to keep up with the swirling lily pad. Their tiny dark eyes glittered fiercely, and they suddenly began to chant together. Their high-pitched calls caused Serepta to break out in a sweat, as they howled in synchronization.

There were so many of them...behind her, beside her, in front of her, in great clumps of dirty white. And the monkeys moved in perfect formations, taking turns swinging down at the princess. Their monotonous, synchronized chanting rose higher in volume as the lily pad began to pick up speed once more.

Serepta cringed as she felt the filthy little claws run through her hair. Another swung down and smashed into her face. She frantically batted it away with her supply sack. The scraggly monkey plunged into the stream, clawing all the way down, trying to drag Serepta into the rushing waters with it. They wanted to make her fall...they wanted to see her give in...

"Stop! Stop already! I'm trying to do something right for once!" the princess cried, tears of frustration springing to her eyes as she struggled to maintain her balance. She couldn't take it any more.

"Don't you little beasts even care? Why do you have to torture me more than I already am?"

Anything, anything would be better than this primal, destroying fear and utter humiliation, this torturous inability to move. A ragged monkey tail scratched her ear, causing her to jerk wildly in disgust.

"ENOUGH! I can't take it anymore!!!" Serepta finally screamed with such ferocity that she didn't even notice the swirling rapids ahead.

Before Serepta could take another breath, she was suddenly flung sharply from the lily pad, and smashed violently into the wall of water below...

Serepta plunged into the roiling waves, and the shock of their cold fists nearly beat the air from her lungs. She felt as though her head was exploding from all sides and all she could see were white bursts of fire in the darkness behind her eyeballs. The waves and the rapids were eternity and eternity...they pounded and stretched and squeezed and pummeled, shoving her body farther and farther down into the murky depths of the dull roar of the stream.

The princess struggled at first, pouring all her energy into wriggling one small finger against the fury of the waves. A merciless coil of water unfolded and cracked like a whip, seeming to snap her entire arm in two. Then there was a lifting, an upheaval...she was brought within moments of the surface...the rippling pattern of sunlight on dark waters was lovely and but an inch from her face...but soon she was shoved violently back downwards again.

Serepta let out a cry of despair, paunchy bubbles escaping her lips. The supply sack had become hopelessly entangled on her foot, and it was starting to weigh her down. There was no escape...no one to help her...nothing she could do anymore...the princess's face dropped in a state of apathy, and she passively allowed her body to be twisted and shredded and torn like a rag doll beneath the waters.

A cannon ball of a wave suddenly slammed her into the hard, rocky surface at the bottom of the stream. There she was, at the bottom, at the bottom of everything she had tried and chosen and struggled for, empty and alone. She had made her choice to take this path, and it had brought her to the bottom. Rafe had been right, she had been wrong, and now she was going to die for it.

Die... dying... death... the words floated like wisps of black smoke through her mind. Was this what death would be like, this cold smoke of not knowing? The dirty tendrils wrapped themselves in clouds around her skull, reducing her thoughts to a dull pulse.

Everything was slowing down around her. Memories began to drift through her darkening mind now. She could hear the thick pound of the king's drums in Shamar...the lazy sound of waves crashing against the shore...everything was slowing...to...a quiet...stop. Serepta's heart gave a frantic last gasp, like the wings of a small bird fluttering against the bars of a cage, but then dropped obediently to a dull thud once more.

Thud. Thud. She could still hear her heartbeat, so she still must be alive. How long would it take to stop living...to stop thinking for herself...to lose control of everything there was...to slip like oil into the world that awaited the dead....

A tiny pebble scratched against her limp toes. It sent a faint tingle of feeling through her cold body. This was what it was like to feel. Serepta quietly acknowledged the pebble. Perhaps that was her last feeling...no more touch of the solid gold of sunlight on her face, or the tingling scent of purple flowers in bloom, or seeing the warm comfort in Rafe's eyes and the glint of silver fur that sent a shiver through her every time she saw it.

Was this to be her fate?

In the pulsing darkness that was her eyes, she began to see a light sprinkling of golden sand. Each tiny grain seemed to twinkle with a separate note of magic...these were her sands of the desert, and she reached for them with all her might....

Was this to be her fate?

The princess felt the warm glow of the sand begin to swirl through her body. She felt tiny buds of life sprout up in each part of her, sending up stalks and blossoming with light. They crackled with an energy she had not felt before, a stirring, a gratefulness, a rebirth....

Serepta's leg reached out, and her toes felt the sucking mud at the bottom of the stream. She was feeling, she was living, and now all she wanted was to live.

There was a great kick. Her arms reached out and felt the coldness of the waters that now were drifting calmly again. The water did not fight her anymore, and she did not let it. Never again. She would not give in any more, and she was elated with the exhilaration at being able to simply resist.

Finally, Serepta's face burst gratefully from the water, and she laughed as she tasted the air once more.

Chapter Seventeen

Coughing and panting, the princess hauled her weary body onto the banks. The dripping lump of a supply sack was still roped around her foot, and all its remaining contents were fortunately intact. Serepta sighed and plowed her fingers into the earth, relishing its gritty wetness.

This is life... she thought, lifting her head back to take in the peaceful scented canopy above. It spun a little as she regained her balance. The sun was beginning to set, and tiny sprinkles of orange light dappled her face.

Serepta sat in a puddle of dirty water, while she huddled silently against a tree. Her limbs rang numbly as feeling began to return to them. She lightly touched a finger to a drop of water that dribbled from her thigh. Water...it was so small and clear now, so harmless as it ran from her fingertip.

Serepta glanced out over the stream and didn't know what to feel anymore. On the surface, the waters drifted calmly now, but she knew all too well that there was a murderous ocean of waves underneath that could have taken her life and not even changed one bit. It wouldn't have cared. It could have drowned Saba, it could have drowned Desmond, and it would still keep flowing.

The sun continued to sink lower in the sky, pulling a silky screen of orange and pink down with it. The princess sighed and looked up at the sky, trying to find the seam where the day ended and the night began. She didn't find it.

As the sun finally disappeared behind the trees, Serepta's heart gave a tiny shudder in the darkness. The princess closed her eyes and swallowed, feeling the lump of moisture slide down her throat. She quietly realized that she was alone, alone under a tree so impossibly far from home. Saba was dead, and Desmond could be right behind her for all she knew. She had abandoned Rafe. She had lost her treasure, her necklace. She was nothing. She was empty.

The princess's face twisted a little and she began to cry. Serepta gave tiny sobs and heaves, and as the tears slid down her cheeks, she was reminded of Sera. Sera...she had lost her, too. Serepta cried even harder. She buried her back against the tree, dug her feet hard into the mud, and hugged her knees tightly as she rocked back and forth. What had she done? Where was she now? Somewhere lost in a place that held no meaning for her. There was no meaning for her anywhere, not without the child, not without her tiger's eye, not without Rafe. Rafe...her heart splintered in two as she recalled the look in his eyes when she had told him to go away. She was sorry, so sorry...

But no. What would sorry do? Sorry would not return her Companion. She would have to get up and find him and apologize to him, hunt through this entire jungle to find him, until the end of her days if need be. The princess knew this with whatever meager scrap of soul she had left, and she rose to her feet.

Serepta did not return to the stream. Instead, she began to pull her way methodically through the jungle on the banks. She was going to do this Rafe's way.

"Stroke! Stroke!" Desmond's sharp voice rang out over his small fleet of rafts. His words chimed and flowed with the rhythm of the stream, lifting the spirits of his men and causing tiny birds to burst from the trees in colorful clouds.

The prince lifted his own oar from the water and felt its woody thickness against his skin. He threw his head back to taste the breeze. "This is the life, my men!" he cried aloud, laughing lustily.

His soldiers cheered and pumped their fists in the air. Their makeshift wooden rafts flew down the stream with ease, and the stallions, which were roped to the logs, swam powerfully alongside.

"Don't you smell it, soldiers? The jungle, the taste of adventure in the air? We're heroes, all of us!" Desmond declared, throwing his arms out wide in the light of the setting sun.

Ratinka sat absentmindedly at the front of the prince's raft, letting his foot dangle in the splashing water. He watched as thick walls of waves washed up around his ankles, to return to the stream once more. One cold wave jumped up and licked at his knee. Ratinka jerked and withdrew his leg from the water. The powerful stream was yanking the rafts along much faster now.

The captain carefully rose to his feet and scanned the stream in front of them with darting eyes. Bright orange light from the setting sun flickered like flames across the surface, making it difficult to see...suddenly, all three rafts tumbled over a steep drop, sending Ratinka flying into the stream.

The captain was jarred by the cold swirling waves. "Help me, you buffoons! Pull me up!" he howled. Ratinka quickly flung out his sharp hands and clung tightly to one of the logs of the raft. White bursts of cold froth leaped up to bite at his skin.

Two of the closest soldiers reached out to haul him onto the raft. One grabbed hold of Ratinka's arm, just when the raft suddenly flew over another quick drop. The soldier plunged into the stream, and Ratinka used his body as leverage to heave himself onto the safety of the logs. The unfortunate soldier cried out in terror as the raft raced swiftly away. The Riders on the last raft leaped up and crowded at the back, watching in horror as their comrade was left behind in the swirling waters.

"Watch out! Watch out! You're going to tip!" Desmond roared, but it was too late. The unbalanced logs capsized, sending all the men flying into the churning stream. Their stallions shrieked as they were pinned underneath the timbers.

"If anyone moves, you're all going to die!" the prince hollered with such agitation that none of the soldiers even dared to turn around.

The remaining two rafts continued to fly down the stream at an alarming rate. Swirling rapids and eddies spun them through the water like furious white tornadoes.

"All soldiers into the middle of the rafts! Hold tightly to the lashings and don't move a muscle!" Ratinka called over the roar of the stream. The sun had nearly set now, and he could hardly even see whom he was talking to, but the shrieks of the swimming horses stabbed through the dark air like knives. Through the entire stretch of the rapids of Jimakana, Raghnall's Riders closed their eyes, clung tightly to one another, and prayed to the gods of protection that this misery would end.

"Look! Up there, ahead! There's a shadow in the water! That must be where the rapids end!" young Admael cried in excitement, squinting into the darkness of the night.

"You idiot! That's a waterfall!" Ratinka roared back at him, causing the soldiers to fly into a panic. They jerked and yelped, the terror of death fully upon them.

"We have to get out now!"

"We'll jump and swim for it!"

"If we do that, we'll all die!"

Finally, Ratinka leaped up at the head of the rafts. "Everyone, quick, grab onto a branch like...." he didn't have time to finish before he had gripped onto a low hanging tree limb above. The Riders watched as their captain disappeared behind them, dangling safely above the rushing stream. They all quickly scrambled to grab onto their own branches.

All of the remaining soldiers leaped up into the trees that hung above them and watched, horrified, as their newly made rafts plunged over the great falls. Their stallions let out wild cries of terror as they followed, still tied to the sides. There were tremendous cracks as the timbers splintered into pieces on the rocks far down below at the bottom. Each sharp sound sent a tingle of shock and gratefulness through every man.

The Riders clambered down the trees and kissed the jungle floor. What had been a full cavalry of men and horses was now a group of dripping foot soldiers, but they were safe, safe for now.

Darkness came creeping into the jungle, first in soft shadows beneath the quiet leaves, but then spreading to cast a peaceful gray haze over it all. Serepta tenderly pulled her way through the brush, moonlight smooth upon her expressionless face. Her dark eyes pooled and focused on only what was ahead of her, on the flowers that had pulled their petals inward for the night, hugging their own softness for protection, and on the brightening glimpse of a starry sky beyond the trees all around her.

Her feet were bare as she trod lightly through the jungle. The princess was strong, however, strong in her purpose and in thought, and she did not notice any pain or discomfort. Her mind was running quietly on one track only, and she knew that she would search the entire night if necessary to find what it was that she sought.

Serepta came to a thinning of the forest. Here the great trees stood magnificently separate, claiming their own soft clumps of earth. The dirt was light and springy under her feet, and the air smelled of life and of strength. The princess closed her eyes and inhaled deeply, rejoicing in the scents. She longed with all her heart to stand among those trees...but it was not her time yet. She was still hollow inside and could not remain still for long. The hollowness drove her onwards.

She passed through more trees and more bushes, and she saw strange flowers that lifted their faces upwards towards the sky. The princess could almost hear their ancient song ringing towards the stars. Serepta lifted her head to join them in that silent song, the one that the flowers and the trees and the howling wolves know.

Finally, the princess stopped, and looked up. With a sense of surprise, she found herself in a rocky clearing. The great jungle had ended. In the shadowy dusk of the night, the princess saw that she had found a small waterfall. The falls drew the last tamed trickles of Jimakana into an oval pond of smooth glass. This waterfall ran steadily and clearly, with none of the glitter of the lagoon that had made her heart sick.

Serepta tilted her head to one side in silence and watched the waterfall slide down the cropping of thick rock. The clean water fell in a sheet that looked like a living pane of glass. Serepta was drawn towards it, drawn into the pond that rippled softly all around her numbing body.

The moonlight shone down, illuminating the waters with a pearly glow. The princess stood up to her waist in the pond, bathing in the clean purity of the light of the moon and the stars. Then she took off her dress and strode gracefully into the falls.

The rippling sheet of water cascaded over her naked body. It liquefied her muscles and caused her hair to hang in thick dark curls. Her skin was made pale in the night as she lifted her head to feel the soft touch of the falls. All of a sudden, as the trickling melody rang in her ears, she had a flash of insight and could finally remember the words to her dream song:

The two Companions have been severed, a move that seems quite bold
The answer to whether this was wise or not, only time shall hold
The Princess will travel down the Stream to a land of young and old
Where the tempter shall arise from the mud and stinking mold...
Keep in mind, impulsive one, for every action there is a toll,
And in the end, are you prepared to pay it with your soul?

Serepta's face fell beside the waters. She finally understood it now, now that it was all over. The princess's instinctive desire to fight back against this truth was soon overcome by a calm acceptance. She had been tempted, she had fallen, and she had lost the only two things that really mattered in the world: her soul in the tiger's eye and her dearest Companion who she missed with all of her heart.

The princess sighed as she felt the cool waters slide down her back. She was empty and sullen in her misery, and she felt as though she were the only being left in the world.

But there was another, one that stood proudly in the shadows, and one whose heart ached as it stared down at the lonely figure in the pond.

Rafe watched through the screen of dark leaves in the forest as the princess bathed in the falls below. His breath caught in his throat when he saw her, and he leaned forward in the night, trying to absorb every bit of the sight of her into his soul.

The wolf felt a deep shame within him. Serepta had thrown him away; she hadn't cared about him, after all they had been through. He shouldn't care what happened to her anymore. But Rafe was mesmerized in her presence, made still and quiet by the glowing figure in the moonlight. The princess' eyes were welled up with an infinite, beautiful sadness, one that seemed etched into her very being. He couldn't leave, even if the urging in his heart wasn't pushing him towards her with all its might. She needed him now. Plus, he had something for her.

The wolf stepped magnificently outward from the shadows. The silver shine of his fur and the crackle of the earth under his feet heralded his presence to the world. Serepta turned around slowly in the water, face lifting in wonder as she saw the creature hurry towards her in the moonlight.

Rafe's muscles slid gracefully under his fur as he ran to his princess. Serepta's body was mostly covered by her long hair and by the water, but she still felt naked in his presence. He looked at her, looked through her, looked inside of her, and she felt the warmth of her dear friend's eyes.

The wolf plunged into the pond, sending thick ripples in all directions. He plowed through the shallow waters until he could finally stand, exhausted, at his full height in front of her.

Serepta eyes filled over with tears when she saw the panting wolf in front of her. He wearily lifted his head to show her the gift that he had struggled so hard to bring to her. Between his jaws, there dangled her tiger's eye stone.

In that moment, the princess's heart seemed to crack, to fill, and to crack again. She reached trembling fingers to reclaim her pendant and tied it around her neck, tingling with an awe-filled joy. She didn't bother to ask how Rafe had found it; she already knew that for her, he would battle a serpent ten times his size and even travel through a desert and over a mountain and into a jungle, just to be with her.

Sobbing softly, tears running down her cheeks, Serepta knelt down in the water besides her Companion and took him into her arms. Rafe had brought her back her soul, and she would never forget it as long as she lived. The princess dug her face into his soft fur and spoke against his body.

"Never leave me again."

Part Four

To the Pyramid

Chapter Eighteen

The Riders collapsed to the soft damp soil, exhausted and aching from their ordeal. The men were dripping wet and devastated over the loss of their comrades in the rapids. They curled up in miserable shivering heaps on the jungle floor.

Ratinka sat alone on a log. His fingers fidgeted and his green eyes darted everywhere in the darkness. The Captain was agitated and jumpy, but he didn't dare go to sleep and risk seeing the shadow man in his dreams again. He had been seeing him much more often lately, drifting among the trees in the moments between soft sleep and wakefulness, haunting him wherever he went. Ratinka's breath grew ragged and cold at the thought.

Desmond lay curled on the ground nearby, black cloak wrapped as tightly around him as dark sleep was. Ratinka watched, lips curling with amusement as the prince's closed eyes twitched rapidly. Desmond's sallow face was wrinkled in consternation, and his lips quivered in the midst of a dream.

"What are you thinking of now, sleeping prince? What demons do you fight? More importantly, are they ones within you or without you...?" Ratinka whispered, closing his eyes against the thoughts that flowed through his mind like the jungle stream in the night.

Desmond lay underneath him, oblivious to it all.

...The young prince's hand reached forward to boldly swing open the marble door before him. He marched into his mother's chambers to find her reclined by the window, her delicate fingers flowing over the strings of an ancient harp. Her white tunic rippled and folded over her porcelain skin, shining in the sunlight streaming in from the open balcony. The woman's downcast eyes lit up when she saw her son.

"Desmond, my darling boy, come here and greet me! Tell me why you have that angry look in your eye," she beseeched him.

The prince glared at her indignantly, squinting fiercely at the golden light beaming all around her. "I'm no longer your little boy, mother. I'm a man now, and you should treat me so."

"A man. A man you say, a man who treats his mother so. What makes you a man? Because you go to the brothels and gambling houses now?" the old woman asked her son.

"It's better than wasting my days up here with you."

The woman paused for a long moment, her face a mask of hurt. "How could you...how could you say such a thing?" she began, putting her hands over her face in distress. "I feel as though I don't even know you anymore! All you do is keep the company of your friends, and I rarely even see you. I feel like you have forgotten me entirely."

Desmond felt a familiar twinge of remorse in his heart, but he turned his head with a sneer, shoving it aside with molten rage. He had to, rather than be consumed by guilt. He was accustomed to it now.

"How dare you! How dare you, you foul woman! You are an embarrassment to the family! You spend your life locked away in these chambers, dreaming of days long ago. You refuse to take part in politics or serve your duty to Shamar, and I think you wish to drag me down with you," he replied, voice ringing with a cold passion.

His mother rose up now, eyes flaring. "So, what Desmond? What do you wish of me? What have you ever asked of me that I have refused? The kingdom is in shambles, and every political faction is struggling to name Raghnall's heir," she babbled, wringing her hands in frustration. "I stay up here because I do not wish to play any part in it."

Desmond let out an exasperated sigh. Politics were everything, how could she not see that? The nobles, the commoners, the intricacies and intrigues and riches of the palace...the young prince shivered with the delight of it all. Someday, he would be at the very center.

"Desmond, please don't be mad at me. I don't think I can bear it. I love you too much," the old woman begged.

The prince put a hand on her shoulder and stared into her deep brown eyes. His heart danced in private glee as he sensed her weaknesses.

"You say you love me, mother. Prove it."

His mother looked up at him, eyes brimming with tears. "I would give you the sun and moon and stars if only to show you how much I do."

Desmond gave her a crooked grin. "Then make me King..."

Serepta awoke slowly, stretching in the soft morning sun. The princess lifted herself up and yawned deeply, staring around the quiet beach beside the falls. Her necklace hung perfectly over her heart, and Rafe lay sleeping beside her.

This was peace...this was right...she could have stayed there forever in that moment. The wolf's chest rose rhythmically with each breath, his head cradled above his large paws. The wolf's dark eyelashes fanned above his silvery white fur, and the points of his teeth protruded slightly from his upper lips. He was a sleeping warrior.

The princess gently touched a finger to her tiger's eye, rejoicing in the fact that it was still there at her heart, that last night hadn't been a dream. As her skin met the cool stone, the waterfall seemed to rush a bit harder, the sky sharpened into a more intense blue, and the sunlight grew even brighter. Rafe woke up.

The wolf's throat let out a rumble. The princess smiled and placed a hand on his head.

"Rafe, I don't think I can ever thank you enough for what you did," she murmured. The wolf was silent, but she could see in his eyes that he understood.

"When I was alone like that...when I was alone out there," Serepta began, recalling with a shiver the fear she had felt. "I almost died. I almost died in the stream, and you never would have even known what had happened to me."

Realizing this made the princess feel hollow inside, but she continued.

"Have you ever almost lost your life like that?" the princess asked, half expecting him to reply. At the wolf's pained look, Serepta let out a sigh.

"There's so much I don't know about you, that I fear I will never know. I know that everyone has their story to tell, though," the princess said, gazing into the falls. She threw her head up to look at the sky, searching the morning blue for eloquence.

"I don't know what my story is. Not yet, at least. All I know is that I want it to be one worth telling, you know? At the end of my days, I want to know that my life created a story worth telling to the world."

Rafe's thick tail slid back and forth over the ground as he digested the words of his friend.

"I don't know," Serepta sighed. "It's just...there are just so many people in the world, wolves too, I suppose, who live and die and never realize that they can do anything they want with their lives. There is so much to see and to do, and so little of them see or do anything. It's a waste. It's one big waste."

The silence that resulted after her dialogue was awkward, yet somewhat cleansing as well. The princess had never given words to these deeply held beliefs of hers. The two friends sat quietly beside the falls, turning their thoughts over and over in their minds.

Then Serepta felt something, a frightful shudder in her chest, a tightening pang of fear. She instinctively grabbed for her tiger's eye stone. The princess closed her eyes, and in her mind, she could see Desmond curled asleep on the jungle floor in the night. His dark form twitched and jerked like a spider in its death throes, as he rolled over in the depths of a dream.

The princess gripped the smooth stone tighter, and it took her into the morning then. She could see shadowy glimpses in her mind's eye of the Riders packing up their gear and eagerly trekking through the jungles of Jimakana. It wouldn't be much longer before they reached her clearing now....

Serepta snapped back to her world when Rafe nudged sharply at her knee. His blue eyes shone with concern at her distant gaze, and the princess laid a hand on his head. "We have to go now. They're coming."

The wolf rose quickly to his feet without a sound, and Serepta grabbed their supply sack. Together, they took off running eastward through the clearing, fear fueling their every step.

"Your Highness, we've spotted the princess up ahead, in a clearing beyond the edge of the jungle," a scout announced, running up to the prince.

Desmond dug his sword tip into the mud. "You've seen her then?" he asked.

"Yes, Your Highness. I saw the witch, and she was with her wolf. They're heading east," the soldier replied.

The prince gave a crooked grin and breathed deeply, closing his eyes in satisfaction. Desmond lifted his sword and felt its cold weight in his hand. He then turned to address his men.

"Riders of Shamar, today we will see our triumph! We will capture the princess, return to Shamar, and you will all be rewarded once I...once I am King," he announced, and then stumbled a bit. Desmond stopped rather suddenly at the end of his sentence, stuttering as a feeling rose up inside him. It twisted him up within his chest and left a bitter taste in his mouth.

"Sir, are you all right?" a Rider asked.

Desmond blinked hard for a moment, instinctively shoving his feelings aside with anger. It was a familiar feeling somehow....

"Of *course* I am! I am invincible!" he roared, causing his men to cheer.

Ratinka scuttled up alongside of him. "Don't you think we should get on the move, Your Highness?" he muttered.

Desmond turned on him with cold gray eyes. "You think I want your advice anymore, soldier? Your idea of trapping the princess with fire was a disaster, and your plan with the rafts nearly got us all killed. And don't think I haven't heard about your imaginary friend, the shadow man," he added cruelly.

Ratinka's eyes blazed a crackling green as the Riders began to laugh loudly at him. Seething, he lowered his head and retreated to the back of the group. The soldiers returned their attention to Desmond and gazed at him adoringly as he issued his orders.

"Here me now, Riders of Shamar! The princess is to be captured alive! You may kill the wolf if you wish, but the witch is to remain unharmed. I will lead a group of two men, Ratinka will hopefully redeem himself with a group of two, and Justinian will lead the rest. We will take the witch from all sides! Onward, soldiers!" the prince cried, pointing his sword into the trees.

The men took off charging, hungry for money, for glory, and for blood.

Chapter Nineteen

Serepta and Rafe ran through the thin forest beyond the jungles of Jimakana, leaping over fallen trees and ducking under low hanging branches. The princess's nerves tingled with a jumpy agitation. This new place was much more open than the jungle, but the scattered tussocks of dry grass blocked her view of the surrounding area. Her heart skipped with fear, and she kept glancing back to see if they were being followed. Her skin crawled with a sense of vulnerability...she knew that her hunters could see her, but she could not see them anymore...nauseating points of fear in her mind caused her to suspect every tree and bush.

Suddenly, Rafe let out a wild bark and Serepta turned just in time to slam into Desmond's thick body.

"Hello, cousin," he murmured, grasping her upper arms tightly.

Serepta let out a wild shriek under his cold touch and kicked him sharply in the knee. With a bellow, his grip relaxed, and the princess frantically jerked away. Shuddering with fright, the princess spun around to find the forms of the Riders materializing out of the forest all around. More and more Riders emerged from the grass, some wielding weighted nets, and others sharp blades.

The princess's heart pained at her ignorance of this planned attack. She took in a breath and gazed fiercely back at them, drawing her golden dagger from her hip. It was a foreign sensation to hold a weapon in her hand and know she actually was going to use it. Her hand felt clumsy, like it had just been given a tool without a handle. The dagger gleamed brightly in the hot sunlight as she quickly looked down at Rafe. The wolf crouched low at her side, fangs bared, face twisting with hatred. She had never seen him look so terrifying before. Serepta knew that he was prepared to fight with her now, to the death.

"Nowhere to run to, witch!" one of the soldiers cried, rushing at her suddenly with a net. Serepta's eyes widened as she quickly slashed across the rope with her dagger, and Rafe took the man down, growling all the way. After that, complete chaos ensued.

The Riders flooded in from all sides, roaring curses and whipping the sharp nets through the air. Serepta gripped her weapon tightly and stabbed frantically in all directions, whirling and spinning to ward off attacks. Rafe's powerful body leaped through the air, taking down several men, but not having enough time to kill any with a final blow. And all around was a cloud of thick coarse rope, singing through the air, managing to catch some of the Riders in its tangles as well.

Serepta's muscles tightened and jerked with fear like springs, launching her in an impromptu dance about the clearing. She had never fought before, but she enjoyed the sense of power that the cold weight of the golden dagger gave her. The princess fought ferociously, knowing that she would rather die, or at least take a few men down with her, than be captured and returned to Shamar. The very thought of it filled her up with grief, emotions overflowing to feed her body with energy. She would never go back to Shamar, and that knowledge gave her strength.

Rafe let out a yelp when he was cut by a spear. The large wolf ripped the weapon from the Rider's hands and broke it in half between his jaws. Serepta could see the dark blood that dripped from his shoulder, and she knew for his sake that they had to try to escape.

"Rafe, we have to break through the circle!" she shouted, ducking under a blow from a club.

Desmond threw his arms in the air. "You see, men? The witch can talk to animals!" he announced, inciting the fighters. The circle closed in tighter.

Suddenly, Rafe launched himself at Desmond and brought the prince down into the dirt. He hated this man, this man that had hunted them down like wild beasts. Anger pounded through Rafe's veins, tightening his muscles and making him hot with rage. The wolf tore and ripped viciously through Desmond's thick tunic, and he would have finished him off if the Riders hadn't come rushing in around him.

Rafe jumped away and saw that his attack had left a narrow gap in the circle of men. Together, the princess and the wolf burst through with all of their strength, ropes and fists flinging at their bodies. Chest heaving, Serepta didn't dare to turn around as she fled full speed after her Companion through the woods. She could hear the pounding footsteps behind her and it sent a shock of fear down her spine. Serepta's legs pumped like pistons, seeming to have minds of their own. Rafe's body flew gracefully through the trees in front of her. He knew that she would follow him.

Desmond ran just behind the princess, shredded tunic dangling limply around his sinewy body. He had a score to settle with the wolf, but that would have to wait until later. Serepta was so close now...he could sense the fear in her swift movements. A gnarled branch tore away part of her dress, revealing a large portion of her leg.

Desmond gave a crooked grin of anticipation and continued after her, the Riders right behind him. His body quivered with the thrill of the hunt. She couldn't keep running forever. Eventually, she would get tired. It was simply a matter of time...

All of a sudden, one of the Riders leaped upon Desmond and threw him sharply to the ground. Just as the prince's head slammed into the dirt, he heard a tremendous, wrenching crack echo through the forest. He looked up timidly from the ground, and saw the limbs of an oak tree above him tremble and shudder. With a loud groan, the massive tree began to lean, as if in slow motion. The Riders watched in horror as it crashed violently to the forest floor, sending dirt and dust flying up everywhere like an explosion. The enormous oak fell, barring their way, just where Desmond had been running moments before. And the princess and wolf were on the other side.

"NO! How can this be happening?" Desmond roared in disbelief, clawing at the giant trunk that blocked their way. All the Riders sprang to help him, except for one.

Ratinka stood alone, off to the side. Face pale and lips trembling, he watched in a terrified silence as a shadowy, dark figure ran away from the fallen tree and disappeared quietly into the forest.

Chapter Twenty

Serepta heard the deafening sound and jerked around in shock to find that she and Rafe were safe, safe for the time being. The massive oak tree lay behind like a great wall, holding back the threat of evil and death. Its quivering leaves and boughs urged her to keep running.

"We're going to make it...we're going to make it, Rafe," the princess murmured through pursed lips. Each breath was an expression of gratitude as they continued to plow through the woods.

The trees and bright young leaves began to thin out now as they ran. The princess and wolf were almost at the end of the forest, and both could sense something greater and open beyond its confining edge. It called to them...it was a golden heated roughness, something new to both of them, yet emanating with age. Most importantly, it felt like the next step along their way. Every step felt like it was bringing them closer and closer to the lulling touch of the oasis at the end of the journey now. They had taken what they could from the jungles and forests and were ready to face this new land they were merging into.

The bits of dirt on the scraggly forest floor began to fall away into earth that was more solid and rocky. Serepta stumbled to a halt to catch her breath and look around in wonder. The hard-packed, grayish ground was dusty and gravelly, and great croppings of reddish boulders rose up all around like the humped backs of camels. The sky shone pure blue, and the sun glittered down on them like a blinding yellow-white diamond.

"Oh, Rafe...I think we might be near a desert...." Serepta whispered excitedly. The princess followed the wolf as he began to meander through the paths between the thick boulders all around. She closed her eyes to taste the heat. Serepta loved the heat. She was a woman of the desert and was born to feel the tingling dry kiss of the sun on her skin. Fire was her element, and she felt in her place again.

The rocky walls rose up on all sides of the lonely two. They were scored with the lashes of ancient winds and stood like mountains, battered yet powerful. Bits of white sand clung in crusty lines to the rock, and Serepta touched a respectful finger to their searing heat as she walked by. Rafe led her cautiously through narrow, dusty paths, ones that must have been carved by old streams long since dried up. Serepta felt a light breeze flicker over her head and she hurried forward, eager to find what was at the end of their path.

When they finally emerged from the labyrinth of boulders some time later, the naked openness surrounded them with a sudden shock. It was as though they had arrived on a foreign planet. The princess and the wolf stood atop a small, wind-torn cliff. There were no boundaries anywhere... Serepta felt as though she was swimming in the open freedom of the place as she threw her arms out wide. The sky curved perfectly up above, bright and solid at the same time, without a single cloud in its vivid heat. And below the cliff stretched a magnificent, shimmering desert.

Subtle glints of gold and copper melded together in the heat, rippling under the glowing disk of the sun. The desert stood like a massive still ocean, perfectly flat and unchanging, boundless on all sides. The wideness of it swept Serepta's eyes around as she tried to take all of it in at once, soon finding it gloriously impossible. The grains of sand below glittered deliciously like flecks of fool's gold. The princess wanted to throw herself into them, to feel their gritty warmth against her body, to feel like she had a purpose once more.

But something felt wrong. Something was misplaced. Serepta couldn't understand why, but as she reached out with her senses, something seemed to ring hollow. It was like a silk flower in a jar of roses, like bits of glass scattered among diamonds. These weren't her sands of the desert, these grains that sparkled perfectly upon the surface. An eerie tingle echoed down her spine like the ringing of wind chimes. The princess remembered all too well the faux perfection in the mirror-rocks of Morad and her heart cried out in warning. This desert drew her eyes, but not her soul...

Rafe stood poised to fling himself off the cliff and into the sands, but Serepta put a hand on his head. The warm fur beneath her trembled impatiently. He wanted to run through the openness, to skip along the top, to go straight ahead to whatever awaited them at the end of the desert. But Serepta knew something was wrong, and he trusted her.

She bent down to pick up a small rock on the cliff's edge beside her. Hefting its solid weight in her palm, the princess drew back her arm and flung it into the desert below. She shielded her eyes, squinting against the golden glow, and watched as the rock hit the ground.

The rock fell with an eerie plop. The sands around it began to send out ripples and waves like water. The stillness of the vast desert was disturbed, and it seemed as though the rock ripped open a great gash where it fell. Suddenly, it was sucked beneath the depths of the earth, and the sands flowed back over to fill the hole. The desert was still again, perfectly flat, and no one would have known that the rock had ever been there.

A chill ran down Serepta's spine. The glimmering gold seemed to be laughing in silence at her, having demonstrated its awesome powers.

"It's all quicksand...." she whispered, lowering herself to the ground in shock. If she had been impulsive, if she had leaped with Rafe over the cliff, they both would have been gone in moments. Rafe slowly sat down behind her, eyes glazed with astonishment. Never again would he doubt Serepta's crazy notions.

"We can't...we can't go this way...my gods, there's nowhere to go!" Serepta cried, heart filling with dread. This couldn't be the end of her journey. Not after all they had seen and done. But there was no possible way around the massive desert before them, and there was nowhere else to go.

When the Companions turned away from the desert, a tremendous wind suddenly rushed and howled, sending sharp flecks of rock flying into the air. Thick black clouds began to roll in from the distance like a flock of darkened sheep. The desert seemed to be angry after losing its victims. A great storm was stirring up, poisoning the bright blue sky.

Rafe's ears suddenly picked up a sound, and he turned around sharply. The cutting whine in his throat told Serepta that he sensed the Riders were somewhere nearby. She let out a roar of frustration.

"Not now! Don't they ever let up?" she moaned. Rafe silenced the princess with a cold glare, and the wolf began to edge his way cautiously back into the maze of rock. The idea of being cornered on that narrow cliff side prodded an instinctive fear deep within him. Serepta crouched low and silently followed him back through the myriad winding paths. Columns of dusty wind began to rise and blow furiously through the tunnels, blackening the sky.

"I see shadows!" a man's voice suddenly called from just around the corner, causing the princess and wolf to jerk backward with shock. Without any thought other than to flee, they spun around and raced back through another fork in the path, their hearts beating wildly as they ran as fast as they possibly could away from the voices.

The pound of pursuing boots echoed on the rocks, and the Companions realized the passageways were getting narrower and narrower. The heat of the air dampened Serepta's senses, and the red-brown of the boulders looked the same wherever she ran. Filthy air clouded everything in sight. Panic began to seize Serepta's body. Her eyes rolled wildly around, and the princess suddenly realized with horror that Rafe was no longer at her side.

Serepta's legs gave out and she fell against the side of the rock. She let out a cry of despair. How could he leave her alone like this, once again? How could he abandon her here? Her heart pounded in her ears and in her eyes, clouding her senses. She could hear the slap of boots on rock and knew that the Riders were close now...her mouth began to tremble, and her hands shook with raw fear. The fear came from the very root of her. She was a deer caught in a trap by lions, and the thought rattled her entire body.

Suddenly, Serepta felt a cold lick at her shoulder. The princess stifled a shriek and whirled around to find Rafe above her, crouched in an alcove in the boulder. His lips peeled back in a grin, and he locked his jaws around the neck of her dress, helping to heave her up towards him.

The princess and the wolf collapsed trembling gratefully within the cave just as the group of Riders marched by.

Chapter Twenty-One

Serepta jerked herself into a dark corner and hugged her knees tightly to her chest. Her rib cage trembled and shook, and she could feel her heartbeat racing in her eyeballs, pooling her vision with soft bursts of light. She shut her eyes to block out the destroying fear of nearly being discovered. She had never known such fear to exist in the world, such a numbing force that paralyzed her into submission and brought her to her knees in its presence. Serepta felt as though any strength she once had fled from her body as the events of the day came flooding back to her. Serepta wanted to cry out, had to cry out, but that was the one thing she couldn't risk doing.

Rafe crouched panting on the other side of the narrow cave, eyes tracing the sick look of distress on the princess's face. The wolf leaped over to her and flowed into her arms, feeling the frightful shuddering of her heartbeat beside his chest. A single tear slid down Serepta's cheek, and he carefully licked it away.

This warm gesture nearly made her sob. *Oh, Rafe...what are we doing?* Serepta's face twisted up with angst. Her eyes welled with tears, blurring her view of the darkened cave. *We've trapped ourselves in here and we might be found and I won't go back to Shamar can't go back to Shamar but I don't want to die...* Serepta's weary body began to shake uncontrollably now. *I really don't want to die...*

She took in a deep, quivering breath and wiped away her tears with the back of her hand, hugging Rafe's solid body tightly against her. The cave seemed safe at least. The rocky walls were warm and dry, and it was high up enough so as not to be seen. They could stay there for a long time...Serepta ached to stay there forever.

We can't go on, Rafe. No farther. No more. I did the best I could. There's nowhere else to go. It would be so easy to fail and die and sink into all that quicksand ahead, and I'm sure other people have. Not me. It's safe here. We can stay here forever…I'm afraid, so afraid…

The princess stole a quick glance at the opening of the cave. It was dark out now, and she saw that the desert winds had picked up even more. She could hear their rushing roar as they whipped past the tunnels in the boulders. Serepta curled up tightly in a ball on the floor, worming up to the safety of the thick rock.

"It's over, Rafe. Here we are safe. Here we will stay," she brought up the courage to whisper, satisfied at last.

The wolf stared down at her as she trembled there on the floor, and his eyes were filled with a terrible, aching remorse at the sight of his princess losing her self into the depths of her fear.

Day was slipping into night, and the Riders continued their merciless search through the bastions of rock. Each man shielded his eyes from the insistent stabbing of flecks of sand that came roaring by them on black winds. A terrible storm was brewing out over the graying desert, beyond the maze of boulders all around them.

Desmond wrapped his thick cape around his head to ward off the sharp pain of the flying debris. He vaguely remembered the bright royal purple color it had once been, but this journey had long ago worn away its luster. This was Serepta's fault. She had taken this away from him. In his frustration, Desmond kept grabbing hold of smaller boulders in the narrow pathways and furiously struggling to the top of them with all his strength, only to allow himself to sink back down once more in defeat.

"Your Highness, we have to find shelter and wait out the storm!" the soldier Justinian bellowed over the roar of the winds.

Desmond turned on him with an evil glare. "Nowhere! We are going *nowhere* until the princess is found. I will not go one more day without her!" he shrieked.

The herd of men behind him let out grumbles of despair, moaning like injured cows. Ratinka stepped forward, black wisps of hair flapping around his head like a warped halo.

"I assure you, Your Highness, the princess isn't going anywhere in this storm. And it looks like we aren't, either!" the captain cried, craning his head to look up at the narrow strip of filthy sky that glowed between the cliffs of rock on either side of them. The vision was eerie and phantom-like.

Desmond seethed quietly for a moment, tension rippling through the air as he ground his teeth together. Finally, weakly, he announced, "All right, men. Find us some shelter to weather the storm."

Ratinka let out a contented grin as he fell in line at the head of the Riders. As they filed into a small worn out cave in the boulder beside them, a furious molten rage began to bubble up inside of Desmond. He hated feeling weak and hopeless, and these feelings were worming their way into his heart.

Suddenly, the prince drew his great silver sword from its sheath and swung it with all his might against the ugly rock face. Bursts of white sparks erupted in the coming blackness of the night, causing showers of light to dance across the prince's twisted face. A tremendous, echoing crash resounded off the rock walls and rang over the howl of the storm.

Desmond lifted his head to roar a single word of rage against the fury of the black winds.

"SEREPTAAAAA!!"

The princess let out a cry when she heard a terrible ringing crash burst forth outside her cave. She closed her eyes tightly and burrowed herself against the snug rock face.

Rafe leaped up and began to pace nervously about the dusty floor. Every howl of the wind caused his blue eyes to dart frantically about and his hackles to rise with the electricity of the gathering storm.

Serepta tried to hush the voices of fear in her head, and she conjured up peaceful dreams in the darkness. The princess dreamed of their little cave all made up with the fixings of a home, and she pictured herself serving food to Rafe in the back corner. That would be the kitchen.

"Oh, Rafe, we can have a beautiful life right here!" she murmured sleepily.

Suddenly, with a thump and a rumble, the wolf landed beside her face, roaring with fury. The princess snapped back into full consciousness to find Rafe's lips peeled back in an enraged growl, his eyes narrowed to slits.

Serepta leaped back with surprise, huddling against the cave walls. "What... what are you doing, Rafe?"

The wolf's face seemed to wrinkle and fold as his anger intensified. After a moment of staring her down with trembling cold eyes, he finally turned away in disgust at her new cowardice. Dust leaped up in hazy clouds around his quivering paws as he sauntered away.

Serepta pulled a hand through her ragged hair and stood up to face him. The princess knew deep down what was bothering Rafe, and it was pecking away at her bit by bit. That foreign creature called fear was inside of her now, but it had become her friend, and she was loathe to let it go.

"I don't...I don't understand what you *want* from me," she began, her head craning with exertion. "There's nowhere for us to go. We can't go back. It would be impossible. And we can't go forward!"

Rafe whirled around to face her again, a snarl on his lips.

"Well we can't!" Serepta cried. "The only way is through the desert and the desert is all quicksand. If we were to try, we would fail for sure. And we can't even leave this cave because Desmond and the Riders are probably camped right outside our door." The princess' lip began to tremble at the thought, and she sunk back down to the floor.

"I can't face them...I just can't face them...." she whimpered. A part of her relished the drama, the feeling of admitting for once that she wasn't all powerful, the revolutionary notion that there was nothing to make her keep trying anymore.

Rafe leaped back at her and snapped his teeth at her hands, tearing them roughly away from her tear stained face. He snarled at her until she finally peeked back up at him.

"Look, wolf, I'm doing the best I can for us. I'm just trying to make the best of a bad situation. I've done all I can! I'm so *sick* of trying..." Her head began to droop again like a dying flower. She felt a little quiver in her heart, as though a tiny part of herself disagreed with her words, but it was soon smothered and drowned with fear. Fear of trying, fear of failing, fear of quicksand, and fear of ever facing Desmond's cold gray eyes again....

But Rafe was looking at her with the same chilly stare. He peered into her eyes, deep within them, past the layer of tears and fear in the thick brown of them, as if he were searching for a part of her that seemed to be lost.

Maybe it is lost... Serepta thought to herself.

A disappointed expression on his face, the wolf finally slunk quietly back to his corner of the cave. He seemed to have given up on her, at least for the time being.

Serepta let out a shuddering sigh and curled up against the wall. The princess was exhausted, and she felt torn apart inside. She hugged her arms tightly around her body, trying desperately to hold back what was rising ever upwards toward the surface. There was no one to hold her, no one who loved her anymore. Her mother was dead, Saba was dead, her father hated her, and even Rafe couldn't even stand the sight of her anymore.

Her greatest fears and her deepest wounds began to rip open. The chilly memories of loneliness and abandonment began to tear gashes through her heart till the point where she could take no more. The part of her that had once wanted to go on had fled from her entirely. Serepta's last thought before she fell into the depths of sleep was: *That part of me is lost forever...*

Ratinka sat in a heap of wet black clothing in the cave by the fire. Exhausted, nerves wrangled, the captain dug his fingers into his hair. Noticing the glances made by of his men, Ratinka quickly assumed a more confident position once more.

Green eyes flared in the firelight as the captain looked around. What had once been a proud company of the most elite soldiers in all of Shamar was now reduced to a band of wet, tired, and horseless riders. Many of their comrades had been lost along the way now, and the rest were beginning to forget what it was even like to be home.

Perhaps there is a good reason why we haven't ventured outside our city gates in centuries, Ratinka thought. These men were weak and pitiful when it came to travel. The captain ground some dirt between his fingers. Each bit of brown dust was another man beneath him, another one he could smash into smithereens. They would be lucky to get stuck under his fingernails. Ratinka laughed.

Desmond, silently huddled against the opposite wall, gave the captain an evil look. For a moment, their eyes locked, shards of green glass against solid gray ice. Tension crackled across the cave, and even the flames of the campfire seemed to leap up. Finally, disgusted and in thought, Desmond flung on his cloak and went out into the storm.

What a troubled young man, Ratinka thought with a sneer. *Certainly not one fit to be king.*

With Desmond out of the cave and underlings all around, Ratinka settled down into a dry corner and wrapped his dark cape around him. The black was soothing, and it would take him into sleep.

Chapter Twenty-Two

Arise, cowardly Princess, get up off the floor
What now seems to be lost shall be found once more
Turn obstacle into advantage, that is your chore
That which seems like a wall is really a door...
Find the ship of sunken dreams, for it shall fly once more
Dream the dream, live the dream, and then the dream shall be yours...

    Serepta suddenly sat up straight as the sound of lightning exploded through the air. Her limbs felt dull and heavy, weighted with the pain of her own failures and fears and doubts. She shook her head to clear away the numbness, and she felt the very electricity in the air send a tingling shock through her entire body.

    Thoughts...more and more began to flow faster and faster through her mind; the shock had dislodged a boulder in her head, and a great river of thought was freed at last.

    Why am I here? a tiny Serepta began to march about in the princess's mind, throwing up her miniature hands in frustration. The clouds of dark sleep were still sliding about.

    You are here because it is safe. You are here to seek shelter, a louder, deeper voice echoed. The essence of wisdom and age flowed with its words, and it came from somewhere deep within Serepta's sleeping heart.

    No! Why am I here? the little one continued to question, pacing about in the darkness.

    You are here because there is a storm and the Riders and a desert of quicksand outside, and there is much fear within, the voice replied.

    But why? Why am I here? the tiny figure beseeched one last time, eyes pleading for the answer she was desperately seeking.

The louder voice was silent for a moment. Its eyes turned inward, gaze penetrating every thread of Serepta's being, searching among every feeling and motive she had ever possessed. But the voice was Serepta, and it felt naked under its own eyes. Still it continued to search. The truth was there, waiting like a flash of gold in the dark recesses of her self.

Finally, with great certainty, the voice began to speak.

You are here because you could not stay in Shamar. You have seeds of greatness within you, ones that were not meant to bloom in the desert. You are seeking your greatness where it lies. You are chasing the part of you that leads you ever on and upward. Your soul is seeking love...

And then came the feeling, the tingling, the pounding of her heart heralding aloud the news from her soul. Its triumphant cry reverberated off the walls of her self, softly awakening each and every fragment of her being.

The princess was quietly awake now, in a cave, miles and miles from home, and a smile was spreading across her face. Why was she here again? Serepta suddenly remembered a time that seemed so long ago. The princess had sat by her precious window, looking out at the world she could see but never touch. Sitting there dreaming of hope, of adventure, and of finally finding love, she would have given anything just to live out her life...and that was why she was here.

Awake, and inspired, she leaped up to her feet.

The princess took a breath of the smoking wet air deep into her lungs and felt it refresh her to the core. She stared around the tiny cave, eyes opening with wonder. It was still nighttime, and the rocky walls were painted with dark shadows. It was so small, so cramped.

The princess threw her arms out wide and let out a tremendous, joyous cry.

Rafe's eyes slid open at the sudden sound, and he warily took in the sight of Serepta moving happily about the cave. The princess lunged over to him and cupped the wolf's head in her hands.

"Rafe, I'm back! I'm here. I'm not...I'm not *afraid* anymore," she murmured, brown eyes glowing with excitement. She bounded across the cave as if dancing.

"I know my purpose now. I know what I have to do," Serepta continued. She felt as though she had been slapped in the face by something, and it seemed to have cleared her vision. "I want to go on! I want to live again. I'm ready for it all!!"

Rafe pranced about her, lips peeled back in a grin as he saw his Companion seem to crackle with an electric aura. The princess danced barefoot about their small cave, torn golden dress flinging about, face widening with excitement and daring.

Serepta looked outside the cave into the black dirty storm, and she shook her fist at it.

"Bring it on, world! Show me your worst. I am better! I have fled across a desert, over a mountain, and through a jungle stream to be here, and you will be conquered next! I know now what I am meant to do, and I will do it!" she cried aloud. She leaped over to Rafe and bent down to look the wolf in the eye.

"Come with me, my dear, because we will find a way through that desert if it's the last thing we do! Come with me, and we will find our adventure out in this stormy world," the princess said. Her face had an ethereal, angelic glow in the light of the crackling night sky.

Rafe nuzzled his face against hers, heart trembling with delight. Then the two were off into the storm, never to return to the safety of the cave again.

The princess and the wolf clambered quietly over the rocks and through the pathways and up to the large cliffs. The only sounds in the night were the tread of feet on stone, the dull rumble of thunder in the background, and the insistent flickering of newfound excitement in their heartbeats.

Serepta felt a recurring rush of joy within herself, a newness, a sense of purpose. This was her passion, her adventure. She closed her eyes and reveled in the glory of the moment. It was as though she had an extra limb, some graceful golden arm that was pulling her onwards. The princess felt deep down that there was something to be found out there in that black wilderness, something that could get her and Rafe past these obstacles ahead. With wide eyes and bated breath, they continued to search.

The two ran together along the coast of the sea of quicksand. To one side of them were mountainous clumps of dark rock, and to the other side was the magnificent vastness of the barren quicksand desert. They couldn't go the left, and they couldn't go to the right, so they took the middle path, searching for a solution.

Serepta squinted her eyes in the dark, trying to figure out a way past the oddly shaped boulder just up ahead. It was difficult to see in the moonless night. She glanced up, shivering and solemn at the eerie heavens. The sky seemed to shrink and contract upon itself, wrinkling up in turmoil like a nervous stomach. Enormous, swollen black clouds loomed overheard, ridiculous in their size and volume, thick and ripe with rain. No drops had fallen yet, but the air all around crackled with acidic anticipation and raw tension. The princess hugged herself tightly against the wind and hurried forward to inspect the boulder blocking their path.

Rafe ran ahead excitedly, the black winds wildly whipping his fur back from his features. He called out to her over their rushing noise, urging her to come forward. Serepta ran up to meet him, eyes wide with surprise to find what the wolf had discovered.

The boulder was not a boulder at all, but an enormous ship, an old wreck that emerged from the earth and rock and sand. In awe, Serepta touched a finger to the ship's warped black wood. It was dry and crusty to the touch. Tremendous, thick masts rose up like mountains from its center and wizened old sail cloths flapped in the wind. The yellowed fabric billowed outward like balloons, and every so often, the ship would be lifted upwards, rocking until falling back to the sand once more. The entire ship echoed with age, something familiar yet distant, a powerful struggle and loss.

When Serepta looked at it, she felt a compassionate instinct wrench her soul deep inside. She would never know how it got there. This ship had a story, one that had been forgotten forever. Its life had died out from the world and never could be returned home again.

On its side, some nameless, ancient hand had painted *The Oneiric.*

"*The Oneiric,*" Serepta breathed. "I wonder where it came from…?" she whispered, walking her way around it, examining it from all sides. It was an oddity there.

"It's a ship that sunk in the desert," Serepta murmured with a smile, putting a hand on Rafe's head. *The Oneiric* continued to heave like an ancient rocking chair, its sails lifting by the increasing winds.

The princess wrapped her dress around herself more tightly as she gazed out over the desert of quicksand. The sand was rippling now, sending out murderous golden waves and currents in all directions. The storm was picking up, blocking out nearly all the light and thrusting hurricane-like winds across the cliffs. It was the worst situation possible for traveling, the most dire circumstances for going any farther at all.

"Unless…" the princess thought out loud, her eyes sparkling with the birth of a new idea. Something was turning in her head, a fragile shell of transformation, a reaping change from darkness into light. She clambered up into the old ship and put her hands on the weathered steering wheel, letting bits of a plan begin to take shape in her mind.

The wolf flowed over to her side, letting out a soft whimper in confusion.

He was uncomfortable there, on top of a battered old ship that seemed so out of place in the midst of a desert storm.

"It...still...works!" Serepta cried, grunting with exertion, as she jerked the big steering wheel. Somewhere towards the back, Rafe heard the groan of a rudder pushing against rock and sand. As Serepta moved the wheel, *The Oneiric* rocked even more precariously in the wind. It rose up higher in the air this time before crunching obediently back down again.

The princess shielded her eyes and gazed out over the rippling desert of quicksand, then up at the ominous sky. She seemed undeterred though, almost peaceful, as she turned to face the wolf.

"Rafe, do you see what I see?" she asked him.

The wolf gazed up at her fondly. He didn't think he could ever see what his dear princess saw, not then, not ever. But there was some new spark in her now, something that illuminated her entire being, and something that made him swell with joy just to be near her.

"A ship. A storm. A desert. Each one is an obstacle, but when you put them together...oh, Rafe, we could *fly* this ship over the desert!" Serepta cried.

The wolf's blue eyes seemed to glaze with skepticism and wonder at the same time. He sniffed his way around the skip, struggling to maintain his balance on all four legs as the ship continued to rock in the winds. Was this possible?

"Think about it. The only things holding this ship down right now are the rocks and clutter that it's stuck in. If we could get rid of all that, it would fly! I swear it would! The winds are headed the right way, and I bet we could make it all the way across the quicksand," the princess continued, running a hand down the wrinkled wood of a mast.

"Someone here, long ago, tried to cross and failed. We'll do this for them. We'll make it for them. And Rafe, why sit here when we can fly?" Serepta breathed, stars shining in her eyes as she gazed out over the tempest ahead.

Rafe's mind flew as he realized that it was possible. There was no other way to cross the quicksand, and if they didn't take the risk now, it would be all over. It was a crazy notion...but as long as there was the smallest chance in the world that it would work, it was well worth taking. The wolf leaped forward and took an old rope in his strong jaws to free another sail, and in doing so, freed a part of himself that he had not felt in a long time.

Serepta leaped up and clapped with glee. "We're going to do it! I know we can. We're going to fly over all this mess, together."

Chapter Twenty-Three

Desmond sat huddled at the edge of his cave, clinging tightly to his worn cape for comfort. His brow knitted and his face twisted with consternation as he watched the awakening storm outside wage war with itself. The prince tossed this way and that against the rock, restlessly seeking comfort somehow.

He couldn't sleep. There were too many dimensions of thought and eerie blacknesses woven into the night, ones that caused fingers of ice to tickle down his spine and refused to allow his mind to stop working.

There was something gnawing away at Desmond. It ate him up from the inside out, causing him to twist with a burning hatred and guilt. These two most vile of all emotions bubbled and simmered like a poison within. There was a slippery iciness of a depression clinging deeply to his heart, and each breath required a heaving effort. He sensed something struggling to fight its way to the surface, and it terrified him to have no idea what it was.

"Your Highness, are you all right?" a voice came from behind him.

Desmond turned slowly to find young Admael, crouched tentatively by his side. The prince let out a wistful sigh upon seeing the eager expression painted on the soldier's face. He sensed somewhere deep down, deep underneath the thick ice, that he would never own such a look again.

"I mean...you're not...I couldn't sleep either," Admael whispered. "Can I join you?"

Desmond weakly gave him a crooked smile. "I suppose," he sighed, and turned once again to face the storm.

"If I may say so...well, I think that once this is all over, you're going to be a great king," Admael chirruped, breaking the silence. "And I really do think that we'll capture the princess soon."

Desmond cringed, feeling slathered with the thickening paste of lust and hatred that came with Serepta's mention. A chilling remorse shot through his limbs, and his heart drew back with pain. The prince let out a tight sigh and put his face in his hands. He wanted to cry. Why, why did he always feel so terrible whenever he thought his dream of becoming king was within his reach? What was this feeling inside that pressed him onward, yet stifled him in his tracks?

I don't understand myself... a voice cried within, seeming to crack him in half.

Admael scuttled closer and leaned next to him against the rock. The young man was clearly not comfortable with silence, and he looked as though something important was on his mind.

"I don't know if I'm being forward by asking this, Your Highness, but I'm just going to ask anyways. I mean, I know that Serepta is a witch and all, and I know that you need her to become king, but...but why is it that you *hate* her so much?"

Weary with fatigue and the ravages of thought, Desmond felt that the night was urging him to say things he might not have said in the daytime. But at that point, he didn't even care anymore.

"Why do I hate Serepta so much?" he let out another loud sigh, and in his gray eyes was a refreshing honesty. "I don't know. I just don't know."

Suddenly, a tremendous, wrenching crack was heard over the blustering of the storm. It sounded as though a mountain was heaved up from the ground and thrown over onto its side.

Admael leaped to his feet. "What was that?!" he cried.

"I don't know," Desmond replied, returning to full alertness. "Rally the men! We're going to find out."

Serepta fell hard to the crusty wooden floor as she finally jerked *The Oneiric*'s rudder free from the earth. She was thrown back by the force of the large steering wheel, and a magnificent crack echoed through the air, dirt and dust spraying up like fireworks. The ship declared its long awaited freedom from its tomb of rock and sand.

The princess laughed aloud, pulling herself back onto her feet. The wolf leaped over to her side. They crouched together by the rusty steering wheel, trembling with wonder.

Above them loomed an angry sky, a rotting blanket of black and mottled purple. She stilled to look, to watch for signs. Tiny gashes in the blanket of desolation appeared within the blink of an eye. The clouds opened up, and the winds sighed as rain finally began to fall. The sharp gusts blew the cool drops tingling against the princess's face.

All of a sudden, the great ship began to rise. The wrinkled old sails ballooned out to their former grandeur, filled with the powerful winds of the storm. Serepta clung tightly to the wheel as she felt herself tipping up into the air. Higher and higher one end of the boat rose, its prow pointed like an arrow to the heavens...

But they were still not off the ground. Rafe gave the princess a troubled look, and then he ran across the deck to the back of the ship. They were too heavy to fly. He hefted some old moldy ropes and sails, tangled far beyond repair, and started to shove them out the back to remove some weight. Serepta stumbled back across the slippery boards to help him.

A burst of lightning flashed through the air. The princess blinked hard, trying to clear her sight from the brightness, when she suddenly noticed a swarming clump of black forms wriggling up the ropes still clinging to the sides. Her heart seemed to stop for a moment, and she flinched again, as another lightning bolt burst overhead. This time, she could see the rain slicked uniforms of the Riders as they scuttled up the back of *The Oneiric* like insects.

"Rafe, quick! Throw the ropes all the way over!" Serepta shouted over the winds. Her hands trembled fiercely as she continued to knock the coils over the side. It was no use though, the soldiers were climbing up too quickly, and the ship was beginning to rise...

Serepta gave a desperate glance over the railing. She saw that they had peeled away from the ground, and were now being lifted clumsily up over the quicksand by the winds. The desert waves pinched and roiled dangerously down below. The princess deftly cut one of the thick ropes with her golden dagger, and the scream of the man clinging to it knifed through the air as he fell, only to be quickly swallowed up by the swirling sands. All that remained of him was the ringing echo of his cry.

Rafe let out a growl as the remaining Riders began to swarm over the railing. They hulked in dripping, black clumps all around Desmond and his silver sword. In a flash of lightning, Serepta could see her cousin's face. The prince's wet black hair hung wildly over his eyes, and his pale face shone with drops of rain as he glared at her with all the hatred of a rabid hound.

I'm never going to get rid of them... the princess realized with a sense of cold finality, shivering in the damp of the dark night.

Suddenly, the ship lurched in the air, sending everyone flying across the slippery wooden deck. *The Oneiric* was buffeted sideways by the winds as it continued to rise in altitude, and Serepta was smashed against the railing. Through cracks in the rotting timbers her face was pressed against, she could see the golden cauldron of quicksand rippling way down below. The princess couldn't even see the shore anymore through the torrents of rain. There was no turning back now.

The ship finally heaved over and returned upright once more. Rafe staggered to his large paws and clamped onto Serepta's dress, dragging her safely away from the side. Together, they scurried carefully up onto a higher deck and clung to a mast for stability, as they continued to rock hellishly through the clouds. Freezing rain poured down all around, drenching them to the bone.

"After them! They're at the top!!" Desmond roared from down below, urging his soldiers back onto their feet as the deck buckled and rolled underneath them. The men clumsily began to draw their weapons and stagger up the stairs, ascending higher into the tempest-tossed skies.

Serepta glared fiercely back at them in the darkness, drawing her golden dagger from her hip. She leaped up to her feet on the narrow walkway, clinging to a rope for support.

"Let them show me their worst. I am not going to run anymore," she muttered through clenched teeth, the fighting spirit fully upon her.

The first two Riders made it up to the walkway. Rafe snapped at their heels, driving one of them towards Serepta, and she lashed out deftly with her dagger. One man's foot stepped on a board of rotting wood, and he crunched through, leg pinned to the floor. The other felt the sting of Serepta's blade across his shoulder, and Rafe shoved him over the side, to fall screaming to the lower deck once more.

The wolf let out an excited howl as more soldiers began to swarm towards them. He lunged towards one to knock him over the edge, but at the last moment, the Rider's cold fingers clamped tightly onto the wolf's tail. Together, the two plunged down to the hard deck below.

"Rafe!" Serepta screamed in a panic. She wrapped her hands around the thick rope tied to the mast and tested its weight with a quick jerk. Praying quickly to the gods of protection, the princess leaped off the walkway and swung in a clumsy arc down onto the main deck. She crashed into an old barrel and rolled across the floor.

Dizzy and distorted disoriented, as the ship continued to heave and toss through the blackened skies, the princess staggered to her feet. Through the foggy air she could see Rafe on the other side of the deck. He was fighting off three Riders with ease. The large wolf could handle himself, at least for the time being.

"Aaah, Serepta. Here you are at last," a voice suddenly hissed from behind.

Chapter Twenty-Four

The princess whirled around to find Desmond only a few feet away. His silver sword gleamed in the darkness, illuminating his sallow face with pointed icicles of light.

"I'm not afraid of you, cousin," Serepta whispered, raising her golden dagger.

A little shock of remembrance quivered through Desmond's mind at the sight of the blade, and he flashed back to the moment so long ago in the princess's bedroom. Liquid fury and familiar hatreds began to simmer back up to the surface.

"You should be!" the prince roared, rushing towards her with his sword.

Serepta quickly heaved the old barrel towards him, and it was violently splintered in half by Desmond's blade. The princess's eyes widened with shock as the sound crashed through the air. Then she turned in fright and fled up the staircase behind her.

"That's right, Serepta! Run, turn your back on me like you always do!" Desmond sneered, pointing his sword up at her.

"You can't...you can't *kill* me, Desmond!" she cried. "How will you ever become king without me?" Serepta spat the words at him.

Desmond's eyes crackled an icy gray. "You are just as good to me without an arm or a leg, although it might make things quite complicated in bed."

Serepta quivered with indignation. "Why don't you come up here and say that!" she cried, flipping her hair to one side.

"With pleasure, my lady!" Desmond growled and rushed up the creaking staircase.

Their blades met with a ringing crash as Serepta countered his blow. The prince's sword was more powerful, but Serepta's dagger was more agile. Her blade stung against Desmond's like the flitting of a golden bee, and together they danced in battle up the stairs and onto the thin walkway above.

The princess's wet coils of hair flapped about in the wind and rain, and her heart raced with adrenaline as she stabbed and parried. Her dark eyes locked on Desmond's, taunting him in the deepest way possible. The prince's face began to quiver a bit, and his mouth erupted in a crooked grin.

Desmond suddenly rushed forward, throwing Serepta's hand with the dagger to the side with one strong arm, pinning her tightly against the mast. With the other arm, he raised his sword high to cut off her limb, a glint of cold, perverted excitement in his eyes.

The princess felt as though her insides were melting away with the icky hotness of fear. The nerves of her arm screamed with terror and trembled under Desmond's tight hold. It was the same arm he had broken when she was a child; that same terrible look was in his eye...the lunatic was really going to do it...but no, Serepta refused with all of her might to allow history to repeat itself.

Without even thinking, the princess kicked out one of her long legs. She struck her cousin hard in the chest, and as if in slow motion, Desmond began to stumble backwards across the slippery boards. His eyes bugged way out and he waved his arms frantically in the air, face frozen in a mask of terror, as he struggled to regain any scrap of balance. It was no use, though. He finally fell over the side, screaming all the way.

The prince struck the deck below hard, his entire body shocked with the jarring blow. Then swirling clouds of black took him into their cold grasps, and Desmond knew no more...

...There was darkness, and then there was light. A bold, triumphant light. The prince sauntered his way through the palace rock gardens, closing his eyes to embrace the desert heat on his skin. His heart began to quiver a bit as the familiar old shadow of doubts and guilt peeled back to reveal a brightening within. Joyful thoughts twittered through his mind, and each step on the worn stones seemed like a swelling of an eternity. He looked over at his mother by his side and flashed her a crooked grin.

"Today is the day, mother," Desmond said, and he took her hand in his.

She gave him a weak smile, but her lined face was darkened under the shadow of an old palm tree. The prince didn't seem to notice, though, as they continued their walk to the palace.

He wrapped his purple cape about himself and rejoiced in its luxurious softness. This was the life he deserved, all of this and more once he was made King of Shamar. And today was the day his fate would be sealed. Somewhere inside the magnificent palace, within its ancient walls of marble and sandstone, a council of nobility awaited him and his mother. Together, they would cast the votes naming Raghnall's heir. Today was the day Desmond had been waiting for his entire life.

"Don't you feel it, mother? The taste in the air? It's simply grand! I swear, the gods themselves are probably about today!" the prince smiled, breathing deeply.

But his mother didn't reply. And in her eyes was the most terrible look of sadness her son had ever seen...

The ship suddenly gave a loud groan and lurched to one side. Desmond's eyes flickered open for just but a moment, and he found that he was alone. The old hollow, black boards creaked underneath his limp body, and deep shadows clung to every surface, casting a blanket of darkness over all.

A distant clatter of steel was heard from somewhere else on the ship. There was a battle taking place, and Desmond had been forgotten. The fallen prince felt with a cold sweat as though he were surrounded by ghosts: ghosts of the future, ghosts of the past, and ghosts of the here and now. And with that frightening thought, Desmond slipped back into the world of unknowing once more.

...The prince anxiously dug his fingernails into the peeling gold polish of his chair. He stole a glance up at the circle of nobles surrounding him and felt the flutter of joy within his heart. He couldn't even bear sitting still anymore, and he longed to leap up onto the oak table and declare his ecstasy to all the world.

"The time has come, my most worthy subjects, to name the man who will one day take my place as the high King of Shamar," Raghnall announced from the raised throne on the other side of the table. His jaw was set as firmly as stone, and his voice as regal as that of a god.

"At this time, the supreme candidate is Desmond, son of my deceased wife's sister, nephew to the Ruler of the Realm. The vote shall take place to name him as my true heir, a vote that must be unanimous, as decided by the council," Raghnall continued, ceremoniously pounding a fist against his bare chest. A golden collar vibrated against his aged skin, and for a moment the king seemed uneasy to continue, uneasy to admit that he was the past, and now had to determine the future.

"But I am the future," Desmond whispered, and his mind then seemed to go even higher into the clouds. He had never known such happiness before. As each member of the council began to announce their votes affirming the prince as their choice, Desmond nearly fainted away with euphoria, and his life as he knew it flashed before his eyes...

This was it; this was the obsession that had taken his soul since the day he was born as a high prince of Shamar. This was his right, his destiny. No matter what evil things he had done in his life, it did not matter. His one true wish was about to be granted, so the gods must be on his side after all.

"And for the last vote is Desmond's mother," Raghnall declared, a wry smile etched in his face. His fist clenched and unclenched around his golden scepter. "Sister-in-law, do you vote yes, or no?"

The bright and colorful world slowed down for Desmond, and all the sights and sounds seemed to revolve around that single moment in time. The prince's eyes began to well up with tears at the idea of his glorious future to come. Perhaps his views on life had been wrong before. The world was beautiful now; he wanted to breathe it all in. His destiny, his heart and soul, was lingering on downy wings just inches from his fingertips...

"No," Desmond's mother choked, tears running down her face. "My vote is no."

Desmond suddenly sat up straight in the air, as though he had been shot from a bow. He blinked for a moment in shock. Then the prince's face wrenched with the sudden shock and pain of finally reclaiming this memory, and his body retched with great sobs. Dry, heaving sobs they were, launched from the myriad dark folds that had remained hidden for so long within Desmond's mind. These folds were being peeled apart with cold fingers now, and random explosions set off like mines inside the prince, causing him to kick and jerk in a ball on the old wooden deck of the ship. His fingers clawed into the wood and tore away at its flesh, destroying outward what was already being destroyed within.

The sharp claws of the dream still clung tightly to all of his senses, ripping at the fine line between the past and the present. He was sliding backwards even then, down into the slippery depths of the dark bogs within his soul. These dusty memories had been stored like boxes firmly in his mind, to open and shut upon him without mercy and without reason forever and ever more, a fickle reminder of the day the only person he had ever loved had betrayed him so completely....

Drops of cold rain pattered upon the prince's face, and they yanked him sharply back into the present. They mingled with tears on his trembling cheeks, and the dream had finally left him completely. Desmond sat quivering on the floor, staring at his open palms, praying that his nightmare had truly flown away into the dark night. And it had. The prince couldn't even remember what he had dreamed about anymore. The boxes of memory were slammed shut, the doors to the cellar of his mind were locked, and the lips of his weeping soul were sealed to him once more.

But the terror remained. That nameless, primal fear that when left to rage within confinement will eventually destroy the cage from the inside out. A raindrop, or perhaps a tear, slid from Desmond's face and splattered against his sword, cold and lifeless.

"Nooo!!!" the man roared and leaped up onto his feet. He began to lope across the deck, arms dangling forward like a monkey's. His chest ached where Serepta had kicked him, and an even worse sense of humiliation throbbed underneath. The ship continued to rock and heave as it was blown through the sky, and flashing bursts of lightning caused Desmond to spin around and around in a maddened confusion. Sheets of rain fell like icicles on the deck, soaking everything to the core.

The prince hefted his sword up high and gazed up at its point, mesmerized for a moment by the glistening steel. Another lightning bolt blazed through the air, and then Desmond could see his reflection in the blade.

A vile man stared back at him. Masses of dripping hair, black as the sky when the day has died, clung to a face of shocking white. Purple lips trembled in the snarl of a wounded animal, and it took all the strength Desmond possessed to look himself in the eyes. The eyes...crackling flecks of an angry gray seemed to ripple across a deep sea hurt. They shone with a pain built up from years of hostility, and back beyond their dilated pupils, within the circular prisons of black there was a man who had been caged for as long as he had known life on this earth.

"*I hate you!!!!*" the prince howled, and he swung the sword with all his might against a wooden railing. The steel cut through the rotting wood like butter, yet the horror of the reflection remained, etched into the night.

He had to get rid of it. He had to scour it from his mind. He would destroy that picture if it was the last thing he ever did. Desmond hoisted his sword once more and took off running across the deck, searching for a body to bloody the blade so he wouldn't have to see the reflection anymore.

Chapter Twenty-Five

Serepta clung to the front mast, her face pressed against Rafe's chest. His body sheltered her from the wind and rain as they awaited the next onslaught of attacks in silence. The Riders would clash with them, draw back to lick their wounds and wait out the worst of the storm, and then return again with even greater fury.

And Desmond wasn't gone... although Serepta hadn't seen him since he dropped over the edge of the deck, she knew within her bones that the prince was made like a rope of twisted knots. He was indestructible. He would be back; there was no doubt of that.

The Oneiric continued to swoop and lurch among the thick black clouds. With each creak of its rotting boards and rusted bolts, the ship seemed to be rejoicing in its newfound purpose. But that did not stop the storm. The storm was growing worse, in fact. It was a roiling black soup of poisonous clouds and shards of shattered lightning. Iridescent green and purple light now shone through gashes in the clouds, as though the black gods themselves were waiting on the other side. Perhaps they were, waiting behind their eerie screens and demonic tapestries, waiting to steal away life and hope, as soon as their claws were in reach.

Desmond was reaching now, straining every muscle in his body onward as he jerked and raced across the ship and up the stairs. He flung his sword in all directions, howling like a madman, barely even conscious with the pain of his newfound memories. A whirlwind of destruction burst up in his path as splinters and chunks of the noble wood were hacked away to fall to the deck, soaking and dead forever.

His gray eyes darted all around, furiously seeking the object of his hatred. She was the one he would torture and wound and drag back to Shamar to make her right the wrong his mother had committed against him so long ago.

His mother...the old boxes of memory suddenly slammed shut hard in his ears, blocking him out, causing Desmond to cry out in pain. There was more...more that even still he couldn't remember...the poison of frustration and guilt seared through his veins and drove him even madder.

"Serepta! Cousin! Show yourself!!" he roared, pounding onto the upper deck.

The princess's eyes widened in horror when they finally locked with Desmond's at the top of the stairs. Time seemed to stand still for one chilling moment as the brilliant bolts of his hatred shot through her heart like arrows.

Serepta suddenly noticed the path of destruction behind him, the parts of the ship that he had razed to the ground, and tears began to fall down her cheeks. He had torn up the deck so terribly that it never could be fixed again. The poor pieces of wood rattled across the deck, severed forever from *The Oneiric,* yet struggling so hard to rejoin it, if only to offer their meager help in fulfilling its purpose. If *The Oneiric* could not have its chance, then maybe Serepta couldn't either. Hope had fled away into that dark night.

"You're evil!" she sobbed. "You're an evil man!"

The words Serepta spat seemed to deepen the look of pain in Desmond's eyes, and he suddenly rushed towards her with the force of a cannon ball. Rafe let out a cry and pushed the princess away, shoving her out of the prince's path. Now was not the time to fight; now was only the time to keep the end in sight; now was the time to climb higher, to new heights....

Serepta and Rafe raced over to the nearest mast and grabbed onto the netting. Then the princess lifted her head against the rain, against the storm, to peer through the darkness at the splintered remains of a crow's nest high up above.

She felt suddenly as though the touch of wisdom was rippling through her body, like that when she grasped her tiger's eye. In that instant she knew within her heart that they would find safety there up above. It was the only place she could be safe from Desmond's murderous wrath, because something seemed to have snapped in him, and not even Rafe could protect her anymore. They would have to climb all the way up the soaking old mast to reach the wooden basket, and sever the ropes that had led them there, and trust in this one final effort to make it to the highest point of the ship. They had to leave Desmond behind, and climb into the tempest that awaited above, into that one miniscule shot in the dark they possessed.

Serepta knew that one shot in the dark was her life and Rafe's, and she was willing to fire it with all the strength she had left. Together, the princess and the wolf clambered swiftly up the mast and finally collapsed, gasping, into the tiny wooden basket high above. With his last ounce of strength, Rafe bit through the netting with his teeth. Their only ladder back down to the ship below was now gone forever.

Serepta sat huddled in a daze in the crow's nest. She crouched there, filled with wonder at escaping Desmond, finding herself at the top of everything that she had ever strived for in her life. It was the highest point of the ship, the highest ship in the world, flying higher than any storm or bug or bird had ever dared. It was humbling, yet glorious up there. She and Rafe were finally safe for the time being, with nothing between them and the gods themselves but a few wisps of wet clouds. The feeling consumed her in an ethereal daze as nature blazed all around.

The princess stood up on shaky legs, wrapping her arms tightly about the spindly wooden railing as she gazed up at the heavens. Her mind seemed to transcend her body then. It drifted away on a stream of golden thought, pressing ever upwards towards the twinkling stars. She could not see them through the twisted black clouds, but she knew with the undying faith that only a human could possess that they still awaited her reach. She could never truly reach out and touch them, but it was her fate to try and try as long as she had life in her body, to pick up the task that every human left behind when they died without ever touching their stars....

This was it, this was her soul and her quest, and this was her life that perched in a wooden basket so very far from where she had started out. Serepta grasped the feeling and bathed in the glory of that moment, for in that moment, she was above the storm, and above the men that scurried like miscrable ants across the deck below.

The men cursed up at her and hacked and sawed at the mast with their swords. Rafe growled at them in return and paced about in a rage. Desmond sobbed and sobbed and pounded his fists against the column, wailing with this new failure, as the rains continued to pour down over him. Serepta would always be just out of his reach, and there was nothing he could do about it.

The princess heard his cries from her throne up in the clouds and a growing smile slid across her face. As it did, waves of warmth and joy blossomed through her body. The princess took Rafe in her arms and held him tight, wanting only to share the birth of this feeling with her friend, and he nuzzled his head against her.

The wings of Serepta's soul, ones that had remained folded and atrophied with fear within her heart, now began to unfurl. She felt her spirits spread out like those of a newborn bird in flight for the first time, and they soared higher than she had ever felt before. She was free to live exactly as she pleased, to learn and to love, or to die if that was to happen. Life and death didn't even seem to matter any more as her heart and Rafe's continued to swirl ever higher into the skies.

"Land! I see land!" a soldier cried from below.

Serepta, exhausted and spent beyond belief, thought she saw a rippling glow from behind the clouds above, and then she could suddenly remember the most glorious song of all:

Arise, cowardly Princess, get up off the floor
What now seems to be lost shall be found once more
Turn obstacle into advantage, that is to be your chore
That which seems like a wall is really a door...
Find the ship of sunken dreams, for it shall fly once more
Dream the dream, live the dream, and then the dream shall be yours...

The princess's face slowly lit up and the bright gold of her smile was reflected in the warmth in Rafe's eyes. They had made it over the quicksand. They had done the impossible, they had tried the untried, they had passed the one great test the gods had delivered unto them and would now be delivered to greatness because they dared to dream.

The old ship continued to rock and groan through the clouds as the sight of stable land past the quicksand and rain began to grow in the horizon. Serepta felt a quick tremor of fear in her heart. If *The Oneiric* didn't come down soon, it would lose the support of the winds and crash to the earth. Serepta and Rafe would be killed.

She put a hand on the wolf's head. But then, what did it matter? They had most certainly done more than anyone had ever done before.

Chapter Twenty-Six

Desmond fell in a heap against the mast, the splinters of soaked wood scraping the skin of his face as he dropped. He had no will left to stand. Instead, he balled up his tunic in his fists, shaking with sobs as he huddled in a fetal position on the deck. And just as one finds it impossible to pinpoint the moment in which they fall asleep, so did the prince find himself slowly drift off into the familiar world deep within his subconscious.

...Desmond squeezed the cloth of the tunic tightly between his bitten nails, deeply agitated. He raised his hand to knock upon the door of the throne room, but the king's guards swung it open before he could touch the wood. They cocked their spears and gestured down the long hall.

Raghnall sat upon his throne at the empty end of the jeweled chamber. His body seemed to be fixed to the hard gold of the throne, and Desmond wondered if the king ever left it. The prince cringed bitterly, supposing the business of kings was no longer his now.

"You may approach, nephew," Raghnall declared. His voice was as hard as his eyes, yet as Desmond stumbled toward him, he saw something new in his uncle. For some reason, the prince could detect a hint of fear, of apprehension, as he moved closer toward the king.

"How are you?" Raghnall asked. His finger tightened around his scepter, and his eyes darted to check the position of his guards.

"Fine," Desmond replied. But fine was a word that meant betrayed in the worst possible way.

"I understand you must be quite...disappointed," Raghnall fumbled for the right word. Desmond was silent.

"The council failed you and failed Shamar. However, there is still a way you may yet become king. I will have no other as my heir. All my life I have struggled to keep a strong monarchy, and I will not have my labor go to waste. I will not have an heir who is not willing to work hard for his kingdom, or to use whatever means necessary to do so. And you, certainly, have proven your prowess in this area." A hint of that same apprehension appeared in Raghnall's black eyes once more, something that Desmond could not understand.

The prince opened his mouth to speak, but then faltered. His limp heart was still too numb to feel any genuine curiosity over this new prospect. His emotions had been shot. Raghnall continued speaking.

"The laws of Shamar state that there are two ways to become heir to the throne: be voted unanimously by the council, and the other, the one for which I called you here today, is to marry a princess," Raghnall said with a hiss, providing fertile ground for Desmond's thoughts.

The prince closed his eyes, and he saw Serepta. He saw her dark hair shifted by the desert breeze, and her dark eyes as she glanced up at him. As she had grown into a woman, the prince had found himself eyeing his cousin more and more. A tentacle of lust shot up in Desmond's heart.

"So you will give me your daughter then?" the prince asked coolly.

"She is yours. You may do with her as you wish. Ever since her mother died, I have had the ultimate say in who she will marry."

"What about my mother? She loves Serepta, and I am sure that goody-goody will object to me marrying my cousin. She never wants anything that will make me happy," Desmond said bitterly.

Raghnall's jaw twitched. He stared down at his nephew strangely, as though Desmond had just said something very odd.

"My sister-in-law doesn't have anything to say about anything anymore," Raghnall replied, the fire returning to his hard eyes.

Desmond bowed lightly. His mind had already been stirred up like a dirty puddle, and he barely heard the rest of Raghnall's words. He turned to leave then, to digest this new card fate had handed him, to plan his next move. A leaden hand on his shoulder stopped him. Desmond gasped, never having felt the cold touch of his uncle.

"I will protect you and cover up what you did. No one will ever have to know," Raghnall whispered into his ear, and with a flick of the scepter, sent Desmond out of the room.

The prince stumbled into the hall. He winced in confusion at what Raghnall had said, and why the King seemed to fear him now. But try as he might, the memory evaded his grasp...

Ratinka seethed as he paced back and forth across the deck. His men were confused and disorganized, set upon by fear and a sense of failure as they flapped about the ship like dark wet crows. Desmond seemed to have left their hell for his own private one. He fell leaning against the mast in a catatonic state, tears still and cold upon his face.

"Soldiers! Riders of Shamar! Rise up, we have not lost yet!" the captain cried, trying to bring them back to attention.

They let out moans of protest, some staring up at the princess and wolf so high above them, others sinking to the soaked floor as rain continued to pour down over them. The glory of flying a ship up into a storm and over the sea of quicksand seemed to have left them entirely, leaving nothing behind but hollow shells of men.

Ratinka knew then that all was lost. The Captain's emerald eyes darted anxiously around the ship as he ran a hand through his ragged black hair. Desmond had lost all sense of what was going on around him, and the men would not follow Ratinka. Their lack of faith was a hard blow to the captain's pride. He sank to the floor in a daze, slowly drowning in thought and despair.

It was impossible to reach the witch and her wolf at the top of the mast. And as the sight of dry land continued to swell in the horizon past the clouds and rain, it seemed even more impossible that they would ever be able to land safely. So what, what then? Would they all die? Would they all rot away in this foreign land with no one to ever find their bodies? Would Ratinka never get his one and only chance at ruling Shamar, at spreading their kingdom east into these new lands?

The captain let out a howl of frustration as he stared at Desmond's limp body.

"You fool!" he shrieked. "You fool! You could have her, but you're giving up! And we're all going to pay for your *weakness*!"

The prince didn't respond, and continued to stare into space with blank eyes.

"I'm better than all of you! I don't deserve this!" Ratinka screeched, slamming his fist against the old wood as he glared around at the Riders. "I could have been great! I could have gone down in the records as the greatest king Shamar has ever known! And now what? I am left to this hell, this rotting old ship flapping about in the storm until it crashes to the ground and all of us die!"

Even as he spoke those words, *The Oneiric* lurched and dropped a long way down as support of the winds buckled underneath it. The closer they got to the land, the more the storm thinned out, and the ship continued to spiral downward.

The Riders let out cries of panic and curled up in balls in the shadows, clinging tightly to one another, sobbing out prayers to the gods of protection. Ratinka continued to cry and rage and slam his fists against the deck, furious at the fates that had brought him to this place as they continued to drop even farther out of the sky. They would crash soon, and it would all be over. Everything Ratinka had ever struggled for in his life, all of his plots and schemes, would be for naught and nothing would be left but the echo of his screams....

Ratinka was screaming louder now, not even being able to fathom why, until he saw a familiar shadowy figure stride across the deck and disappear into the lower part of the ship. The captain shrieked and tore wildly at his hair, at this phantom that had haunted him for months now, that even in these last moments of his life would not give up. Ratinka twisted up on the ground in pain and fright as the shadowy man vanished to the deck down below, leaving him to writhe in the poisonous puddle of the last remnants of his miserable life on this earth.

The Oneiric then slammed into the hard, rain soaked ground, and wood and dust burst up like an explosion all around. A jarring shockwave of force rippled through the ship, and darkness consumed them all.

Chapter Twenty-Seven

Up a mountain, through a stream, and over a desert flown,
From what I can see, O Princess strong, how great your spirit has grown.
This journey is not over yet, there is one skill left to hone
Listen to that which comes from the heart, and that is all you need to know.
The time has come to take what you've learned, and make the power your own,
And when all is finally said and done, meet me in the Pyramid of Stone...

A tiny sliver of bright blue pierced Serepta's eyelids and pulled them apart with a gentle warmth. The princess blinked hard, slowly, feeling a quiet rush of joy, as she was filled with the sight of the cloudless new sky above. She was alive, for some inexplicable reason. Serepta felt different, as though something had shifted inside of her. She felt...older. For once, her thoughts were quiet, and her emotions were steady. In the stillness, peace prevailed. It suited her and refueled her. Serepta was alive, and a brand new day awaited her.

Rafe lay next to her in the dirt, great chest heaving with exertion after the crash. Serepta could see that he was exhausted. The wolf's beautiful fur had lost its luster, and his fair features were drawn tight and pale. As she gently urged him awake, she awakened for the first time to the devastation all around her.

The Oneiric rose jaggedly from the sand like black heaps of broken glass. Scraps of wood were scattered everywhere, twisted and warped with the damp and heat. The sails dangled limply from wizened masts. Even the steering wheel was falling apart, and Serepta knew then that the ship was dead.

The princess clasped her hands together, quietly staring at the ancient structure, as the breeze rustled gently through her hair. She whispered a silent prayer in her heart for the ship, but felt no sadness. *The Oneiric* had done what it needed to do. The noble wreckage had lifted itself out of the trap on the other cliff, soared above the most frightful storm possible, and made it to the glory of this golden desert. It had fulfilled its purpose, and that was all that mattered.

The wind, the sky, and the sands under Serepta's body ran like a river into her heart and stirred her deep within, lifting her head up off the dry ground. This was a different place she found herself in. It was a new desert, a solid one, and it was drenched with sunlight all around. The bright golden light lifted Serepta up to a tentative crouch as she reveled in this foreign land.

Dunes of tawny sand rose up for miles all around like sculpted waves. These were real though, nothing like the fake pools of quicksand she had crossed before. Faint rippling patterns of the wind echoed across the surface, but other than that, the desert was empty. It was empty of life, yet somehow throbbed with vitality, emanating a nurturing essence capable of supporting even the smallest being. The key was simply in getting there...

The sky peaked high up above in a rich blue dome and melted down to meet the desert at the horizon. The horizon was perfect; impossibly far away, but always there and always a constant line. Serepta thought that the myriad dunes would disrupt the line where land met sky, but she realized that as far as the eye could see, it all evened out in the end.

One point far off in the distance stood out as she gazed across the glimmering sands. Serepta squinted hard and brushed the grime away from her eyes to look harder. Slowly, as if watching clouds move across the sky, the princess could see the image of a tremendous pyramid appear, standing above the desert.

The pyramid rose majestically in the distance like an emperor surveying his lands. No, that wasn't it. It was more like a great philosopher standing at the height of his accomplishments, peering over a stack of knowledge at the vast wisdom he commanded. The pyramid came from nature, perfected it, rose even up above it, and in doing so, made the world a better place. It was greatness embodied in the ancient stones of the desert, and Serepta knew that she was drawn to it like a wolf to the moonlight.

The princess's eyes wandered farther. In the dark recesses of the body of the ship, she could see the still forms of fallen men. Some were alive, some were dead, but their black presence had followed her still. And Serepta knew in her heart that Desmond was alive. No matter what, he would always come back. He would always come back as long as she ran, as sure as cold winter pursues the fleeting summer.

That was when Serepta knew that the running had to stop, right then and there. Desmond was her burden, her nightmare, her greatest fear in this world, and she would have to deal with him once and for all. The princess knew that between her and the pyramid there was only open desert, and if she chose to run, he would follow. And she would rather die than taint those hallowed stones with the evil presence of her cousin.

Serepta rose to her feet and stretched. Her arms tingled as they flung way out into the sky, seeming to cast off the heavy cloak of fear that had enveloped them all her life. The princess reveled in the touch of the sunlight on her naked skin as it tasted the sweet gold for the first time.

This is what life is about, this growing and shedding of skins, Serepta thought to herself. She knew that as long as she had breath in her body, she would continue to do so. The princess would have to shed her old skins and emerge reborn; not once, not twice, but as many times as she was called upon in the series of events that was life.

Rafe leaped up to her side, and Serepta knew she was ready for the final confrontation. And if there were any doubts left in her mind, they were wiped clear when she noticed a tiny purple flower sprouting valiantly up out of the desert sands...

Desmond emerged from the wreckage, clawing and tearing at the broken boards and filth. He seethed under his black cloak, blinking under the bright light of the sun. The searing heat blinded the prince and made him dizzy.

Slowly, his men began to pull themselves out of the ship. They were dirty, bruised, and battered, but quite alive. Ratinka seemed to be more anxious than usual, jumping at the sight of any shadow. His green eyes darted about the rotting boards, seeking something and coming up empty as he picked compulsively at his tunic.

The sounds of a breeze drifting high overhead and the droning sizzle of burning heat on the sands greeted Desmond's ears as he staggered farther away from the ship. The cloudless sky shone blue up above, so blue that none could bear to look at it for long. Other than the movement of his men, everything seemed to be empty.

Emptiness was all that the prince felt as he stumbled out into the desert. His mind seemed to be slipping away from him, riddled with befuddled imagery and worn bits of old memories. Desmond couldn't feel anymore...his senses were burnt out, razed to the ground, and he rang with a cold detachment. That and the desire to kill.

Desmond felt bitterness rise up in the back of his throat, as though he had vomited up old feelings from the past. Serepta lingered on the edge of his consciousness, burning a hole through his weakening exterior. But he had the upper hand now. The prince's eyes slid across the desert, and he realized that she couldn't run far in its vast openness. In fact, for once, she hadn't run at all.

Serepta stood atop a nearby sand dune, dark against the glowing halo of sunlight all around her. The wolf stood large and protective at her side. Her golden dagger was ready in hand, and both princess and wolf were ready to fight.

A crooked grin slid across Desmond's face as he drew his sword from its sheath. His men soon realized what was happening there on that small dune, and they fell into formation behind him.

The time had finally come for Desmond to claim his princess.

Chapter Twenty-Eight

The prince strode forward with great purpose, his men trailing behind him like froth in the wake. Shafts of sunlight echoed across Desmond's unshaven face and danced among the golden sands, rippling like waves under the hushed glory of the sky. The great dome of blue rose high above, illuminating the land with its brightness. All of nature seemed to fall into silence as the Riders of Shamar came forth to the bottom of the dune.

"Are you finally ready to face me now, Serepta?" Desmond questioned, voice ringing peculiarly in the cool air. His shadow flickered sharply over the ground.

The princess glared down at him, dark eyes glancing back and forth as she surveyed his features. She hadn't taken a good look at him in months. His face seemed to have changed. There was a haggard emptiness in his look, a ring of cold exhaustion. The skin around his eyes was the color of dead leaves. She knew those eyes, those familiar flecks of icy gray. They had petrified her in childhood and haunted the caves of fear within her mind for as long as she could remember. But Serepta's eyes were steadied upon them for once, and she stood ready before him.

"I will not run anymore. And I will not go back to Shamar. And there is *nothing* you can do to stop me. If you try to kill me, you'll never become king," the princess flared, stating calmly what she knew in her heart to be true. Rafe stood firmly at her side, and his warm solidity under her hand seemed to feed her strength. She had longed for months now, to speak these words to the prince. Along the way, she had become caught up in the escape, and the escape had brought her there.

Desmond flashed her a crooked grin. His soldiers began to squirm with hatred for the witch, and swords flashed in the hot sunlight like the gleam of a dozen fangs as they were taken from their sheaths.

The princess stood firm, however, atop her dune. The prince squinted up at Serepta. He was unused to seeing her standing so calmly before his gaze. On this journey, she seemed to have finally grown a spine to back up her sharp words, but that would soon come to an end.

"Ha!" Desmond cried aloud. He took a moment to examine his silver blade, testing its edge for sharpness. Then he suddenly whirled around, eyes transfixed upon his cousin, brimming with a cool hatred. "You think I need you to become king? The only thing I need is to see you *dead*," he snapped.

Serepta stared down at him, face tensed with confusion, as he began to pace about the sands.

"I don't even know why I kept you alive this long. Don't you realize how simple it would be to forge documents saying that we got married out *here* in this hellhole of a desert? Of course, I had planned to do the whole wedding thing, and the wedding *night*, but the sight of you really does make me sick now," the prince babbled. He was tired of this hunt, so sick and tired of it all. Seeing Serepta standing before him loosed a poisonous hatred upon his soul, and he relished this new look of shock on her face.

Serepta's grip on her dagger seemed to loosen. "You...you actually think my father is going to believe you? He knows I despise you," she said, trying to keep her voice strong, though it wavered with new fear. Fear was beginning to burn away at the edges of her proud exterior.

Desmond picked casually at his fingernails. "Even if he doesn't believe that we got married and you died *tragically* on the way home, he'll make me king anyways, once he sees all the lands I've claimed."

"Lands?" Serepta breathed. She blinked hard, staring blankly ahead, as all the power and strength she thought she once had slipped through her fingers like sand. The princess was left empty and motionless upon the dune. It was Desmond now who held all the power in his grasp. He was going to kill her, and he would still become king. But that wasn't all.

"Yes, the lands I've claimed. No one has inhabited them for ages. It is time Shamar moves from its gates and claims what is rightfully ours!"

The princess clutched at her hands and blinked in horror. All the lands she had passed through, all the glorious places she had seen, were soon to be consumed by Shamar. That hideous kingdom with its rotting institutions and rotten inhabitants would spread eastward into the lands of her journey, destroying everything in its path. And Serepta suddenly knew that she wasn't just fighting for her life anymore.

Desmond was destruction incarnate. Everything he ever touched turned to a festering black. Serepta's heart raged silently when she thought of Shamar spreading like a cancer into her lands, and her golden dagger seemed to rise by itself into the air.

"I will kill you first!" she roared, words flying through the air like electricity. Rafe sprang in front of Serepta, blue eyes flaring, as the wolf prepared to slay anyone who came near. The Riders lifted their blades in response and charged up the dune.

"Soldiers! Kill the wolf!" Desmond commanded, but he need not have spoken. The band of men flooded in around Rafe in attack. The wolf leaped with alacrity into the soldiers, eager to help his Companion and finally taste the blood of his hunters. Serepta could hear the sound of claws on armor as Rafe fought at the bottom of the dune, and she trusted in his ability to handle the Riders. Now was the time to focus all her attention on Desmond.

O enemy of enemies.... Serepta thought to herself, heartbeat thundering in her ears.

"The time has finally come, cousin," Desmond whispered, and suddenly leaped up onto the dune, flinging off his black cloak. His silver blade seemed to fly through the air of its own accord, metal singing as it crashed into Serepta's dagger.

The princess felt the blow reverberate down her arm as she jumped backward. Together, the cousins circled one another about the dune, hearts racing and weapons stabbing in all directions. Sweat dribbled down Serepta's face as she leaped about the sands. Desmond was strong and wiry, and he was well trained in swordplay. Perhaps even worst of all was the surprising lack of emotion on his face.

The prince swung and stabbed his great blade, features devoid of any passion. Staring into his eyes was like staring into the empty sockets of a skull. His entire body, his entire being was focused with all its might on the dance of battle. Without emotion, there could be no weakness...the thought sent Serepta spiraling into a fearful daze. Fighting Desmond was like trying to pick up a piece of broken glass; it appeared transparent, but there were jagged edges everywhere, just waiting to cut you.

Rafe's snarl of rage from down below snapped her back into clarity. She could not give up, not now. Desmond's sword was bearing down on her, and her weakness was beginning to show, but she could not give up.

"It all comes down to this, eh? Come on, cousin! Your soldiers are watching," Serepta mocked, struggling to keep her voice strong. She saw a fit of emotion dance across Desmond's countenance, but his sword was steady as it stabbed in all directions. The princess leaped back, a smile playing on her face. For a brief moment, she had seen a loss of concentration in Desmond's eyes. There was weakness there, and she would have to tweak at it.

The silver blade swung at her, again and again. Desmond's sword bore down on her in a cold fury. His body ached to destroy her. If she wanted to play games, he was more than willing to join.

"You know, your father never has loved you. You were simply a brooding mare for the kingdom," the prince mentioned calmly as he thrust his sword towards her.

Serepta felt the point of the tip pierce the front of her dress as she leaped back. Her reaction had been lagged by his words, and she trembled with nausea as a thick trickle of blood slid down her stomach. The prince was a clever man. He was playing her game, using her emotions against her...the princess fled across to another dune, regathering her wits like a shepherd herding his flocks about him.

"Yes, and I wonder who father will name heir once I have escaped and you are dead!"

Hatred seemed to crackle through air, prickling the hackles on the back of Desmond's neck. The prince was stronger than Serepta, but in her eyes, there was a fierceness that rattled him terribly. There was something deep within him, some nameless parasite of emotion that burrowed itself even deeper into his soul the more he stared at her.

Desmond suddenly lunged across the dune to join her. He swung his silver blade, and sparks flew as it struck her dagger. Thoughts and ideas and patterns from old sword training pulsed through his mind as he ravaged it for archives of psychological weaponry. A box of memory was flung open, and he grinned, presented with the most lethal possibility imaginable.

"You know what I'm thinking about? I just can't help but to wonder how our dearly departed grandmother is doing in the land of the gods. You must miss her terribly," the prince's voice dripped with sympathy.

The breath of air in Serepta's throat suddenly snagged, as if caught on a hook. Her entire body tensed. It began to crumble then, piece by piece, as she reeled in shock at his words. Her hand instinctively flew to the pendant around her neck, and her soul betrayed her then.

Everything came flooding back to her...Desmond beating their grandmother again and again, forcing her frail body to the dusty floor, and finally the sound of the rush of wind echoing around Saba's body as it fell...

Her stomach leaped into her throat, and she grew insane with fury. Serepta's blade faltered for a moment, and then she suddenly lunged at Desmond with all her might. The prince struggled to parry her blows as she whirled about, so filled with rage that she was barely even conscious. Serepta felt the cool tiger's eye stone bounce across her throat as she moved and tears of indignation stung in her eyes. Pain welled up inside of her, and her body shook with hurt.

Desmond grinned, taunting her, prodding her deepest wounds with each look, and Serepta knew that he could see her cracking inside. She took in a sharp breath and slowed her dagger, struggling with all her might to hold back the emotions that bubbled to the surface. She had to hold them back…it had all come down to this final battle…everything she had ever done and tried for swung on the delicate balance of this fight, and if she could not be a more skillful actress than she had ever been in all her life, everything would surely be lost.

Desmond's gray eyes darted sharply back and forth like the jerk of a pendulum as they watched the moves of her golden dagger. The princess smiled, fighting to hold back the bitter tears that pooled in the corners of her eyes.

"I'm pretty good with this thing, aren't I? I would have thought you would have remembered that, after our little incident in the bedroom. You seem to have a problem with the word 'no.' But that's okay," Serepta began, heart leaping with joy as she pulled off the dialogue with perfection. "We can keep that our little secret…"

Desmond suddenly drew back, losing some grip on his blade. His eyes fluttered and twitched as the biting memory of the golden tip at his throat replayed over and over again in his mind. The very sky seemed to twirl around above him, and he stumbled about in shock at the feelings that began to pound through his veins. Hatred rose like a wave deep within his throat. Burning hot lava seeped around his blackened heart, flowing more fiercely than he ever had felt in all his life.

Then Desmond's countenance grew rigid as he snapped back to full alertness. Suddenly, he kicked sand up at Serepta's face. The princess stumbled backward, clawing at the sharp flecks in her eyes. Desmond roared and moved in on her with the flat of his blade, and he slammed her in the side with all his might. The cold metal exploded against her body with the force of a battering ram.

Serepta crumpled to the ground in pain and shock. Her eyes burned and her side throbbed as blood began to seep out. When the princess's sight finally cleared, she could see the point of Desmond's silver sword hovering right above her bobbing throat. Her heart felt as though it stopped in that second. The sky and sands all around seemed to fall into a deafening hush, watching in silence at the battle of the fates unfolding before their gaze.

Chapter Twenty-Nine

Desmond stared down at Serepta for a moment, relishing finally seeing her lying before him in fear. He prodded her throat with the sword tip, and then he began to speak.

"How does it *feel*, cousin?" Desmond whispered slowly, taking his time, enjoying himself immensely. Dark shadows played across the prince's face, clinging to each enraged feature as he leaned in close. His face twisted as he spoke.

"Did you really think you could win? I'm a desperate man, Serepta. I have nothing to lose and everything to gain," Desmond murmured, his words oozing from a festering wound deep within.

The words didn't make sense to the princess, until she detected a quivering voice of the broken man inside of him. For reasons she couldn't understand, she realized her cousin didn't even value his own life anymore. How could she possibly know of the nameless vultures of emotion that had picked away at his heart for months? Serepta tried to speak, but the shaking of her throat caused her skin to drag across the sword tip.

"Now. Cousin. Here is what's going to happen," Desmond began, speaking more to himself than to her. "I am going to slit your throat now. You are going to die, and I will become a happy man. Then your wolf will die, too. Maybe I'll make him into a nice new cape, if his pelt isn't completely full of holes. Yes, that's a splendid idea. My purple one is ruined, thanks to you. And then…let's see…ahhh, and then we'll go back to Shamar. I will hold a funeral service for you, being the dutiful widower I am, and I will *finally* become King. Isn't that wonderful? And *then,* Serepta, *then* I will lead Shamar in taking over all these new lands. Does that sound good to you?" he asked, leaning his face in next to hers, blasting her with his foul breath as he dug the point a little deeper into her neck.

She let out a terrified squeak. Time seemed to slow down all around her, revolving around the icy silver point that pricked into her throat like the prodding claw of death.

Serepta shut her eyelids tight and shivered. She was surprised to find a great sadness begin to take over her soul in those last few moments. It swam like a dark ocean wave through her body, sweeping through every inch of her being, seeming to wash away everything she had ever felt and was.

Serepta realized that for once this sadness was not for herself, though she knew she would surely be gone in moments. Her heart felt sick with grief over the lands that would soon fall into the grasp of Desmond. The mirror-rocks of Morad that had reminded her who she was...the fairer side that had brought her the child...the beautiful stream of Jimakana, where she had lost her soul and reclaimed it once more...even the desert of quicksand, for without it, she never could have attained such heights. The Kingdom of Shamar would spread through them all like a disease, destroying everything it touched, and it made Serepta want to cry.

Through the warped noises that echoed all around her, through the thundering of her heartbeat in her ears and Desmond's own rasping breath, she could hear the dim sounds of the battle taking place below. Rafe was down there. Rafe was fighting alone against the beasts.

Serepta cringed. She loved the wolf with everything she was and would never be able to tell him. Her heart was made sensitive with this cleansing grief, and the princess could feel the tug of her Companion's presence on her soul. It beat with every quickening touch of her pulse, slowing time all around as it sped up.

So this is love.... the thought slipped through her mind. If she was destined to never have found her soul mate, the wolf would have been enough.

Hot tears welled up in her eyes when she thought of her soul mate lost somewhere out there in the big wide world. It might have taken her a lifetime to find him, but whoever he was, he was worth it. For better or worse, her life was still worth it....

The princess fiercely shut her eyes and felt the coolness of the tiger's eye on her chest. She focused all her attention on its smooth touch and dug down deep into the stores of knowledge her mind held. The princess reached, strained, prayed, and ached with everything she had for a bit of an idea that could save her life, because there was no time left for her in the world.

Serepta's eyes suddenly snapped open, and she took in a shuddering breath. There was still one more option. There was one last weapon she had left in her arsenal, one last arrow in her quiver, one last shot she thought she would never have to use against her cousin because it was impossible to predict the shattering explosion there would be...

"Go ahead, Desmond. Kill me. Kill me just like you killed your mother."

Chapter Thirty

"What?"

The word slipped loose from Desmond's mouth, tumbling outward from a pit inside his stomach.

Serepta blinked hard underneath him. "You heard me," she whispered.

The silver blade dropped to the sand with a dull thump. The princess let out a ragged sigh of relief and sat up slowly. She couldn't even believe she was telling him this. This story, this wretched history, had been chained in the basement of her mind for so long that it almost seemed unreal to be finally telling him. His mind was surely dangling on the precipice of insanity, had been for some time, and Serepta was terrified to send him over the edge.

The prince stood motionless in front of her, face a mask of white shock.

"We were never supposed to mention it again," Serepta began hesitantly. Each word was tensed with anticipation of a sudden outburst from her vile cousin, but still it did not come. "Under the threat of death. My father said he would kill anyone who said anything about it to you, because for some reason, you just couldn't remember after it happened."

Desmond's eyes rolled back and forth in his head, and he felt as though stitches in his mind from long ago were starting to rip open, black thread unraveling all over his senses.

Serepta saw that she held him captive by her words, so she continued. "It was after your mother voted for you not to become the heir to the throne. She knew your soul, knew what you were capable of, and she couldn't bear to let you into power. So...you killed her. My gods, you *killed* your mother. And afterwards, you didn't even remember a thing. My father covered it all up, because if you hadn't murdered her, he probably would have. He wanted you as his heir that badly. You ended up doing the dirty work for him," the princess reflected bitterly. Her words came forcedly from her mouth, and Serepta didn't know if what she was doing now would simply delay her own death. But time gave her hope, and the final release of the truth fed her courage.

The truth...the truth was this still life of Desmond standing catatonically over his cousin, while she told him how he murdered his mother. It was not real. The prince was inside a glass case, watching the scene unfold around him, and the walls kept pressing in closer and closer. Serepta's words were dull blurs, like the thick pounding of wood against cotton. Meaningless. They couldn't be real, not without the memory.

"Shut up! Just *shut up!*" the man in the glass box heard himself bellow. He sank to his knees in the sand and put a quivering finger to Serepta's lips to silence her. In an involuntary bolt of rage, he suddenly slapped her across the face. She dropped to the sand in terror, crying, crying....

... "Desmond... my gods! I could go on for years and years and never be able to tell you how sorry I am!" the prince's mother sobbed. She wrung her hands, searching frantically for the words to apologize for ripping her only child's dream away from him. The words dropped like boiling oil onto Desmond's soul, sizzling as they burned away into a smoking blackness. He stared blankly around his mother's chamber and realized he didn't even remember coming up there with her after the council meeting.

"Speak to me. Say something," she begged.

But Desmond could not think; words could not form in his mind nor spring from his lips. He was made empty with her betrayal. He was drifting a million miles away from her, floating upon a sea of flickering rage.

"Desmond! Son! Please," his mother dropped to her knees on the marble floor. Her tears smeared his tunic as she hugged herself against his legs.

Those arms...those trembling things, those poisonous snakes, those limbs of a blackened tree...they dug deep into Desmond's legs and inflamed his soul. This side of her was nauseating.

"Get up, mother," the words fell from his mouth.

She stared up at him with tearful eyes, not daring to believe he was speaking to her. After a moment of silence, she staggered to her feet.

"I know this is terrible for you, but I know you will get past this. You will move on with your life and find something you are more suited to do. You must believe this. I love you, I love you more than anything else in the entire world!"

"Oh, and I love you, too, mother," Desmond replied, voice devoid of emotion. He pulled her into a hug, and, embracing, the two moved out onto the sunny balcony.

The old woman squeezed her son tight and then tried to release herself. But Desmond continued to hold her in his arms.

"What is love?" his words sounded peculiar in the cool breeze outside. "Is love… is love this… this thing I feel inside of me?" Desmond asked.

"Yes, I know you still love me deep down," she murmured against his shoulder, grateful for his touch.

"Does it… does love come in waves that seem to tear you apart at times?" the prince asked.

"Yes, love sometimes does feel that way," his mother replied, anxious now, trying to free herself from the Desmond's hug that was lasting too long. But still he held her tight.

"And does it ever climb into your soul and whisper into its ear, telling it to do things that it normally wouldn't dare?" the prince beseeched.

"Yes, love does. And you should always listen to what that voice tells you to do. Desmond, son, let me go. You're hurting me."

"Then I must do what my voice is telling me to do," Desmond whispered, and he pulled her even tighter to him.

The old woman's heart beat frightfully against his chest, and her fingernails dug into his back as he continued to squeeze her tighter. His muscles clenched and shook, as he struggled to bring her even closer to him, so close that perhaps she could hear his thoughts and feel his pain and know for once who her son really was.

But then, no one did.

Desmond began to move towards the edge of the balcony, dragging his mother with him. They moved together in a demented tango, each one struggling against the other. Desmond was much stronger than the elderly woman, though, and that voice whispering inside his head blocked out any cries of protest uttered into the still air.

There was a scrape of silk on stone, as the woman's back finally came pressed against the railing. She saw in Desmond's eyes what he was going to do, and then her eyes bugged way out of her face. Her countenance was distorted with abject terror, and she fell limp against the body of her son. The old woman wet herself, and it dribbled all down her legs.

"I love you, too, mother." He kissed her cheek, and then gave one last shove.

"Desmond! Noooo!" her scream shattered the sky into millions of little pieces, and the rippling wind around her falling body whistled like the shrill cry of demons, etched into the glassy blue twilight.

It was then that the boxes of memory slammed shut in Desmond's mind, the bolts twisted in, and the locks secured, to torture him with this secret forever more...

Reality began to sift slowly back in, blown by the soft winds across the open desert. Desmond was lying in the sand. His fingers curled around it, and he clenched the grainy flecks between them, embracing the painful scraping across his skin. His face was buried into the ground, and sand was bitter in his mouth. Sand was harsh against his bare skin, and it seemed to find its way into every line and crack. These sands of the desert were everywhere, inescapable in the end.

Desmond lifted up his head. Serepta huddled warily in front of him, and the terror in her eyes reflected the prince's twisted shock. He sat there for a moment, eyes closed, and he could feel each and every surge of blood his weakened heart pumped through his veins. Trembling, the prince stared down at his hands. Then he looked at Serepta's.

Hands are all hands but for the tasks they have wrought in this world... he thought to himself. And then he hated his. He hated the misshapen palms with sand forever embedded in the lines, he hated the grayish bony knuckles, and he hated the fingers that twisted with their own sins.

The prince's insides folded and wrinkled like a dripping wet cloth as he stared at Serepta. With a tremendous roar, he suddenly clawed his fingers deep into the dust. The princess leaped back in terror, and then Desmond hated what he had become.

He was the most vile creature the gods had ever set forth on this earth. He was a demon flung from the bowels of hell to torture those who were good and just. He was ugly, and Desmond cringed with self-loathing. He closed his eyes tight to shut himself out, but it did no good. Wherever he went, there he was: a wizened empty husk of the soul he had never possessed. And now he would bear the image of his mother with him always.

"I *remember*," he finally choked. The rush of stale wind trapped in old boxes of memory wheezed out as it tasted the air once more. The words came out of Desmond's mouth, burning like the seepage of blood from an old wound ripped open. His guilt, the pile of black knots that had been twisted up inside his heart for what seemed countless eons, began to unravel and spread throughout his being. They melted his insides and wrenched his limbs and racked his body with great sobs.

Serepta tried to speak, but she couldn't find the words, and for a moment, she felt as though she could almost feel a fraction of the pain he was feeling. Her body ached with it, and for the first time in her life, she was surprised to feel a searing sense of pity for her miserable cousin. She couldn't understand it. He was cruel, he was a vicious murderer... but he was also a human being, and he was suffering.

Tears rolled down Desmond's cheeks, as if even they fled in horror from the cold touch of his skin. Each drop was a tiny splinter of his soul, and the guilt was expelling it all. It forced the tears to fall from his eyes and the weight of his head to feel huge. The prince's head bowed as he knelt forward, blood thundering in his ears. He had come to a point in his life where he no longer seemed to exist anymore; he had forfeited that right long ago. He hated himself now with such certainty, with such passion and such fervor, that it was as though he no longer even *was*...but Desmond could still feel the touch of sunlight on the back of his neck, and it felt good, as he bowed down before the heavens. It cooled him like the healing kiss of the gods.

Something changed in Desmond then. For one sweet, brief moment, the prince hoped that his nature had changed, that he was no longer evil. But that wasn't it. His heart had been decaying all his life and could never be repaired. No, this change was different...for the first time, he was finally made aware of himself and his intentions.

A shaft of light seemed to pierce through Desmond's being, and its golden brightness blinded him. He retreated back into the dark recesses of his mind like a rat into a sewer, his old rotting dwelling places familiar. He could not face its purity, not after facing the horror that was himself. But the great light continued to sweep forcefully through it all, into every dilapidated cranny, expelling the darkness and clearing out the battered old boxes of memory. As Desmond sat kneeling in the sands before all of nature, the merciful touch of this release seemed to wipe him clean. Sins of the past fled away into the air, their black tails whipping him like a thousand lashes as they flew by. The guilt began to dissipate, buckling under its own weight, folding away into oblivion. All of everything seemed to finally be gone, empty, and only one question remained.

"What is there left for me to do now?" Desmond whispered.

Serepta's chest tightened at the remorse in her cousin's voice. His pain was nearly visible in the glowing desert heat as they sat huddled together in the sand. She wanted to speak, but her mouth seemed to be glued shut.

Desmond's eyes flicked up at her, and incredible hurt shone in the icy gray. "My gods Serepta...my own cousin is terrified to speak to me," he murmured. The prince let out a haggard cry. "It wasn't *you* I hated...I loved you, I wanted you, I needed to have you with me. My *mother* loved you," he choked.

Serepta was quiet.

"And I hated you! You started the madness; you awoke it inside of me...you dared to tell me no...you...you looked at me the same way that *she* did," he continued. His voice rang with complete exhaustion.

Serepta was still made speechless by her cousin's change. She did not need eyes to see that something had transformed in him. Something had come, something had left, and Desmond was a different man. The princess tried hard to look upon him with the same consuming hatred she had felt all her life, and for once, she could not find it. She reached blindly for it with outstretched fingertips of logic, and it eluded her grasp. But Serepta had learned to trust herself above all, above anything, and she knew that somehow another bit of herself and her cousin was emerging new.

"Desmond...you can still...it's...it's not *over*. You speak like there is nothing left for you anymore. You could still have a life in Shamar without me, without these lands. Just go home," Serepta murmured. She put down her dagger. Its cold glint seemed useless now, almost shameful in its violent promise.

"There is nothing for me there, or anywhere. My life...it's like an endless night where I just can't fall asleep...I have no future, and if I do, I loathe it. Every waking moment is *agony* for me. There's only one thing left for me to do now, can't you see it?" Desmond cried. He saw the beauty of it, and it could have blinded him with its goodness.

Serepta was quiet for a moment until his meaning finally washed over her.

"No. No. You can't...you can't give up yet...you can still change; all of us can. I see it everyday. You can change!" she babbled, surprised to find herself actually pleading with Desmond to save his life, but she didn't even care. For she had changed, too.

"Change. Ha! Look at me," Desmond spat, staring at his quivering hands. "I am a rotting puddle of stagnant water," the prince said. Then his voice grew calmer.

"Finally, I am to pay for my sins...I must know for *once* in my life what it feels like to do the right thing," he whispered, voice strung tightly. His eyes were blank and staring as he picked his silver sword up off the ground. He felt the weight in his hands, shifted its coldness back and forth like it rested upon a scale, a light of peace in his eyes.

Serepta stared back at him, surprised to find her eyes welling up with tears, for she could see his soul had already died and left him long ago. All that remained was the mortal shell, empty and aching to go.

"Desmond, no...please, no...just go home!" she begged, trying to take the sword away from him, but he brushed her hand aside.

Tears shone on his face, and his tears were redemption. For once, his homely features glowed with peace. He would never know happiness in his life, but for now, perhaps peace was enough.

Desmond ran the silver sword deep into his body and finally fulfilled the need to bloody the reflection he once saw in its surface. The pain, the sins, would end now. The prince fell down dead into the sands of the desert, never to change, never to feel, never to hurt anymore.

Chapter Thirty-One

As her cousin fell to the ground, Serepta unleashed such an anguished cry from her lips that her very heart shook with it. She reached for Desmond, but it was too late. The prince was already dead.

The princess knelt, trembling in the sands beside him. She took his hand in hers, tears of shock rolling down her cheeks. Blood ran in warm rivulets all down his arm, but the skin underneath was cold and hard. Serepta cradled Desmond's hand tenderly as she stared down at it. These were the hands that had shattered a little girl's arm with a rock, the hands that had murdered his own mother, the hands that had beaten Saba to the ground, the hands that could have ruled over all of Shamar. But they were also the hands of her cousin. This blood, *his* blood, that ran in warm rivers all down his arm, flowed through her veins, too.

Serepta looked at Desmond's fallen body, and she shook with great sobs. A part of her was dying with him. She saw him lying there in the sand and saw herself in the heart of her enemy. Who was she to say she had never felt cold ambition driving her every move? Who was she to say she had never let her emotions run rampant over her soul? Who was she to say she had never allowed herself to hate? No, had little things gone differently in the course of events that was life, it could have been her lying there instead.

"You could have been so *different*. My gods, you could have been great...." Serepta mourned. Her words, simple as they were, served as an epitaph for him. There was nothing left for her to say anymore, no more words to leak from the pain of all that could have been.

The sun was there, and then it was not. The princess glanced up from the ground to find the Captain of the Riders suddenly standing over her. His mass of dark hair eclipsed the bright heat of the sun. He pointed his sword down at her, reality returning in the sharpness of the silver.

"Princess, I am impressed," Ratinka smiled.

Serepta's eyes flickered up at him. She didn't like the cold ring in his voice, his indifference to the broken body lying before him. And she was tired, so tired.

"Desmond is gone. Go home. Leave this place," she commanded. She needed time to mourn for the cousin she had never even known. A breeze rippled across the dunes, silently stirring the golden flecks.

Ratinka fell quiet for a moment. He closed his eyes, tasting the wind against his worn skin. At the bottom of the sands, the battle between Rafe and the Riders had subsided for a moment, as they both peeled away to lick their wounds. Some fell about to sit in the shade of the wreckage of the ship, and others gathered in closer to leer at Desmond's fallen body.

"Go home. Go home? What is home?" Ratinka spun around. "All I have eaten, slept, and breathed for months is this hunt!" His glittering green eyes narrowed as he gazed down at Serepta. "Home? No. I will not go home. Not until you are dead."

At those words, Rafe struggled to pull himself up onto the dune. The wolf was beaten bloody from the battle, and he staggered onto the edge of the sand. His eyes met with Serepta's, and together they nurtured each other with that one look.

"Why do you care if I am dead? Have Shamar! Take it. I will never return with any claims to power. Judging by your uniform, I'm sure you have wriggled your way into a high enough rank. You've earned that horrid kingdom," the princess replied.

Ratinka kept his sword trained upon her. "It's not as simple as that. You see these men here?" the Captain gestured around at the ring of soldiers. "These are my men. My loyal Riders. Their prince lies dead at their feet because of you. You are a witch, just like your grandmother before you! Now what kind of a future king would I be, if I didn't destroy your evil?"

The remaining Riders jeered at her and slung their weapons through the air.

"You have cast your vile spells upon me, sorceress. The shadow man you sent has been hunting me for months! I haven't had any peace!" Ratinka added in a harsh whisper, voice trembling with rage. His words rang like the vibration of cold steel, and he was entranced by this chance of final retribution for his recent lunacy.

The princess stared back at him in confusion. Then her heart suddenly grew heavy. She saw Rafe struggling to move closer to her, and the wolf's pain became hers. The creature was a mass of fur matted with blood, and his face was bruised with dark contusions. She could feel the dull ache of his wounds and the trickle of blood across his fur. She could feel his presence rippling through the still blue air, and the way it crackled like a cool electricity. The Riders were approaching, but Rafe was nearby, and that was all that mattered.

Ratinka suddenly grabbed Serepta's forearm with one hard fist. The wolf was waiting for this. Quicker than his injuries should have allowed, Rafe lunged from the ground and soared towards the Captain. In an instant, several Riders were there to meet him. Their blades slashed in all directions, searing through fur, tearing across flesh, and Serepta felt each cut like a knife through her own skin. She let out a ragged cry of anguish, and then everything seemed to go into a blur.

Ratinka's cold fingers pressed deeper into her arm, the weight of iron in each touch. He lifted his sword high in the air. It swung down in a deadly arc like a waterfall of silver, and just before it reached Serepta's head with that final ending blow, something very strange seemed to happen.

A bolt of oak wood suddenly grew out of Ratinka's chest. It pushed forth like a seedling emerging from the crusty soil, and in moments, the Captain's body flopped limply to the sand. The wretched man had only enough time to let out a screech of protest. Perhaps if he had more time, his scathing eyes might have seen at last the error of his ways, and how everything he had wasted his life trying to gain was stripped from him in that last moment. Blood flooded in dark rivers over the ground, and the Riders flew about in confusion.

Serepta's pulse thundered in her temples as she leaped up to her feet. Her darting eyes, swimming in the heat and hysteria, were drawn towards the wreckage of the ship. There, emerging from the bowels of *The Oneiric*, was a man in the tattered rags of what used to be a uniform fit for Captain of the Riders. His dark blond hair was plastered to his face, and his features were lit with the joy of a triumphant warrior. He was the man who had finally fulfilled his promise to himself. He was the man who had haunted Ratinka for months now, his shadow ever present, as he followed the path of the Riders. He was the man who had lost everything he ever had and regained it in that instant.

"Sanjay…" a soldier murmured.

The man called Sanjay leaped from the hulk of the ship. His muscles trembled and he clenched his jaw tight to keep it from chattering, to keep it from spilling out the joy that threatened to tumble from his mouth. His lips had not uttered a word since the betrayal, not once, as he had tracked the path of the Riders through the wilderness. Glory gripped his chest, and pride made him move out onto the sands. The warrior ripped his spear from his slain enemy's body, and he sounded a great cry to all the world. His bellow was like the explosion of warm rocks tumbling down a mountainside.

The Riders began to tremble and quail.

"But...but we killed him!"

"That must be the shadow man Ratinka said was following him!" another cried.

The Riders disintegrated into abject terror at the sight of their old Captain living and breathing before them. Dust flew into the air as they scrambled over the dunes, and their cries disturbed the stillness of the desert as they fled. Serepta could see every muscle tense in the man called Sanjay. He wanted to chase them, hunt them down, and kill them, as he had finally killed Ratinka. But he had the power of self-restraint in his quiet warmth. Instead, he leaped down from the ship and knelt at Serepta's feet. Shaking, he carefully touched his dirty lips to her feet.

"Your Highness, I am here to protect you," Sanjay whispered.

Serepta put a hand to his sunburnt shoulder and bade him rise. "I don't...I don't understand. Who are you? Where did you come from?" the princess asked. Her head was still numb from what had just happened, at how she had just seen the pointed glimpse of death over and over again that morning.

"My name is Sanjay. I used to be the Captain of the Riders until that man betrayed me. They all thought me dead, but I have been hunting them all along, waiting for the right moment to strike," the man replied. His voice was strung tightly with emotion, but in his face there seemed to be release, as well. Staring into his face was like staring into the trunk of a solid oak tree, brilliant in its aliveness and powerful to the core.

Serepta gazed around at the vivid array of colors surrounding her world, drew in a deep breath of the desert air, and felt as though her entire body rang with gratitude at simply being alive.

"You saved my life," she said. The words flowed out, affirming what was right and true in the world, burying Desmond and Ratinka into the sands and scattering the Riders like motes of dust on the wind.

"It was my duty," Sanjay replied firmly.

"If it was your duty to protect me, then where have you been all along? Where were you on the ship? And where were you now, while I was fighting Desmond?" Serepta found herself asking. She did not mean to sound ungrateful, but she had a thousand unanswered questions.

"Throughout your journey, I followed every step of the Riders. I never let Ratinka out of my sight. I haunted him, and made him begin to doubt himself, but I knew I could not kill him until the right moment. It had to be at a time when he would have everything he ever wanted stripped away from him in one moment, because that is what he did to me," Sanjay said. His light eyes danced with what he knew to be right, to be justice accomplished at long last.

"As to your question of where I have been all along, I have been sabotaging the prince and his men. I clouded Ratinka's judgment. I cut down the oak tree that kept them from capturing you at the edge of the forest. And on the ship, while battle was taking place above, I was lashing down the sails and steering us in such a way that we all were not killed during the crash. No one even noticed me during the fierceness of the storm," Sanjay continued.

Serepta silently took in all that he said, and she was beginning to understand this man who had saved her life. In fact, she did not even need an answer to her last question, but he chose to answer her anyway.

"And finally, I did not interfere with you and Desmond, because that was your battle to fight, not mine. We each have our own battles and enemies we must face. Mine was Ratinka, and that is why I chose to step in when I did." He felt alive, safe, and powerful with the accomplishment of his purpose. Satisfied at last, the warrior slung his oak spear over his broad shoulder.

"Wait! Where are you going?" Serepta asked, as the man turned to leave.

"I have done what I came to do. Isn't that all that matters?" Sanjay asked, a smile emerging on his face.

Serepta glanced over at the wreck of *The Oneiric*, and she smiled, too. "I understand. But...where will you go?"

The man squinted out across the desert. "I'm going to follow the Riders. I will help them find their way back to Shamar. But don't worry. They will be sure to know that if they ever speak of these lands to anyone else, I will be waiting for them out in this wilderness. I will protect these places, and I will protect you."

"But why do you want to help them if they betrayed you?"

"They are not evil, just weak. And I am strong. The strong must protect the weak, always," he said, shouldering his spear. "Goodbye, Your Highness, and good luck."

And then he was off into the desert. Soon, his faint image had faded far away into the hot air flickering above the dunes, gone as quickly and mysteriously as he had come. Their fates had become tangled together for a brief time, a crucial time, but now his was leading him elsewhere. Serepta was left alone, sitting upon the sands in a daze. The princess found herself wondering whether the encounter had ever actually occurred.

"That man is so brave. He saved us, Rafe," she whispered.

There was no reply.

"Rafe?"

But the wolf lay still upon the golden dune, quiet and deathly cold.

Chapter Thirty-Two

The heap of silver shone up from the dust of the earth, its rippling sheet of fur interspersed with jagged bolts of blood. Those eyes, those sparkling eyes of a brilliant turquoise sun were closed shut to the world.

Serepta frantically crawled over to Rafe and put her ear to his chest. It was still warm, but she could almost sense the life inside of him flowing out onto the sands. There was scarcely a breath, and her nerves screamed with it.

Serepta tore at her hair and cried up at the sky. It curved perfectly dull blue up above, its skin unwrinkled and untroubled by the events playing out down below.

"Help me! Oh gods, somebody, please!" the princess shouted. But there was nobody there. Sanjay and the Riders were long gone by now. She was alone in the middle of the desert and Rafe was hurt so very badly and she wanted to save him, had to save him, but she didn't even know if he was already dead...

"Is there anybody left? Is there?" she sobbed wildly. Her mother was dead and Saba was dead and Desmond was dead and the Captain of the Riders was dead and if Rafe died would he just be added to the laundry list of fatalities?

"Not him! Not him, please!" Serepta screamed up at the sky. She put a hand on Rafe's head and smoothed down the mussed fur of his forehead. The princess tried to look down at him, to search for any minute sign of life, but her eyes were overflowing with desperate tears and were of no use anymore. Her mind was of no use anymore. She couldn't even comprehend the possibility of living without the sound of Rafe's feet padding alongside her, without the familiar glint of silver in the corner of her eye. The wolf had come with her everywhere, down into the bowels of hell and back out again.

"Bring him back to me! Or take me, too. We can have adventures for all eternity in death together, but don't you dare take him away from me!" the princess begged.

This wasn't meant to happen...she was meant to go with Rafe to her oasis and finally be safe there. That was the point of it all, wasn't it? The point of this impossible journey? But Serepta couldn't tell, because the only point of anything there ever was in the entire universe was that her dear Companion was lying quiet on the sands. It was wrong. Her heart screamed to her that it was wrong. She wanted to lie down alongside his body and die right there in that desert with him but her heart screamed to her that it was wrong....

Up a mountain, through a stream, and over a desert flown,
From what I can see, O Princess strong, how great your spirit has grown.
This journey is not over yet, there is one skill left to hone
Listen to that which comes from the heart, and that is all you need to know.
The time has come to take what you've learned, and make the power your own,
And when all is finally said and done, meet me in the Pyramid of Stone...

"The pyramid..." Serepta breathed. Her dark eyes sought it out on the horizon, and there it stood, peaceful and waiting like a sentinel of security. If there was any chance at all for her and Rafe, it awaited her in the pyramid. The woman of the song awaited her in the pyramid.

The princess glanced down quickly at the wolf. Every second that passed, more of his precious life left his body forever. She had already wasted enough time. But would he even survive the trip, this one final run?

Serepta looked up at the pyramid again. It seemed impossibly far away, over miles of mounds and dunes of thick sand. The very sight of it sent a shiver of exhaustion through her. The princess slid her hands under Rafe and cradled the big wolf in her arms. It seemed unfathomable that she could find the strength left in her body to carry him all the way across the desert, but her heart was placing her on the starting line, giving her the signal to go, and that was enough.

Hugging the wolf tightly to her chest, tears falling down her cheeks, Serepta took off running with all her might toward the Pyramid of Stone.

Chapter Thirty-Three

Thud, thud, thud – one foot after the other, as the princess strained forward with every tiny bit of herself. Her bare feet were seared by the hot sand and the muscles inside of them were forced to work like frantic shovels, carving away at the thick earth with each step, tearing chunks away from the surface so that she could only keep on running. Rafe's limp, broken body was the weight of the world in her arms. She hugged him tightly against her chest, feeling the soft fur against her skin, struggling to feed some of her strength to the wolf. She would give all for him, give anything, but the pyramid was still eons away...

"There's nothing left!" the princess let out a heaving gasp.

Those words took a huge gash out of her, and she fell silent once more. The only sound was the ragged sigh of her breath, wheezing like a torn flag flapping in the wind. The world around of gold and bright blue swam together and danced around her pulsing head. Her heartbeat drummed against the hardness of her ribs, pounding through her body. What was feeding her heart? Where could it draw its strength, when there was none left? Her body rang with total exhaustion. Every cell in Serepta screamed for her to sit down and rest. They begged with her, pleaded, all the while collapsing and committing suicide and feeding off each other, scrounging for any ounce of energy left, any crackling ripple that might force her aching muscles to take one more step.

She had never known such agony before, such brutal sparring between her body and emotions, such vicious warfare that played out within the battlefield of herself. Serepta would go on though...the princess saw failure glinting out of the corner of her eye and she raced ahead, clenching her jaws and shutting her eyes until that possibility was left far behind. No, she would not fail. She could not fail. She could not do her best either, because Serepta knew then that her best was not enough, not nearly enough to save Rafe in time. She would have to push herself over the peak of her best again and again and again. She saw the limits of her own self and knocked them down, tore them down frantically, for all the necessity of life.

The pyramid drew closer.

The bright yellow-white fireball of a sun cast its rays down upon her body. Serepta was drenched all over in sweat as she kept up a dogged pace. Her head swam with it, and in her delirium, she found herself flickering back and forth from Shamar. Shamar – the land of stones worn weary with age, and soil barren like the face of the moon. Nothing would grow in the cold marble corridors; nothing would nurture them there. But Serepta had planted seeds there long ago, seeds of rage and fear and bitterness and hate. They had stayed dormant under the icy dirt, until this journey had come and torn up the dirt and ravaged it over and over again until it became something else. The seeds were gone; they were blossoms now, of love, and strength, and courage.

Running across this endless sea of a foreign desert, her thoughts were befuddled, but everything now made sense. The journey seemed so fragile to Serepta. It was the edge of a dagger, a flimsy screen that could be flapped back to reveal a life underneath that never would have been. Never would have been. She would have been asleep in Shamar under a starless sky with Desmond beside her and a body chilled and cold but now it was Desmond who was chilled and cold and she was beside herself, holding her own hands and pushing up on her body to keep it from caving in. This was the purpose...to run by herself and know herself like this for once. Serepta had known this when she left Shamar eons ago, but there was a difference now. She was no longer running *away* from something, away from someone. She was running *to* something, with someone. She knew the purpose and the purpose did not change but grew deeper, grew thicker with dimension that could not be denied.

The pyramid drew closer.

Saba probably knew all these lessons from the start and could have told her, but it would have meant nothing without the experiences. The experiences had etched them within her soul. The experiences were life, and the purpose of life was to snatch up as many of them as possible. Maybe someone should have told her mother that before she caved in and died, without ever tasting the sweetness that could have been her own life to hold.

This is life...

Serepta was running and dying and using up every bit of energy there was in the world and the weight of it all was in her bare, smooth hands. The weight of love was in her hands, the solid fluid pulsing beauty that was love. Her skin thrilled with its touch.

Strands of dark hair, plastered with beads of sweat and sand, lashed her face as she ran. It felt as though her head was melting around the edges. Her eyelids bore the weight of a thousand mountains, and her lips were as dry and cracked as a sun-baked plateau. Her body was falling apart bit by bit, self-destructing. Serepta knew she could keep running forever; it was when she would finally have to stopped that terrified her. Her entire body might crumble into pieces. But as long as she kept running, feeling Rafe's warmth in her arms, she would hold together. Everything seemed to make sense under the thick clouds of heat and feverish wisps of delirium. Thoughts blipped through her mind like pebbles being tossed about in a wild river.

The sands of the desert were underneath her dirty feet. Her feet trod them down into the dust because the ones on the surface didn't matter; it was the darker hidden ones below that held the support of the world and kept it from caving in. Serepta could feel her own sands within, keeping her own fragile body shell from collapsing and melting away into nothingness.

It was the sands that meant everything, that had set her on the path. She had found them and they were hers and she was theirs, and together they could do magic in the world, magic for the wolf who was dying, dying, deadening and there was almost no time left. Time was falling apart as it screeched to a halt and ran underneath her and hauled her over a mountain just to prove her strength and pulled her down the length of the river to test its vitality with her own and hurdled her over a desert just to see how high she could fly and now she was running, running, running – the final test, the last part and she would do it and Rafe would not die and he would not die and he would not die and that was final and with that, she finally collapsed on the floor of the Pyramid of Stone.

Part Five

The Sands Come To A Rest

Chapter Thirty-Four

Serepta's body was a beach. A long, thick, curving beach. It seemed so entrenched in the earth that it would not move for a long time. Somewhere in the middle of the packed solidity of it, there was a narrow gash in the surface. It was as though the black gods had stabbed a snarly claw deep into the pillowy mounds. The gash was on fire...hot liquid spilled out from the abyss and singed the beach, sending up plumes of vile smoke and pain as it sizzled away at the earth.

Footsteps echoed down a hallway.

Gulls cried aloud on the beach in response. Blankets of warm water washed against the entire length of her body. Pools of it flowed into the pockets of destruction in the sand, filling them with soothing mud. The gash seemed to lose its fire, if only for a moment.

Somewhere in the distance, a door creaked open.

"Pyramid...." Serepta heard herself whisper slowly. Her voice was the breeze drifting over the ocean. The pulse of a nearly forgotten purpose throbbed softly.

The vision of the beach split in half, and then it peeled apart. The princess opened her eyes and blinked hard.

She was curled on her side in a large feather bed. The white mattress was a thick cloud of linen, held up by a frame of dark wood. The princess had nearly forgotten the meaning of a bed. She closed her eyes again, savoring its warmth, as she let her body melt into the softness of it. Three straight days of sleep now felt like a million years.

Clarity was slowly beginning to return, like circles of glass sharpening her senses. Serepta tried to sit up rather quickly, but the hot poker of pain in her side made her stop. She could feel the harsh discomfort of raw flesh rubbing against the clean bandage around her waist. She hadn't even realized the wound that Desmond had given her so many days ago.

Carefully, Serepta sat up in bed and looked around the small, empty room. The walls and floor were made of blocks of smooth reddish stone, and rays of sunlight streaming in from the window formed bright patterns on the floor. It was a comfortable room. The princess rubbed her eyes, struggling to massage some clarity into them, and she paused for a moment to think. Serepta could barely even remember how she had gotten there...everything about the past week seemed to blur into one big heap of biting memories. But she was safe now, safe at last.

"You should be able to stand up. Come on, give it a try," the princess urged herself softly.

Serepta swung her legs over the side of the bed. She found that her old golden dress was gone. It had been replaced with clean white robes, and the thick bandage was wrapped expertly around her side. Carefully, the princess pressed her feet to the floor. Holding the wooden bed frame for support, she slowly pulled herself up off the bed.

The princess inhaled deeply, savoring the taste of the foreign air, as she tottered back and forth. Somewhere in this pyramid was the woman who had sang to her and led her along her journey. Somewhere inside was Rafe, and the possibility that she had just not run fast enough lay heavy upon her heart. She would tear this place apart to find him.

As Serepta pushed open the great carved wooden doors and stumbled out into the pyramid, a million questions buzzed through her mind like flies. But the princess had the feeling that all would be answered soon, here in this glorious pyramid that seemed to veritably glow with wisdom.

A hallway awaited the princess on the other side of the door. It was made of the same light, smooth blocks of stone as her little room, and the floor was cool and hard under Serepta's bare feet. Bright, pure light streamed in from slits in the slanted outer wall. Narrow columns lined the hall, and lengths of ancient ivy were entwined in the rock like wreaths of laurels.

The princess drifted down the hallway, the open slits singing with fleeting images of the outside world. She pressed onward, using the columns for support, as she regained the use of her weary feet. This pyramid seemed immense. Its long halls faintly echoed faintly with age, and Serepta had the feeling that she wasn't on the bottom floor, or the top.

"Where is everybody?" the princess breathed, fingers clinging to her nightshirt.

Finally, she reached the end of the great hall. Serepta began to turn the corner, but something else caught her eye. It was a long reflecting pool rimmed with gold, and the still allure of it drew the princess near.

Serepta gazed down into the motionless waters, and she suddenly took in a sharp breath. The princess blinked hard and looked again, dread seeping through her heart. She found the woman from the mirror-rocks of Morad staring back at her. The same golden skin clung to her form, the same dark hair flowed down her shoulders, and the same eyes of black crystal shone back at her. Had this woman followed her here somehow? The princess tentatively stirred the cool waters and looked closer, heart pounding.

No. It was not that same glittering portrait of perfection. It was only Serepta, it was herself, and she was a woman now. There was a welcome roughness around the edges. There was a crude bandage tied around her waist. A smear of dirt lay like war paint across her cheek. Even the pendant of tiger's eye, still in its familiar place over her heart, was not free from imperfection. The princess knew herself, and not even a glassy reflection could convince her otherwise.

Serepta smiled, and then she turned the corner.

This new path soon merged into a small foyer. To one side was a staircase leading up into darkness. To the other side, another set of stairs descended into a brightly lit chamber below. Serepta leaned against the wall and peered down the stairs, mesmerized by the warm amber light flickering from sconces on the walls and the faint sound of voices below.

A party was going on down there. Serepta closed her eyes in order to listen better. Her royal ears were highly attuned to the sounds of a gala banquet. The chamber flourished with raw people and noise, their chatter rising like identical leaves scratching against one another, drawing the princess in like static winds.

She began to go down the steps when something drew her back. She paused, rocking back and forth upon her toes. There was another option. Serepta's eyes were drawn to the second staircase, the one that went higher up into the pyramid.

The ancient steps climbed upward like the worn side of a mountain and merged with soft darkness at the top. The princess blinked hard, peering into the upper regions. Finally, her eyes seemed to adjust to the light, and she could see what awaited in the other chamber.

It was an earthy tower that stood like a sentinel at the top, walls carpeted with thick books. From this library, the musky scent of the yellowed classics of the world rained down upon Serepta. Tentatively, the princess climbed a few steps to get a closer look.

The rows of volumes waved down at her from the shadows like the flames of a long-burning candle. The princess was in awe of the fact that so much writing existed in all the world. Surely, this was greater than the paltry collection of superstitious tales her father held in Shamar. Her mind ached to devour the words, ached with a burning curiosity. With the excitement of a wide-eyed child, Serepta started to hurry up those stairs.

Once again, the princess halted in her tracks. Thinking for a moment, she stepped back down into the foyer. She needed someone who could help her to find Rafe and the wise woman from her dreams. Should she go downstairs or upstairs?

The party was still going on below. The princess closed her eyes and swallowed hard. She could feel the familiar longing returning. Serepta knew that her old habits would never die. This was just like the grand parties in Shamar. Everyone was expected there. She could still visualize the men, tanned chests adorned with golden baubles, eyes glittering with lust as the king's concubines danced all around. Women of high blood dressed in robes of silk, drifting among the men like lost souls, hunting for husbands, laughing loud and high with a superficial joy.

Greed seemed to lick at Serepta's throat, but it was more than that. She burned with a need to be among the young and the beautiful, to dance among them and feel their eyes glitter with envy. Serepta was a high princess of Shamar, one who had been born into a life of beauty. She ached to be surrounded forever by this beauty...she glanced down at her own weary body clothed in an old nightshirt and felt the damp tightness of shame close in around her.

But it was not the beauty that mattered. The beauty was fleeting, the beauty was treacherous, and the beauty was a being in and of itself that could turn in a moment's notice. The memory of the flashing gold of the serpent rattled Serepta deeply, and she grasped her tiger's eye protectively. No, it was not beauty and riches that mattered. It was Rafe. It was her soul. It was the mystery of the woman who had led her along this journey; that was what mattered. It was something as true as her heartbeat, and the way her fingers trembled against the tiger's eye.

Her eyes flicked up at the other staircase. There might be more people down below, but Serepta knew they could not help her. Not when this shrine of wisdom waited just above her. But could she find someone to help her up there?

The princess paused, tensed in the grips of indecision. Worse still was the feeling of urgency that nipped at her heart. She had to know if Rafe was all right...the princess was in awe of the grand, thrumming culture of the pyramid, but now all she could think about was seeing Rafe again. Everything else was just wisps of smoke that were there and then not, fragile amusements that could flicker and die. She had not been separated from her Companion for this long the entire time she had known the wolf. Dark pangs of loneliness lapped up against her ribcage.

Silence was all that responded to her indecision, silence in the very atoms of the walls. Serepta couldn't understand why it mattered which way she went, but either path seemed fraught with regrets and faults to come.

The people below cried out, and it was impossible to tell whether it was the pain of blind joy in their cries. The books above whispered, and it was impossible to tell if an eloquent trap was spun in their deepening secrets.

I don't know where to go... Serepta thought, her heart paining. She took a deep breath, and looked up, and looked down.

No. There were people down below, but not ones who would help her. They would stare at her, yes, adorne her, yes, make idle chatter and jokes, but they would lure her into their world, and there was no escape from that. That was where the woman in the glass belonged, and that was not Serepta.

The princess gritted her teeth and looked up once more at the other staircase. The shadowy outline of ancient bookshelves awaited in a dusky silence. Her heart was speaking to her, and she had to listen. Proudly, she wrapped her old nightshirt tightly about her. Right or wrong, she would go to the top.

"I'm coming, Rafe."

Chapter Thirty-Five

At the top of the stairs and to the right, the first thing Serepta saw was light. Brilliant, beautiful, milky beams of light poured in from an opening at the very pinnacle of the pyramid. She hadn't been able to see it from the bottom. The light lifted her spirits and soothed her weary body as she gazed around in wonder. This room was not as dark as it had seemed.

Shielding her eyes from the brightness, the princess found the small chamber to be entirely lined with books. Rows upon rows of thick volumes carpeted the walls, and the room radiated with the musky scent of the yellowed pages. There were scrolls, too, bound by ancient hands, and shelves of herbs and potions. Earthy shades of rich red and soft brown clung to the walls. For once, Serepta seemed to understand the comfort her grandmother once took in her Tower. The princess felt as though she could spend an eternity bathing in this knowledge, devouring all the wisdom from the pages.

Others saw the greatness that lay in this room, too. Most were children, children who sat upon soft pillows, stacks of books all around. These children of the mind seemed to inhale the words off the pages, tiny brows furrowed in concentration. Watching them, Serepta felt herself tremble at the sense of where their destinies lay. These children would be philosophers, leaders, and movers of continents – people who were bound to change the world in some way.

The chamber had a rhythm to it, a heartbeat, and a silent dance that seemed to echo in the walls. Finally, beneath the column of light shining in from above, Serepta could see where all the activity of the room revolved around. An older woman sat cross-legged on the floor, illuminated in the light.

Her eyes were closed, and her face was poised in an expression of peace as she meditated. Her countenance was like that of a portrait, painted with gossamer layers of bright silk. The sunlight shone upon dark hair streaked with silver. The woman's face had few wrinkles, but Serepta knew that if she could look inside those wrinkles, she would find experiences to last a lifetime.

The princess moved closer, mesmerized, lulled somehow by the sight of this woman. How could one sit so still in a room full of people and things? How could one sit cool and composed before a million thoughts and ideas sparkling all around? Serepta would have to learn someday. She felt an urge deep inside her, an ancient urge, one that compelled her to curl up in this woman's lap, to lose herself in the warmth and softness. There was something familiar, a taste in the air that rang like the peace that comes before a sunrise.

All of a sudden, Serepta's nose was made aware of the scent of herbs and purple flowers. Her heart seemed to stir, and the voice of little Sera inside cried out.

That was when the woman opened her eyes. Serepta found herself staring into disks of melted oak wood. They were eyes hardened by fire, yet softened with love. The princess quietly soaked herself in the dark pools, warming her entire body with the heated liquid. From inside this woman's eyes, from inside her body, Serepta could hear the drums of the ages pounding along with her heartbeat.

These were the eyes of Saba, the eyes of Serepta, the eyes of little Sera, and that was when the princess knew who the woman was.

"Mother," she choked.

The room fell silent. The young children ceased their chatter, and the sound of pages turning halted like a flock of birds alighting in a tree. The silence was deafening.

The woman beamed, her face glowing with such an illuminating joy and beauty that everyone in the small room turned to stare. Something was happening there at the top of the pyramid, something that had been written in the poetry of the stars long ago. The woman on the floor savored the feeling as great puzzle pieces seemed to finally lock into place.

"You found me," the wise woman said. A faint smile danced across her face. Her voice was that of the songs that had rippled through Serepta's mind in the night and guided her there like a light out at sea.

The princess could not speak. She stood before her mother, leaning forward, face and body tensed like a harp's string.

"I have prayed to the gods for years that if only you would recognize my face, I would know then that my life had not been in vain." The woman's dark eyes seemed to crack and refill.

Serepta felt as though her insides were melting, and her eyes flickered with disbelief. "You are an impossibility. You are...a miracle! I don't want to look away, because you might just disappear like Sera did. Tell me, how can this be real?" the princess breathed.

"For years I have searched for the words I would tell you once we met again, but they seem to have flown away at just the sight of you. My daughter, you are beautiful," the woman whispered, her voice trembling. She rose to her feet, shedding thick blankets onto the floor, and extended her arms out wide.

Serepta flew into them without any reserve, drawn into the woman, drawn into her arms, and took her place with the mother she had always had but never known. The princess clung to her with such fervor that she could feel her pulse clamoring wildly against her chest. Tears ran down her cheeks, for herself and for Sera. She knew in that moment she would surrender any treasure she had ever owned, just to know the warm solidity of her mother's hug, and the scent of herbs and wild flowers. She had never known how much she needed this, how much she needed to feel safe in the arms of a big mother bear, a blood mother, who would lay down her life for her child. Serepta could not stop crying, for the floodgates of her heart were flung open once and for all. Nothing could stop her from loving then, no fears or vulnerabilities or doubts.

Serepta had found her mother.

The woman clung to her daughter tightly, slowly rocking back and forth. She had waited for the soft warmth of her daughter for years now, and every nerve in her body strained to feel what it was to hold her. She had seen Serepta before, as a baby and in visions, but memories were nothing without the experience...

"You have been through so much pain. Too much, for one so young, and it's all my fault," the woman murmured, soft lips moving against her child's head.

"Tell me why," her daughter replied.

The woman sat down upon the floor and took Serepta onto her lap. The princess was far too big, but that didn't seem to matter. "Everyone told you I had died, but that wasn't true. The only other person who knew the truth was my mother."

Saba... Serepta's heart cried out. The woman sensed this, and she pulled the princess closer.

"When you were just a baby, I made it appear to everyone that I had died, and I came here."

"Why? Why would you leave me?" Serepta asked. The question burst out on its own accord, a question that had been lying dormant for years.

The woman's face stiffened. "I never wanted to abandon you. I left for the same reason you did. I couldn't bear staying married to your father, any more than you could stand marrying Desmond. This place came to me in a vision, in a dream. The dream came to me every single night, haunting me, and I could not refuse it any longer. I didn't want to leave you alone there with those cruel beasts all around. The trickeries and deceits of the palace were bound to tear you apart. But I had to make the same journey you did. I wanted to take you with me, away from that horrible kingdom, but a baby never could have survived the trip!"

Serepta saw the sharp glint of a tear in her mother's eye. Her face seemed etched with trauma, as she relived the terrible choice she had to make all those years ago. Serepta marveled at the horrendous task of having to leave her baby behind in order to gain freedom, and with a peace and compassion not naturally born within her, understood it.

"I nearly died after I left you. I couldn't bear it. Looking back on it, I think that's the first part of the journey for anyone who might choose to take it. I lost you, and you lost your grandmother. The only thing that kept me going, the only thing that propelled me through those lands, was knowing that I would some day see my daughter again. I made Saba promise she would send you to find me, as soon as you were ready," the woman continued.

"So you think I was ready?"

"No." Serepta's mother laughed. Her laughter was like the peal of a rich brass bell. "Far from it. You were selfish, and spoiled, and weak. Saba sent me visions of you from afar, and I knew you were not ready. But Desmond was forced on you so soon, and sometimes we do not always have time to prepare for our destinies. That is why I tried to help you along the way. And that is why I sent you a Companion," the woman said, cheeks folding with delight.

Serepta's face stiffened, and she blinked slowly. Rafe. Through all their times together, through all their adventures along the way, even when the wolf lay dying, the princess had scarcely stopped to wonder where her friend had come from. The room seemed to spin for a moment, and she put a hand to the floor to steady herself.

"You...you sent Rafe to me? This is where he came from? But...how? Why?" the princess babbled.

The woman looked deep into her daughter's eyes, searching the dark brown. "It was a wise decision. You have learned so much from each other. You love Rafe, don't you?" she murmured, eyes twinkling.

"I never could have made it here without him. He's the most wonderful friend I've ever known. I miss him so much. I haven't seen him since...since we got here, and I want to know if he's all right. I couldn't bear it, if anything were to happen to him!" Serepta replied.

"He is all right. However, I must warn you, he is not the Rafe that you know. He will never be the same Companion you knew. He has changed much," the woman smiled.

"Then I will nurse him back to health. I will make him better," Serepta said firmly.

"I don't think that will be necessary. Ah! There he is now," her mother exclaimed, looking over her shoulder.

Serepta turned, and she suddenly felt as though the earth crumbled away beneath her feet.

Chapter Thirty-Six

In the small entrance of the chamber, past the worn wooden shelves and stacks of dusty books, in this nook draped with curtains of soft darkness, a form moved. It was a large shape that shifted in the shadows, powerful and strong, yet injured, somehow. Steadying itself for a moment, swaying upon feet made like the roots of a mighty oak, the form finally moved out of the darkness and into the light.

A young man strode in from the doorway, past the stacks of volumes and scrolls. A slender arm, sculpted with thick muscle, reached out tentatively to run a finger down a column of books. The soft beacons of light played against the man's hair as he stared about in wonder, casting it with a silvery glow. He seemed to have an innate grace in him as he moved, one that served to counteract the restraints of bandages about his body. He was wounded, yet moved with the grace of a king.

The children in the room put down their books and dropped to their knees before him. Their little faces glowed at the sight of the young man, and they whispered excitedly amongst themselves. The man did not notice, however. All his eyes could see was the princess standing before him in awe. Finally, the full force of the light streaming from the top of the pyramid collided with his face in a solid brightness. That face locked upon Serepta's, poised in tension with the impacting emotions, brows slanting with a sense of wonder, eyes dancing with recognition.

The eyes were domes of the fresh blue of the sky. They were turquoise mires that Serepta could lower herself into. Flecks of gold danced in the pools, soaking up the clean fresh waters, sparkling merrily and forcefully under thick lashes of ebony. The princess would know those eyes anywhere.

"Rafe...." Serepta breathed. The word could have melted on her tongue. It could have disintegrated into chaff and be borne away on the wind for all its frailty and disbelief. Something shifted, and the princess needed to steady herself, to remind herself of the firmity of the pyramid beneath her feet. But Serepta had never been one for composure, especially now, with exquisite, melting planes of reality colliding in front of her face.

"Serepta," he returned softly. His voice was strong and lilting in his throat, a voice that could turn into a rumbling growl to protect the ones he held dear or sing poetry up at the moon. It was a voice that had been caged for far too long.

The princess was left speechless. Her heart hammered against her ribcage, its pounding language speaking things that Serepta had never even once dared to believe. She reached up her fingers to touch the man's face, to trace its somehow familiar features.

The two encircled each other tentatively, with the clumsy grace that only the human form can possess. Their eyes greedily took in the sight of each other, both finding themselves becoming more and more accustomed to the oddness of Rafe's new stature and form. The princess's mother moved to one side, watching the dance that was unfolding before her. A growing smile slid across her face.

Rafe gently took Serepta's hand away from his face and held it, rubbing his fingers over hers, relishing the feeling of being able to touch her, to speak to her, to finally stand up to his full height in front of her.

"I think this is what I meant to do, the first time we met, I mean," he said. With that, he took her hand in his and kissed the soft skin. His lips burned and his cheeks seared and his eyes flicked up at hers.

Butterflies danced across the skin of her hand, and she felt as though she was dreaming.

"Speak, speak more. I feel like I've always known your voice inside my head, but to actually hear it out loud..." Serepta stopped talking, afraid she would start to cry.

Rafe's throat bobbed as he struggled to find the right words. He had waited so long to reclaim his voice, and now that he had it, was rendered speechless. It was difficult to even think at all, with the way Serepta was looking up at him.

Finally, he blurted out, "How are you? You're not hurt, are you?"

The princess blushed and looked down at herself. For a moment, she had forgotten that she was dressed in an old nightshirt and bandages.

"Certainly no more than you!" she exclaimed, and smoothed down one of his own bandages. "You were dead when I brought you here...your body was cold, you had no breath," Serepta's voice turned hard as she remembered.

"I know...they told me what happened. All I could remember was that captain grabbing you so roughly," Rafe started, a growl rumbling in his throat, as his shoulders tensed. "I still don't know how you made it away from them alive. Or how you managed to carry me, running, across half a desert. I'm not exactly a light-weight," he said, standing up proudly to his full height.

"Well, you were a lot smaller then," Serepta replied. She was still reeling from this shock. "I don't understand...how did you...change?"

"The doctors here work miracles," Rafe grinned. "Seriously, they are the most gifted healers in perhaps all the known world. With their wisdom and love, they possess powerful magic to do great things. And they are my people," he declared. "This pyramid guards the way to the oasis. My oasis, where I am the prince."

Serepta was now too numb to feel shock; she was absorbed by the mere sound of his voice, and she felt as though she could wrap herself up inside of it.

Rafe began to pace about the chamber in thought. He gazed around at the beautiful carved shelves, and at the storehouse of knowledge they held. Finally, he turned to speak once more.

"My father was getting old. He told me that my time to rule was approaching. It took me by surprise," the young man recalled. "I didn't feel...*ready*. I doubted myself and my ability to rule as well as my father had, and I couldn't understand why. So I went to your mother, because she was the wise woman of our kingdom. Of course, I didn't even know about you then."

After he said those last words, both of them felt the strangeness of it. Rafe continued, savoring the ability to finally tell his story.

"I went to your mother and told her I wasn't ready to become king. I didn't think I was strong enough, or wise enough. I knelt before her in this very room and told her I wanted to know all the wisdom there was in the world."

Serepta's mother finally stepped forward at the mention of her name, for she had been listening the entire time in silence. The old woman's eyes glazed over in memory.

"Ah, yes, I remember it like it was yesterday. You said '*You are wise, far beyond anyone else in all the lands. If I am to be king someday, I should like to know all the wisdom in the world. I believe it is my fate. Tell me of fates, wise woman.*"

Rafe turned to her, affection in his eyes. "And tell Serepta what you told me."

The old woman closed her eyes, and then she began to speak.

"Our fates to choose are numbered as the sands of the desert. The golden, sun-kissed grains that swirl about the surface may tempt us, but the cooler, more obscure ones underneath may lead us truer. And some, young prince, never would have been found had we never chosen to dig at all..." she reminisced, a smile playing upon her face. It all seemed so long ago.

Serepta closed her eyes and swallowed hard, clutching her tiger's eye tightly. So it was fate now that had come to touch down upon her life, hers, and it was as miraculous as choosing a single star and pulling it down from the heavens. The princess found it difficult to talk; her lips could not move while her soul did the speaking. Something was whispering within her, some faint glittering arm of the galaxies was prodding her and washing against her, and she did not know where the wave would take her next. She turned to Rafe, and the sight of him sent a new thrill of shock down her spine.

"So how was it that you came to me, in the form that you did?" she asked.

"I told your mother I wanted to learn to be wise, and strong, and loyal. I wanted to learn all these things before becoming king, so your mother took it upon herself to turn me into a wolf. Then she sent me to you," Rafe replied with a smile. "I was furious with her. That is...I...I was, at first."

The sun was beginning to set, and it cast dusky pink rays through the hole in the top of the pyramid. Time continued to flow outside the ancient place. Once again, Serepta's mother rejoined her daughter and Rafe. She seemed to have an elusive quality about her, some faint magic that pulled the shadows about her at will. Now, an impish twinkle came to her eye.

"Wolves are marvelous creatures, you know," she returned. "So did you learn what you set out to learn? Did you find what you set out to find?"

Rafe heard her words and closed his eyes to let them take full root in his mind. The prince turned his gaze inward and saw the wolf waiting within. It had always been there, phantom of the night, beautiful in its savagery and raw in its poetry. It howled aloud to him now, and what it said firmly answered the wise woman's question.

"More. I know now what I found, and it is more."

Rafe looked down at Serepta's hands in his, and then into her dark eyes. He found himself remembering their journey together, the way they had been separated and returned to each other once more, time and time again. The most important thing he seemed to remember from it all was the way that Serepta had held him when he was dying.

"Come with me," he said to her.

"To where?" she asked, thought it would not have mattered.

"To the next room, the one with the big window. The night is beautiful, and I have much to say," Rafe murmured, and he took her arm in his.

Together, the two walked quietly out into the adjoining room, into the sweet calm of the darkness that awaited them in silence.

Chapter Thirty-Seven

"This was my room, a long time ago," Rafe whispered. He lit a small torch on the wall, and its flame flooded the area with warm light.

Serepta smiled and her eyes looked all around. The chamber was fairly small, but warm and comfortable. The hard stone floor was covered with thick rugs. A large, pillowy bed sat on one side, and the walls were lined with bookshelves and rows of ancient weapons. What immediately caught the princess's eye, however, was the great open window facing west.

Serepta moved over to the window, drawn to the peace of the night like she always had been as a child. She tilted her head, feeling the cool grace of the starlight against her skin. The night hung softly over the pyramid, poised quietly in the shadows between rock and ivy. The great desert unfolded below like a midnight sea in the moonlight. The princess faintly recalled a time long ago when she had sat alone in front of her bedroom window, watching the night sky over the desert of Shamar. This was a new desert, though, and a new sky.

Rafe joined her at her side, his presence vibrant and powerful against the windowsill. "This was the room I stayed in when I wanted to get away from the crowds of the oasis. I used to stand here like this when I was a boy. I would look there, out to the west," he gestured with his hand to the lands where the last traces of sunlight were melting away into the horizon.

"I would dream about new places far away, and people...people I dreamed I would someday meet," he continued. He paused to look down at Serepta, hoping she would not think him strange.

The princess let a small laugh escape her lips, and her eyes lit up with wonder. "I used to do the same thing. I had a window in my room just like this in the palace. Mine faced here, faced east towards this window," she murmured.

All of those nights spent in loneliness by the bare windowsill, all those quiet dreams and hopeless prayers, had not been in vain after all this time. They made the same journey she did. They flew from her heart, across the world, and into this very window a thousand miles away. It was a miracle, and Serepta was made silent by it.

Rafe's blue eyes seemed to darken and pool in thought as he looked out at the stars, and the way they gently lit all the world below them like a stage.

"Do you believe in fate?" the young man asked, rather suddenly. His face seemed tensed in thought, as though tiny enigmas were working themselves out in his mind.

Serepta opened her mouth to speak and then stopped, pausing to think for a moment. She looked at the stars hanging in the sky, and at the sands of the desert, and then she realized that something must have brought her there.

"I think that fate sets us on the path, and it is our choice whether or not we take it."

Rafe turned to face her, and he grinned. "We certainly took the path, didn't we?"

Serepta smiled back. They were the only two people in the world who could have understood the depths of his jest.

"There were so many times on our journey when I really didn't think we would make it. There's just so much out there in the world. It's almost too much to bear, to overcome. But that's life," the prince continued. In his eyes there was the glow of understanding. Rafe leaned over her, and a lock of his dark hair brushed against hers.

"We made it. You and I, we actually made it," the prince whispered into her ear.

So this is love... Serepta suddenly remembered thinking those words as she lay pinned beneath Desmond's sword. She had known it then, somehow known it in her heart, and she knew it now. It had come like a tiny growing thing, buried beneath the soil for so long. Now it stood poised just beneath the surface, and it would take only a tiny shake to set it free.

Serepta closed her eyes and put her head upon Rafe's shoulder, praying that the feelings sprouting up inside her heart dwelled within his. They were alive. They had made it to the pyramid. Serepta didn't know what awaited them in the last leg of their journey to the oasis, but she knew that they could handle absolutely anything in the world as long as they were together.

She laid her head against the soft skin of his throat. "If I am still enough, and quiet enough, I can hear your heart beating," she whispered.

Rafe put his arm around her, and he grinned. "Since when were you ever still and quiet?"

Serepta laughed aloud and shoved him playfully. "You know what? I think I liked you better when you couldn't talk!"

"Then I won't." And with that, he kissed her.

The stars above seemed to burst into a shimmering applause, those fated stars that shone only for them. And when the golden sun replaced them in the morning, the two would travel to the oasis, together.

Chapter Thirty-Eight

A great caravan set out the next day, one as such that desert had never seen or felt upon its roughened back. A group of the tiny children of the pyramid skipped along, scattering flower petals over the dunes as they went. A company of armed soldiers, in smart uniforms of dazzling crimson, rode on the backs of camels in a ring around the other travelers. Their wise woman of the pyramid led the way on a brilliant white stallion.

This grand procession, this parade of joyous colors and people, was circled around the prince and princess who rode together on the back of a mighty elephant. Rafe and Serepta sat poised like gods in a wicker basket canopied with silk on the giant beast's back. The two were wrapped in the luxury of one another's arms, oblivious to all around them.

Rafe was clothed in a soft white tunic, his strong arms and dark hair free to taste the breeze. His face was a mask of magnificent power and contentment. The princess sat in grace and beauty beside him, dressed in lengths of golden cloth and silk. Her sun-burnished skin seemed to glow with a new radiance. She had grown in stature and in presence, and she possessed a new quiet confidence in herself and her capabilities.

Serepta closed her eyes and reveled in the glory of the world. The princess that had once run terrified from the gates of a prison would now enter the oasis like a goddess upon a cloud. Her heart beat with a quickening excitement at finally reaching the endpoint of her journey, the image of which had kept her going through some of the most terrible times of her life.

The princess's mother rode ahead, the brilliant whiteness of her robes and horse leading the caravan onward and onward. Serepta smiled and toyed with her tiger's eye. She knew that her mother would sing to her again.

Rafe sat beside her, constant as the warmth of the sun. The sight of his face, the sense of his soul in human form, sent new waves of joy through

Serepta's heart. The feelings of hope and love inside her had been given a face now, and she could no sooner tear her eyes away from him than she could stop breathing.

All day, they rode over sand and earth. The sky was shimmering and cloudless above, dancing with the heat of the midday sun. The great creatures began to bear their riders faster, anticipating the cool waters and shade of the paradise to come.

"Look, look there! The gates to my city!" Rafe cried, pointing ahead.

In the distance, the line of the horizon pooled into a dark shape. It shimmered in the hot sunlight, and if one were to stare directly at it, the image would disappear before their gaze. Soon, however, as the caravan drew closer, Serepta could make out the brilliant fanned shapes of palm trees sprouting above some rocky crags.

The princess leaned against Rafe's strong form, and he wrapped his arm around her. She could hear trumpets in the distance heralding their arrival, and she had never felt so lightheaded with excitement before.

"Look, the gates are opening!" Rafe cried. "I bet they'll have a celebration planned for my return! There was one like it for my father once when he returned home from battle. I was only a little boy, but I still remember it. There was lots of music and people and food...I haven't had decent food in months!"

Serepta laughed. "Hey, what did I tell you about talking too much?" she grinned, lifting her head to kiss him. Afterwards, they laughed. The two then sat there for a moment in a contented quiet, the gnawing silence of reflection afflicting them both.

"You know, I didn't like you when I first met you," Rafe finally said.

"I liked you."

"Not until you got to know me."

"Yes, I suppose that's right."

"So how can this be right? How can you feel for me, what I feel for you? Until last night, you thought I was a wolf!"

"But...there was always something different about you. Do you remember when we played with Sera in the fields?"

"Yes, of course. I shall never forget it."

"I placed a crown of white flowers upon your head," Serepta began. "And I said, *There you are, Your Highness. You are truly a prince among wolves.*' I suppose I just didn't know how right I was."

Rafe laughed aloud. "Perhaps you are a witch."

"Then, Your Highness, you dare admit you're in love with a witch?"

"I suppose I do."

"The audacity! What would your people think?"

"They would take one look at you, as I have done many times, and want you as their queen."

The playful banter stopped, and Serepta fell silent. Rafe's jaw twitched as if holding back more speech. He closed his eyes tightly, and he took a deep breath. The prince turned his head to face Serepta, serious for a moment, and his eyes shone.

"Marry me. Be my queen over this oasis, because I couldn't see anyone else at my side for the rest of my life besides you."

The rocking gait of the elephant below seemed to sway her, and the trumpeting music in the distance filled her ears like soft ribbon.

"Yes," she finally replied, closing her eyes to wrap up that moment and place it in her heart to remember for all time.

The gates opened, and the caravan entered the oasis.

Chapter Thirty-Nine

A tremendous explosion of music burst into the air as the parade of people and creatures entered the city in the oasis. The buildings themselves seemed to be carved out of the natural rock structures, and they were shaded by a grove of ancient palm trees. Masses of cheering crowds danced in the streets, celebrating the return of their beloved prince. Acrobats and gymnasts flipped across the carved stone archways, and merchants loudly hawked their wares in the streets.

Little children in robes of silk tossed flower petals over the travelers, and they fluttered down upon them like a fluorescent rain. The rest of the people waved at their prince from stone balconies and gazebos, bursting with excitement and joy.

Serepta's heart skipped faster at the sight of these spirited people and this magnificent city. Everything she had ever strived for and believed in her entire life had led up to this very moment. As the roar of the crowds grew higher and higher, she could barely even comprehend that she would soon rule over these people...

Rafe plucked a blossom from a tree as the elephant continued down the main street. Gently, he placed it in Serepta's dark hair. "I don't think I've ever seen you so happy!" he laughed.

"I have never been so happy!" she cried.

The masses of people followed the caravan in a parade now as they marched through the city. The wide stone walkways rippled like a colorful sea.

"Where are we going?" Serepta asked.

"To the palace!" Rafe shouted above the roar of the crowds. "Then I can announce our marriage to them all!" his eyes danced.

Serepta wanted to leap across the rooftops and sing it to all the world.

Her mother had raced ahead on her white stallion, and now stood poised atop a tremendous staircase at the foot of the palace. She dismounted her horse and threw her arms out wide. Immediately, the crowds fell to a respectful silence towards their wise woman. Her brow furrowed for a moment as she looked out over the audience. Her dark eyes shone, and she began to speak.

"I have never seen a sight more wonderful than the welcome you have prepared for your prince!" she cried, face lit from within.

Applause rose once more like a rushing wind.

"He has traveled farther than any prince before him, and he has sacrificed more for his people. He nearly lost his life on this journey, but he has brought you back something much greater in return. The woman at his side is my daughter, and your future queen!"

If Serepta had thought the crowds were loud before, now their applause was deafening. The sound echoed off the rock walls and rolled down the streets, rising in volume and fervor. The princess laughed as Rafe struggled to stand up atop the elephant, wriggling his arms to keep his balance. Finally, he waved wide to his people, unable to stop a goofy grin from spreading across his face.

Serepta could see the eyes of his people examining her, and she sat cool and composed before their gaze. Some of the young women of the oasis had visible disappointment in their eyes at the news of Rafe's engagement, and it made Serepta's heart swell with pride. She and Rafe had found each other, and they would be together always.

Finally, Rafe sat back down and put his arm around her. "I better sit down before I fall! You wouldn't want a husband with a broken neck."

Serepta laughed and touched his face. "I would want you even if you were a wild animal."

"And I would want you even if you dragged me over half the world, you crazy witch!" he laughed.

"You didn't seem to mind, as I recall."

"Not as long as I was with you," Rafe concluded, and he kissed her.

The crowds went wild with applause.

Chapter Forty

The next day, Serepta stood in a stone gazebo, clothed in a magnificent gown of white silk. The gazebo, engraved with images of the gods, rested on a bridge over a waterfall. The gentle falls ran down into a pool of clear water below, and sunlight rippled across the surface. It was peace, and it was right.

It would be a private ceremony. Serepta's mother would perform the service, as well as the coronation. All the princess could think about was her wedding, though, and the life she would have with her husband.

Finally, Rafe stepped up into the altar, clothed in the royal white robes. His wounds were nearly all healed by now, and he moved with even more grace and power than ever before as he took his place at her side.

As Serepta's mother took both of their hands in hers, the princess closed her eyes hard and marveled at where she was standing. Everything could have been so different...had she never decided to take the journey, she would be back in Shamar now, wed to Desmond. She would have never even known that her mother and Rafe existed. Serepta's eyes snapped open, and they hungrily took in the sweet sight of her mother and her soon-to-be-husband, and her very heart seemed to beat with triumph and pride.

She had made her choice. She had taken her path. Desmond was gone, having finally cleansed himself in death. Sanjay had saved her life, and he would make sure that the people of Shamar would follow their old tradition and never leave the city walls again. She and Rafe were safe and together, and that was all that truly mattered.

Rafe wrapped his arm around her and spoke into her ear.

"We have done more than any other rulers before us. We have seen more than most people could ever wish to see. But it isn't over yet. We will rule this oasis together. The journey will go on," he murmured, kissing her head.

Serepta smiled up at him, and their pact was sealed.

Her mother beamed down at them. "Saba and I prayed so hard for the well-being of you two. I think she knew this would happen, somehow. She foresaw it, and she was right."

Serepta looked back fondly on her grandmother's memory. Suddenly, she was reminded of the last words Saba had ever said to her: *...I have one last thing to tell you, and I pray, dear child, that you will remember it. Rafe is, and always will be, your Sole Companion....*

"My Sole Companion...." the princess breathed.

"What was that?" her mother asked.

"It was...it was something that Saba said to me. She told me that Rafe was, and always would be, my Sole Companion," Serepta replied, and as she said the words out loud, their true meaning finally dawned upon her.

"Oh! Mother! She didn't mean Sole Companion, she meant..."

"*Soul* Companion," her mother interrupted, laughing at the look of understanding on her daughter's face. "Your grandmother was always one to play on words."

"I hate to interrupt, but isn't there a ceremony to perform?" Rafe asked.

Serepta laughed and joined her hands with his, ready to become his wife.

With joy in her eyes and peace in her heart, Serepta's mother led them in their vows to one another, and in that altar atop the waterfall, the two were made man and wife. Rafe took Serepta into his arms, and he held her there tightly.

The princess smiled against his strong shoulder. For a moment, she was almost sad, for it seemed as though their adventure had come to an end. But then Rafe's words came to her head, and the princess knew that he was right. She would hold his words in her heart for all of time.

The journey will go on...

Epilogue

After the wedding, Serepta stole off by herself to venture outside the oasis, never being one to observe the restrictions of city gates. The princess was a woman of the desert, and the desert would be a part of her, always.

She sat in the warm sands and threw back her head to take in the heat of the sun. The warm gold danced across her face and lifted her heart with joy. Something, somehow, had conspired to bring Serepta there. But the princess knew nothing about fate.

"Tell me of fates, wise woman," her husband had once beseeched her mother.

Serepta felt her tiger's eye stone cool against her throat, and the pendant helped her to remember the answer her mother had given long ago.

"Our fates to choose are numbered as the sands of the desert. The golden, sun-kissed grains that swirl about the surface may tempt us, but the cooler, more obscure ones underneath may lead us truer. And some, young prince, never would have been found had we never chosen to dig at all..."

Serepta blinked hard and sat up, fingers still clutching the tiger's eye. She had a feeling now, a feeling that she had been there for an eternity, sitting upon the sands. On an impulse, the princess thrust her fingers into the soft grains and began to dig. Her labor was not in vain.

Lingering just inches from the surface of the earth, a tiny purple flower bloomed up out of the sands, flickering softly in the desert breeze.

"Ah, I see you have joined me at last," Serepta smiled. She gave the flower a bit of water from her canteen, but she had no doubt that the blossom would live, and live well. With that, she returned back inside the gates to find her beloved husband.

The wise people of the oasis would never understand how the purple flower got there. There was something odd about the bright little thing on their side of the world, and they did not know if it would survive. But survive it did, longer than any flower they had ever seen. The tiny purple flower would flourish there, growing up out of the sands of the desert.

* * * * *